CW00951095

Another unique species

Patterns in human evolutionary ecology

Robert Foley

Longman Scientific & Technical

Copublished in the United States with
John Wiley & Sons, Inc., New York

Longman Scientific & Technical,
Longman Group UK Limited,
Longman House, Burnt Mill, Harlow,
Essex CM20 2JE, England
and Associated Companies throughout the world

Copublished in the United States with
John Wiley & Sons, Inc., 605 Third Avenue, New York, NY 10158

© Longman Group UK Limited 1987

All rights reserved; no part of this publication
may be reproduced, stored in a retrieval system,
or transmitted in any form or by any means, electronic,
mechanical, photocopying, recording, or otherwise,
without the prior written permission of the Publishers.

First published 1987

British Library Cataloguing in Publication Data
Foley, Robert
   Another unique species: patterns in
   human evolutionary ecology.
   1. Human evolution
   I. Title
   573.2 GN287
   ISBN 0-582-44690-2

Library of Congress Cataloging-in-Publication Data
Foley, Robert.
   Another unique species.

   Bibliography: p.
   Includes index.
   1. Human evolution.   2. Human ecology.   I. Title.
   GN281.F64   1987   573.2   86-23442
   ISBN 0-470-20728-0

Set in Linotron 202 10/12 pt Palatino

Produced by Longman Group (FE) Limited
Printed in Hong Kong

In Memory

David Clarke
Glynn Isaac

Contents

Contents

List of figures

List of tables

Preface

One of the first books written on human evolution was by Charles Darwin. *The Descent of Man* is still one of the best books on the subject, laying out many of the issues that remain central today, and yet it was written with virtually no reference to the fossil record and at a time when hominid fossils were almost unknown. Despite this, there is a common assumption that developments in the study of human origins come about through the discovery of new fossils. Advances occur when a new 'missing link' is unearthed, and another branch is added to the human family tree. But, as important as the discovery of new fossils is the framework into which the story of human evolution is placed. Darwin's book remains important because he dealt with the issues of how and why human evolution proceeds. Other books have also lasted because they have provided a durable and ultimately 'useful' framework that does not have to be discarded like a conceptual razor-blade dispenser with each new find.

This, too, is a book about the framework for studying human evolution. If there is a context for looking at the evolution of any species, including humans, it must surely be ecology. Developments in evolutionary biology over the past 10 years have emphasized that the patterns of evolution are firmly embedded in those principles of ecology that structure relationships between individuals, populations and species, and their environment. Evolutionary ecology is emerging as more central to evolutionary biology than the often sterile debates about classification and phylogeny. As Michael Ghiselin has argued, this is far closer to the spirit of Darwin's original formulation of the theory of evolution. Furthermore, the ecological basis for evolutionary patterns has been recognized not simply for morphological and physiological characters, but for aspects of behaviour as well. In this book I have attempted a consideration of the patterns of evolution in one group of animals – the hominids – in terms of their ecological basis.

The ideas that have inspired this work are not really anthropological. Studies of human evolution have traditionally been separate from other branches of evolutionary biology. Despite the Darwinian revolution – the idea that humans are just another animal – human evolution has been treated as a rather special subject. That we are very different from most other species on this Earth has greatly influenced the way in which the problems of human evolution have been approached. This book tries to avoid treating humans and their ancestors as anything more than just another species that has evolved over the past few million years. In using the title – *Another unique species* – I hope to show that uniqueness is paradoxically a characteristic of all species, not just humans. The scientific context, therefore, is perhaps less that of biological anthropology and archaeology, and more the fields of evolutionary ecology. To this end, the ideas and models developed here have been greatly influenced by such biologists as John Maynard Smith, Eric Pianka, Robert Martin, Paul Harvey and Tim Clutton-Brock. Another evolutionary biologist whose work has been influential here is John Eisenberg, and it is perhaps interesting to note that in the introduction to his book *The Mammalian Radiations* he cites the anthropologist Daryll Forde's *Habitat, Economy and Society* as pointing him in the direction of considering the relationship between environment and behaviour. This relationship has been greatly underplayed in many parts of anthropology since Forde's book, and it is now from zoology that the ideas for human evolutionary and behavioural ecology must come.

Although this is a book about human evolution, it is not supposed to be a comprehensive account of a historical event. Human evolution can be told as a story occurring through time, with a strong chronological theme. This approach has not been adopted here. I have been more concerned with getting across the way in which human evolution should be approached and analysed, and ultimately accounted for, than in presenting the basic facts in chronological order. The first chapter presents an outline of human evolution as a relatively simple story, but after this the emphasis is on the analysis of particular problems in human evolution from an ecological perspective. The book should therefore not be treated as a straightforward textbook, but more as an ecological and evolutionary companion to an outline of human evolution. In order to maintain this thematic approach much of the raw, descriptive material that forms the core of many human evolution textbooks has been omitted. I hope that it will be of interest to those readers specifically interested in the evolution of the human species – anthropologists and archaeologists – as well as biologists more generally. In writing it I have tried to avoid the use of technical jargon wherever possible and so make the book widely understandable. Many of the sections are therefore preceded by an introduction to and discussion of some of the basic concepts, terms and issues involved. I hope that this does not detract too much from the 'enjoyment' of those already familiar with the principles of evolutionary ecology. A further limitation that should be pointed out is that I have concentrated on the earlier stages of hominid evolution – the period from five to one million years ago, when the hominid lineage was emerging and radiating within Africa. This is not because this period is necessarily the most important or interesting, but because it illustrates well many of the processes and mechanisms of evolutionary ecology. There is no reason why the later periods of hominid evolution should not be treated in the same way.

A large number of people have helped, intentionally or not, in one way or another with this book. It was written while I was at the University of Durham, in between the more exacting duties of sorting out the timetable and trying to keep the coffee room from bankruptcy. My colleagues at Durham provided the ideal academic environment – friendly and argumentative. In particular, Gilbert Manley could always be depended upon for lively and critical debate. Shared courses with Robert Layton and Malcolm Smith acted as a great stimulus to me in the development of the ideas that lie behind this book. Michael Carrithers, despite his reluctance to take the title of this book seriously, was a source of encouragement, support and wine, for which I am extremely grateful. Others in Durham, especially Martin Jones, provided many helpful comments and ideas. Above all, though, I am indebted to several generations of students for putting up with my various intellectual hobby horses, although I often wished they wrote shorter essays. I must also thank the students and staff of the Department of Anthropology at the University of New Mexico for their hospitality and interest while I was there as a visiting fellow.

Robert Martin read and commented at great length on an earlier draft of this book, and any coherence or value it may have owes a great deal to the effort he put in. Parts or the whole of this book have been read by Clive Gamble, John Speth, P. C. Lee and Elizabeth Cruwys. All have provided me with many useful suggestions (some of which I took!). The errors that remain are my sole responsibility. Sarah Bunney has done much to improve both the style and the scientific content of the book. I am also especially grateful to Polly and Giles Courtice for their kindness and hospitality in Cambridge. To all these people, and to many others, especially Jill Goudie, I owe a great debt of gratitude.

Finally, as an undergraduate and graduate student, and during the start of my career, I had the privilege of being taught, encouraged and befriended by two very great archaeologists, both of whom died tragically young. This book is dedicated to the memory of David Clarke and Glynn

Isaac, without whose inspiration it would not have been possible to attempt this type of work.

Robert Foley
Cambridge
June 1986

Acknowledgements

We are grateful to the author, Jared M Diamond and Academic Press for permission to reproduce an extract from p296-7 from Sunda & Sahul (1977) and to the following for permission to reproduce copyright illustrations:

Academic Press for figs 7.12, 9.9 & 9.10 from figs 4.2, 4.5 & 4.6, and Tables 6.5 & 9.10 from Tables 4.1 & 1.3 (Foley 1984a & b); Academic Press and the authors for fig 6.7D from fig 6 (Clutton-Brock & Harvey 1977), fig 8.3 from fig 4 (Harris 1980), fig 8.11 from fig 4 (Hladik 1977), figs 2.14, 2.15, 5.9 & 5.10 from figs 2.1, 2.2, 2.3 & 2.4 (Roberts 1984), figs 6.17 & 10.3 from figs 3.3 & 3.2 (Stringer 1984) and Table 8.3 from Table 2 (Dunbar 1977); the American Anthropological Association and the authors for fig 8.21 from fig 1 p 26 (Dyson-Hudson & Smith 1978) and for fig 2.4 from fig 3 p 302 (Pilbeam 1986); the American Geophysical Union for fig 2.13 from fig 6 (Kennett 1977) copyright by the American Geographical Union; the American Museum of Natural History's James Arthur Committee for fig 6.16 from fig 16 (R. D. Martin 1983); American Scientist for fig 7.16 from the graph in fig 8 (Potts 1984b); Annual Reviews Inc. for Table 6.4 from Tables 6 & 7 (Frayer & Wolpoff 1985) (c) 1985 by Annual Reviews Inc, The Athlone Press for figs 1.3, 6.2 & 9.2 from figs 4, 43 & 38 (Eisenberg 1981); Blackwell Scientific Publications Ltd for fig 6.10 from fig 3 (Western 1979); Dr. Bonnefille for fig 5.9 from fig 1 (Bonnefille 1984); Cambridge University Press for figs 6.5 & 6.6 from figs 6.9 & 6.11 (Schmidt-Nielson 1975); The Ecological Society of America for fig 6.7a, b, (c) from fig 1 (Harested & Bunnell 1979); Harvard University Press for fig 9.16 from fig 30.6 (Maglio & Cooke 1978); Little, Brown & Co for fig 7.13 from p 89 (Weiss & Mann 1975) Macmillan Journals Ltd and the authors for fig 7.10 from fig 1 (Martin & May 1981) copyright (c) 1981 Macmillan Journals Ltd; Plenum Publishing Corporation and the authors for fig 2.8 from figs 8 & 10 (White, Johanson & Kimbel 1983); Princeton University Press for Table 6.4 from a table in figure 1, p 278 (Smith 1954); the Royal Anthropological Institute of Great Britain and Ireland for fig 5.4 from fig 7 p 401 (Foley 1982); and Taylor & Francis Ltd and the authors for fig 7.14 from fig 1 (Aiello 1981) and fig 7.6 from fig 1 (Andrew 1981)

Introduction

'Why a duck?' was one of the more interesting questions asked by Groucho Marx. Although he has had rather less influence on anthropology than his namesake Karl Marx, the question 'why a human?' is a particularly important one. Traditional answers to this question have been philosophical or theological in nature. However, the true lesson of the Darwinian revolution is that this question is essentially a technical one within evolutionary biology, susceptible to empirical enquiry rather than just metaphysical, ethical or teleological discussion. The neo-Darwinian answer would be that humans evolved because human, and hominid, characteristics endowed their bearers with a reproductive advantage over those that did not. The problem, then, is to define what those advantageous characteristics are, and to show under what conditions they will be advantageous. The problem of 'why humans?' is thus one of specifying the type of environment, both natural and social, in which the benefits of being human exceed the costs. It is a question of locating human origins in time and in space.

This approach may lack the grandeur of more philosophical ones, or the romance of theories that see human origins as the result of visiting spacemen or ape miscegenation, but nonetheless it is one likely to reap results. Asking 'why humans?' takes us beyond the fossils to the evolutionary ecology that produced those fossils.

Fossils form the centre piece in the study of human evolution. Palaeoanthropologists – those in search of human origins – are best pictured with suntanned knees scouring some inhospitable part of the world for small fragments of fossilized bones that might give clues to the mystery of our evolution, or, better still, provide the missing link that is in the popular imagination the Holy Grail of the subject. Each human fossil discovered, blazoned across the newspapers of the world and accorded some cute nickname and a rather more unpronounceable scientific one, has been another piece in the jigsaw. As more and more such fragments of our past have been recovered, the story of human evolution has been unravelled: the more fossils, the greater our knowledge.

Although the pattern of human evolution is undoubtedly better understood than at the time in which Darwin wrote the first book on human evolution, *The Descent of Man*, the major questions addressed by Darwin in that book remain the same, and as open to dispute now as then. The accumulation of fossils has provided answers to many of the questions of human evolution – *what* did the early hominids look like?, *when* did they evolve?, *where* did they evolve?, and *how* did they evolve? – the most fundamental question – *why*? – is still a contentious one.

In this book I shall be suggesting that 'being human' has solved problems that ancestral forms faced in the remote past. Being a 'hominid' proved to be a better adaptive solution than the various alternatives produced by the genetic variability present at that time, and the alternatives used by other species that are now extinct. The reason for this is that evolution is a problem-solving process. Natural selection favours those 'solutions' that best solve environmental problems; these solutions spread through the population because the bearers of them have a greater level of reproductive success. Populations and species thus come to adapt to their environment. There is no grand scheme to evolution, no master plan, and no predetermined direction. Rather, what we see in the pattern of evolution is the way in which alternative solutions to environmental problems have been produced by the genetic and phenotypic repertoire of vast numbers and types of organisms, and from which selection has favoured those that provide the 'best' solution.

This process has happened to hominids and to humans as much as any other organism. The pattern of human evolution is one that can be seen in the fossils and in the archaeological record. It is also stamped into our current biology and behaviour. This pattern, though, is shaped by the problems that the early hominids faced. To answer the question 'why a hominid?' we need to identify what those problems were, and why hominid characteristics provided the best solutions.

Where, though, do these problems come from? How can they be identified? The problems come from two sources. They come firstly from the type of animal we are – mammals, primates, terrestrial, etc. – and they come also from the environments in which we live. Ultimately, then, they come from the interaction between the two. The purpose of this book is to define the problems that the early hominids faced, and to relate these problems to the evolution of hominid adaptive strategies.

Such a task calls on three things. It calls on the approaches available for studying the arena of early hominid evolution – the past. It calls on the specific characteristics of the hominids – the domain of anthropology. And it calls on biological and in particular evolutionary and ecological theory as a framework for linking the characteristics of an animal to the context in which it lives and evolves.

The book takes its structure from these considerations. A brief overview of the current status of early hominid studies is provided in Chapter 2. Then the principles of evolutionary ecology – the analytical framework – are outlined in Chapter 3. The difficulties of applying these to the archaeological and fossil record are discussed in Chapter 4. With the theoretical and methodological basis established, the actual adaptive problems can be analysed and interpreted (Chapters 5–10). To some extent these problems must be arbitrarily imposed, for in the 'real world' of survival there are no categories, only a continuum of selective pressures. However, in order to make the study manageable, I discuss in turn the problems of living in tropical environments, as a large mammal, as a terrestrial primate, in seasonal environments, facing interspecific interactions, and colonizing new habitats. Each of these, it can be shown, has played a part in shaping the direction of hominid evolution.

Central to the aims of this book has been the bringing of palaeoanthropology closer to the mainstream of evolutionary biology. The barrier to this aim has been the long-held view that humans are unique, a totally new type of organism, that thus require a special type of explanation, different from that used in understanding the rest of the biological world. The development of human evolutionary ecology therefore depends on solving the problem of human uniqueness.

1 The problem of human uniqueness

Are humans different?

Levels of uniqueness

The modern human is undoubtedly a very special type of animal. Speech, unparalleled behavioural flexibility, a peculiar upright stance, a brain far too big for comfort, and complex technology all cry out as the markers of human uniqueness. Darwin may have shown that we are descended from more lowly forms, and chimpanzees may be making some telling attempts at language, tool-making and some of the less-pleasant aspects of human behaviour such as cannibalism and forms of warfare, but in our hearts we know that humans are protected from the onslaught of the common herd of animals by an unbridgeable chasm. The walls of human uniqueness are in pretty good shape after more than a century of Darwinian battering.

Two divergent strategies can be identified in the history of research into human evolution. On the one hand, there are those who have sought to emphasize the uniqueness of man, and so have looked for the discontinuities in evolution and have searched for uniquely human characteristics in the remote fossil record. On the other, are those who see in the primates the mirror of man, and who consequently have minimized the differences in behaviour and anatomy and argued for a recent evolutionary divergence between humans and their closest evolutionary relatives. This book lies in spirit with the latter strategy, but recognizes that no amount of observation and argument can get around the fact that humans are a very special species. The difficulty lies, then, in how uniqueness can be accounted for.

Modern man – *Homo sapiens sapiens* – is a unique subspecies. Uniqueness becomes a problem when we try to relate unique phenomena to a general class and then try to account for patterns of variation in that class in terms of general principles. However, two points should be made about the applications of general biological principles to our own subspecies. The first is that the term 'subspecies' is itself a biological one, and if man is to be placed into a biological context by such terms as 'species' and 'subspecies', then it is appropriate to use biological concepts to study the characteristics shown by them. And, second, all biological taxa are unique. This is the basis of biological taxonomy and the diversity of life. All species are unique because they constitute 'groups of actually or potentially interbreeding natural populations, which are reproductively isolated from other such groups' (Mayr 1963: 120). They are thus genetically unique. Genetic isolation may be the result of geographic isolation, but in virtually all cases it also involves phenotypic and thus adaptive differences. All species are physiologically, ecologically and behaviourally unique in the same way that modern humans are. Ecologists recognize this adaptive particularity by using the concept of the ecological niche to describe the unique multidimensional biological space that a species occupies (Hutchinson 1957). Although *Homo sapiens sapiens* is unique, so too are all other subspecies. This applies back through time as well, so that *Homo erectus* is also unique and distinct from other hominid species.

It follows from this that the inappropriateness of biological principles cannot rest on the uniqueness of modern humans. However, two further criteria might be used to set us apart. Either the differences between hominids and other taxa might be far greater than that between other species, or the human species may be the product of unique processes that do not operate on other organisms.

Turning to the first of these criteria, how different are humans from other organisms? Our closest relatives are the great apes. The physiological basis of the relationship has long been demonstrated by Darwin (1871) and Huxley (1863); genetically the differences are remarkably few, of the order of less than 1 per cent (Sarich 1971). Behaviourally, though, the differences are considerable, although as Passingham (1982) has shown, humans still lie broadly within the primate frame. However, the distances between living species can be misleading, as Darwin (1871: 152) pointed out:

> The great break in the organic chain between man and his nearest allies which cannot be bridged over by any extinct or living species, has often been advanced as a grave objection to the belief that man is descended from some lower form; but this objection will not appear of much weight to those who, from general reasons, believe in the general principle of evolution. Breaks often occur in all parts of the series, some being wide, sharp and defined, others less so in various degrees . . . But these breaks depend merely on the number of related forms which have become extinct. At some future period, not very

distant as measured by centuries, the civilized races of man will almost certainly exterminate, and replace, the savage races throughout the world. At the same time the anthropomorphous apes . . . . will no doubt be exterminated. The break between man and his nearest allies will then be wider, for it will intervene between man in a more civilized state . . . and some ape as low as a baboon, instead of as now between the negro or Australian and the gorilla.

In other words, ignoring the somewhat dramatic and racialist tone of Darwin's terms, the extent to which an organism is considered unique depends on how similar its closest living relative is, and this in turn depends on how many related forms have become extinct. Like so many evolutionary issues, therefore, the problem turns on historical conditions and is subject to only relative measurement. Human uniqueness, we now know from the vastly improved fossil record from that available to Darwin, is exaggerated by the extinction of *Australopithecus*, of *Homo erectus* and of neanderthals, not to mention the possibility of now-extinct great apes which were more closely related to hominids than are chimpanzees and the gorilla today. Even in behaviour, the archaeological record of the development of tool-making illustrates the intermediate technologies that once existed. In considering early hominids, the apparent gap between them and other organisms should not constrain the closer alignment of palaeoanthropology with evolutionary biology.

The second criterion that might be used to determine human uniqueness could be not only that the product (humans) is unique, but that the processes and mechanisms by which that product was brought about are unique also. Thus, although all organisms from hornbills to horses are unique in the ways described above, the processes by which they evolved were common to them all – that is, natural selection leading to adaptation, genetic isolation and a distinct set of behaviours and morphologies. What it is necessary to consider here is whether that process may be expected to hold for humans as well.

The inadequacy of culture

If there is a new evolutionary process to be found among humans it is cultural evolution. Culture is a concept central to anthropology, epitomizing much of what we think of as distinctly, or uniquely human. Regrettably, there are almost as many definitions of the term culture as there are anthropologists, but broadly speaking it refers to the non-biological aspects of the human species, incorporating such features as language, tool-making, increased behavioural flexibility, symbolic thought and expression, and it is transmitted through learning and teaching rather than through any genetic system. Although the capacity for culture may be species specific and genetically endowed, the behaviour that it allows is not. With the development of these characteristics human evolution became separated from the mainstream of biological evolution. For humans, natural selection is at the very least complemented by a parallel process of natural selection, if not actually supplanted by it. Models of gene-culture coevolution have been developed in recent years (Lumsden & Wilson 1980; Cavalli Svorza & Feldman 1981).

Is culture, though, a particularly useful concept in the study of human origins? I would argue that it is not. Culture is a composite term, bringing together a whole series of attributes that are important in the life of humans today. However, in studying the origins of these cultural features it may not be particularly useful to link them together. We do not know – indeed this is the very thing we are trying to find out – when any of them first occurred within the hominid lineage. Each of them – the enhanced capacity for learning, speech, tool-making, etc. – may have evolved separately, subject to independent selective forces, and so to lump these all together as 'culture' is to remove the possibility that hominids may, in the past, have possessed only part of their present behavioural repertoire, or that repertoire combined in different ways. There is little advantage in using a term that bestows the advantages of a descriptive shorthand if it begs the very question we are asking and so occurs at the expense of analytical precision.

When looked at separately many of the features of human culture can be found in at least rudimentary from in non-human animals. Chimpanzees are known to be tool-users and tool-makers, and tool-making, as well as the extensive modification of the materials found in the environment (such as occurs in nest-building), are found in other parts of the animal kingdom. Chimpanzees are capable of systematic use of gestural language (such as American Sign Language) in ways that suggest a grasp of symbols and grammatical structure. Futhermore, in their natural state primates use a wide variety of communicatory systems; Seyfarth, Cheyney & Marler (1980), for example, have shown that vervet monkeys (*Cercopithecus aethiops*) use vocalizations in precise ways that are close to what we understand as 'words'. Learned behaviour is also, of course, extremely widespread among animals, from blue tits learning to open milk bottles to saddlebacks learning songs from their neighbours to Japanese macaques acquiring the skill of cleaning the sand off their food. In each of these instances not only is learning involved, but there is also rapid transmission of information and the development of 'traditions' within populations.

When treated independently, therefore, most of what is known as culture occurs elsewhere in some form in the animal kingdom. Use of the term culture in palaeoanthropology obscures this continuity. In investigating the origins of modern human behaviour it is far more productive to adopt a reductionist approach to deal with the minimalist categories of behaviour, and not to assume, through the use of the term of culture, on *a priori* grounds, that we are dealing with something different.

This is not to say that once these characteristics have emerged that they do not result in novel patterns of evolution. However, at this stage it is best to treat these as *consequences*, not *causes*, of behavioural evolution, altering the nature of the selective pressures operating on hominids but not the mechanisms by which they act. To assume cultural evolution or coevolution at the outset of an analysis of human evolution is to predetermine that natural selection is inadequate. It is the purpose of any evolutionary ecological analysis to determine whether this is the case, not to prejudge the issue. Accordingly, in this book the term culture is avoided on the grounds that it is an unnecessary and not particularly useful concept. Behavioural, not cultural, evolution is an adequate term, making the fewest assumptions and providing the greatest flexibility. This does not remove the characteristics that make humans unique – a vast capacity for learning, innovation and imitation, complex communication, and extreme plasticity of behaviour – but deals with them in ways that make comparisons between species feasible.

Methodological reductionism

This research strategy is a reductionist one, which perhaps in an anthropological context requires some further comment. 'A reductionist is one whose objective is to account for even the most complicated phenomena in terms of elementary interactions between more or less elementary entities' (Anon 1983: 301). In this case, a complicated group of organisms – the hominids – are being accounted for in terms of elemental ecological and evolutionary processes – natural selection and adaptation. Such an approach is justified, as I have tried to show above, by the shared ancestral history of hominids and the methodological difficulties involved in determining human release from natural selection. 'The value of reductionism is . . . to help more accurately define the constantly moving boundary between what may be described as known and the rest' (*op. cit.*). The 'known' in this case is the general biological character and evolutionary history of humans, and the 'rest' or unknown is the nature of the processes and mechanisms of separation between man and his close biological relatives. The critical justification in using a reductionist approach is that while intriguing emergent properties may be apparent, the units and mechanisms of reproduction of these properties remain speculative. Only by attempting to account for the maximum amount of variation in terms of minimal entities and their interaction can we discover the properties of whatever might be emerging.

In summary, it has been argued that elementary principles of evolutionary ecology are appropriate for the analysis of hominids. They represent the most suitable way of trying to define and explain the differences and similarities between humans and other organisms. Our apparent uniqueness is not a sufficient reason for adopting special techniques and concepts; uniqueness is a characteristic of all species, and the degree of difference between species is a function of differential extinction, not an absolute quality. Furthermore, it is methodologically unacceptable to assume a different set of rules for hominids before analysis. These should arise out of the analysis. These conclusions provide the justification for the approach adopted in this book.

Hominids, then, represent a unique group of animals. In trying to apply the general techniques and concepts of evolutionary biology to them I am not trying to remove this uniqueness, but rather trying to explain it. The purpose of this book is not to pursue human character-istics back into the primeval swamp, but rather to bring to bear on a special evolutionary event a powerful set of analytical and conceptual tools. We are indeed a unique species, but we should also remember that we are also just another unique species.

Our place in nature

The human animal

The idea that being human can be understood through the application of evolutionary and ecological principles rests on one key assumption – that our species can be treated as a biological organism, that each of us is essentially an animal. The claim that humans could be treated as biologi-cal organisms stems from the notion that they evolved through natural selection. This claim was based on a comparison of the similarities and differences between modern humans and other species. Despite the limited data available at the time, Darwin, in the *Descent of Man* (1871), was able to show that our anatomical, physiological and developmental characteristics were remarkably similar to the order Primates, and that certain behavioural attributes, such as facial expressions, could also be usefully compared between humans and other primates. The conclusions that Darwin was able to draw have formed the basis for subsequent work over the past hundred years, and provide the basic assumption under-lying this book. Archaeology and physical anthropology have been concerned to document the precise nature of the relationship between humans and other animals (Le Gros Clark 1964). Before the publication of the *Origin of Species* the character of this relationship was unproblematic, for an unbridgeable gap lay between humans, the crown of creation, and all other organisms (Foley 1984a). However, once the notion that we had clearly identifiable animal connections was established, the relationship between humans and primates became an issue.

The present situation has been critically assessed by Passingham (1982) in a comprehensive analysis of primate structure and behaviour. While recognizing the importance of changes in form – bipedalism, manipulative ability, etc. – he places particular emphasis on the changes in the brain. However, the conclusion that Passingham reaches (1982: 332–3) focuses on the key to the relationship between humans and the biological world. We may differ widely from even the apes, but these differences can be accounted for in terms of elementary biological principles. He identifies three such principles by which the transformation could occur. First, that quantitative changes can have effects that are qualititative in character. Using the analogy of a computer, he states that a larger computer does not merely do the same as a small one on a larger scale, but is capable of carrying out operations of a different kind and with greater efficiency. Second, that radical reconstruction is not a necessary prerequisite of major functional changes, and that small changes can have fundamental effects. And third, that 'the adoption of a new code for handling information can have revolutionary results'. That code is language, but again it is a code (communication) present in other organisms but expanded and transformed to new functions, principally internal mental activity.

The overall conclusion that can be drawn is that modern humans can be compared in most respects with other species, but that some significant and discontinuous changes have occurred. However, the central point is not uniqueness, but that both discrete and continuous uniqueness can be acounted for by basic biological principles.

The primates

The group with which modern human populations share the most biological characteristics and the longest evolutionary history are the primates. These shared characteristics serve both as evidence for the evolution of man, and also as a source of ideas and questions. Primates provide the context for human evolution.

Primates are an order of mammals characterized by the retention of several primitive traits and the evolution of more specialized features relating to tree-dwelling and high degrees of sociality. Several trends can be identified in their evolution (Le Gros Clark 1949; Napier 1971) (Fig. 1.1). Primates have retained the basic mammalian body plan and structure, for example the five digits of the hand and foot. These have become progressively more mobile, providing many primates with an extremely dextrous grasping and manipulative hand and foot. The eyes have become more frontally positioned, allowing binocular vision, and the snout has become reduced, with an associated loss of olfactory ability. The brain is enlarged relative to body size, and many species live in complex social and natural environments. There is also a trend towards greater body size, with changes in the relative and absolute lengths of

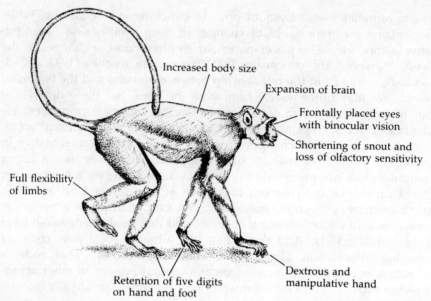

Increased body size

Expansion of brain

Frontally placed eyes
with binocular vision

Shortening of snout and
loss of olfactory sensitivity

Full flexibility
of limbs

Dextrous and
manipulative hand

Retention of five digits
on hand and foot

Figure 1.1 Principal characteristics of the primates (based on Napier 1971).

both particular phases of the lifespan and longevity as a whole. In dietary terms the primates are remarkably flexible, but there is a trend from insectivory to frugivory and omnivory. However, it must be stresed that these are general trends, and any particular group of primates may have either elaborated or reversed these trends.

Living primates are divided into two main groups (Fig. 1.2) – the Strepsirhini and the Haplorhini (Szalay & Delson 1979). The former are the more ancient lineage, comprising the prosimians, the smaller, largely nocturnal and insectivorous species – lemurs, lorises and related forms.

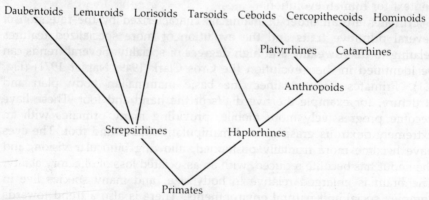

Daubentoids Lemuroids Lorisoids Tarsoids Ceboids Cercopithecoids Hominoids

Platyrrhines Catarrhines

Anthropoids

Strepsirhines Haplorhines

Primates

Figure 1.2 Relations between the higher taxonomic categories of primate.

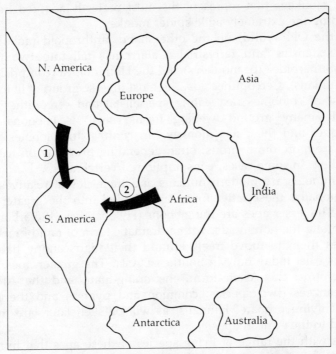

Figure 1.3   Relative positions of the continents in the Eocene epoch,
about 55 to 35 Ma ago, showing the alternative routes of
dispersal for the platyrrhines; 1, from Africa across a
reduced Atlantic; 2, from North America before the
formation of a link between North and South America (see
Ciochon & Chiarelli 1980 for a discussion of this; map after
Eisenberg 1981).

The other, haplorhines, consists of three major taxa – tarsiers, platyrrhines and catarrhines. Tarsiers are a relict, geographically localized group
restricted to Southeast Asia of essentially prosimian-like forms that have
re-adapted to a nocturnal way of life. Consequently, many of their
characteristics have converged on those of strepsirhines. Platyrrhines and
catarrhines are the anthropoid (monkey-grade) primates of the New and
Old Worlds, respectively. The Americas have been isolated from Eurasia
and Africa for at least 35 million years (Ma) (Fig. 1.3), allowing anthropoid primates to evolve in isolation. These two groups thus represent a
classic example of parallel evolution, where the same selective pressures
have produced similar evolutionary patterns. Platyrrhines have remained an entirely arboreal group, living in the tropical rainforests of
central and southern America. They have produced both very small
species (marmosets and tamarins) that have at least partially converged
on some of the vacant prosimian niches of the New World, as well as

larger monkeys that represent the most perfectly adapted tree-dwellers, including the extremely agile spider monkey.

In the Old World, on the other hand, anthropoid radiation was far more extensive and terrestrial. Catarrhines fall into two groups: the Cercopithecoidea (or monkeys) and the Hominoidea (comprising the apes and humans). Cercopithecoids, the most diverse group of living primates, consist of colobines (leaf-eating specialists) and cercopithecines (which include many ground-dwelling forms, such as baboons, mandrills, macaques and the patas monkey). In contrast to colobines, cercopithecines are more omnivorous, often depending primarily on fruits but also including, in some cases, consumption of vertebrates.

Hominoids are modern humans and their closest relatives, the apes. Traditionally, these latter forms are divided into the greater and lesser apes. The lesser apes are the gibbons (Hylobatidae), the arboreal specialists among the hominoids, with a dramatic form of rapid brachiation that enables them to move freely around their high canopy habitat. These species exist today only in Southeast Asia. The greater apes really form two groups: the Asian form, the orang-utan, and the African apes, chimpanzees (two species, common and pygmy) and the gorilla, the largest living primate. Humans, as will be seen later, are most closely related to the African apes.

It is with the range of living species of these apes that humans share the closest genetic, morphological and evolutionary relationship. As the evolutionary biologists were quick to note, humans are clearly primates, possessing many characteristics derived from common primate ancestors, as well as modifying successful primate features to their own ends. From the perspective of palaeoanthropology, the central characteristics of primate adaptations – the grasping hand (and foot), the importance of vision, the loss of olfactory senses, and the high level of sociality represent the starting point in any consideration of human evolution, while departures from the primate form – for example, bipedalism – may be considered as particularly important in human evolution.

Even after many years of research primate taxonomy has still not been settled, and is presently being modified as new biochemical approaches to classification are developed. This is true at the highest taxonomic levels – for example, relationships of tarsiers to anthropoids and prosimians, and relationships of Old and New World monkeys – as well as at the lowest – for example, the extent to which the various forms of *Papio* baboon are separate species. But a basic classification of the living primates is shown here for reference (Table 1.1).

Hominids and humans

The variability of these characteristics provides the basis for classification, as primates fall into greater and smaller groups according to shared

Table 1.1 A classification of the primates (modified from Kavanagh 1984)

	Informal or common name
Order	
Suborder	
Superfamily	
Family	
Subfamily	
Genus	
Primates	Primates
Strepsirhini*	Prosimians
Lemuroidea	Lemuroids
Cheirogaleidae	
Microcebus	Mouse lemurs
Cheirogaleus	Dwarf lemurs
Phanerinae	
Phaner	Dwarf lemur
Lemuridae	
Lemur	Lemurs
Varecia	Lemur
Hapalemur	Lemurs
Lepilemuridae	
Lepilemur	Sportive lemurs
Indriidae	
Avahi	Woolly lemur
Propithecus	Sifakas
Indri	Indri
Daubentonioidea	
Daubentoniidae	
Daubentonia	Aye-aye
Lorisoidea	Lorisoids
Lorisidae	
Lorisinae	Lorises
Loris	Slender loris
Nycticebus	Slow loris
Arctocebus	Angwantibo
Perodicticus	Potto
Galaginae	
Galago	Bushbabies
Haplorhini*	
Tarsioidea	
Tarsiidae	
Tarsius	Tarsiers
(Platyrrhini)†	Platyrrhines
Ceboidea	Ceboids
Callitrichidae	
Cebuella	Pygmy marmoset
Callithrix	Marmosets
Saguinus	Tamarins
Leontopithecus	Lion tamarin

Table 1.1 (contd)

Order
  Suborder
    Superfamily
      Family
        Subfamily
          Genus
	Informal or common name

Callimiconidae	
Callimico	Goeldi's monkey
Cebidae	
Saimiriinae	
Saimiri	Squirrel monkey
Aotinae	
Aotus	Night monkey
Callicebinae	
Callicebus	Titis
Alouattinae	
Alouatta	Howler monkeys
Cebinae	
Cebus	Capuchins
Pitheciinae	
Pithecia	Sakis
Chiropotes	Sakis
Cacajao	Uakaris
Atelinae	
Lagothrix	Woolly monkeys
Ateles	Spider monkeys
Brachyteles	Woolly spider monkey
(Catarrhini)[†]	Catarrhines
Cercopithecoidea	Cercopithecoids
Cercopithecidae	
Colobinae	Colobines
Colobus	Colobus monkeys
Presbytis	Langurs
Nasalis	Proboscis monkey
Simias	Simakobu
Rhinopithecus	Snub-nosed monkeys
Pygathrix	Douc monkey
Cercopithecinae	Cercopithecines
Cercopithecus	Guenons
(*Miopithecus*)[§]	Talapoin
(*Erythrocebus*)[§]	Patas monkey
(*Cercocebus*)[§]	Mangebeys
Papio	Baboons
(*Mandrillus*)[§]	Mandrills
Theropithecus	Gelada
Macaca	Macaques

(contd)

Order
  Suborder
    Superfamily
      Family
        Subfamily
          Genus
	Informal or common name

Hominoidea	Hominoids
Hylobatidae	Hylobatids
Hylobates	Gibbons
(Symphalangus)§	Siamang
Pongidae‡	Pongids
Pongo	Orang-utan
African apes + humans (?)	
Gorilla	Gorilla
Pan	Chimpanzees
Homo	Man (humans)

* An alternative classification would divide the primates into two suborders, the Prosimii and the Anthropoidea. The principal difference between the two classifications would be the positioning of the tarsiers (belonging to the Prosimii). The term prosimian is still used informally to refer to primates below the grade of monkey.

† The infraorder Platyrrhini (platyrrhines) are the New World monkeys; the Catarrhini (catarrhines) are humans, apes and monkeys of the Old World.

‡ Revisions of hominoid taxonomy have led to terminological confusion. The traditional classification is three families: Hylobatidae (gibbons and siamangs), Pongidae (orang-utan, gorilla and chimpanzee) and Hominidae (humans). It is now recognized, though, that humans share a closer relationship with the chimpanzees and gorillas (the African apes) than any of them do with the Asian ape, the orang-utan. In formal classification, this would mean that the African apes fall within the Hominidae. However, this would lead to considerable confusion given that the term hominid has been used extensively to describe humans and their direct ancestors. In the absence of a resolution of this problem no formal assignation is used here.

§ Some authorities consider these taxa to be subgenera.

features. The precise recognition of which group is referred to is of considerable significance in an evolutionary analysis. In particular the definition of *hominid* and *human* is critical here.

In the past, it has often been assumed that hominid and human could be used interchangeably. However, at this stage we do not know what the degrees of difference between extinct and living hominid taxa are, and only confusion can arise if the distinction is not maintained. The term *hominid* (which is derived from the family name, the Hominidae) should be used to denote all populations and species with which we share an evolutionary history exclusive of any other living primate. In this text 'early hominid' refers to hominids before the evolution of *Homo sapiens*. The term *human* should be reserved solely for members of the only living subspecies of hominid, *Homo sapiens sapiens*, or for characteristics found among living populations. For extinct or anatomically distinguishable forms it is better to use the general term hominid, as it is precisely the differences between extinct and living forms that provide the key to hominid evolutionary ecology. Furthermore, although the term 'man', used in a biological sense, refers to all members of the subspecies *Homo sapiens sapiens* and not just to the male sex, it should also be avoided on the same grounds. Table 1.2 summarizes the taxonomic place of humans and hominids in the biological world.

Table 1.2   Hominid taxonomy: the place of humans and hominids in the biological world (based on Le Gros Clark 1949; Szalay & Delson 1979)

Taxon	Linnean name	Common name	Group of animals
Class	Mammalia	Mammals	All warmblooded animals with hair that bear viviparous young
Order	Primates	Primates	Prosimians, monkeys, apes and man
Suborder	Haplorhini	Haplorhines	Tarsiers, monkeys, apes and man
Infraorder	Catarrhini	Catarrhines	Old World monkeys, apes and man
Superfamily	Hominoidea	Hominoids	Apes and man
Family	Hominidae	Hominids	Man and ancestors thereof
Genus	*Homo*	Hominines	Man
Species	*H. sapiens*		Recent man
Subspecies	*H.s. sapiens*		Anatomically modern man (humans)

2 The story of human evolution

The scale of human evolution

The evolution of *Homo sapiens* is the evolution of just one among millions of species that have lived on this planet. To understand this, and the evolution of the hominids in general, it is necessary to see them in the perspective of the evolution of life in general.

Geological time

The Earth is currently estimated as being 4600 million years (Ma) old. The time between then and now – geological time – is divided into a series of periods that mark off the evolution of the Earth's climate, geography and biology (Fig. 2.1). Each period is distinguished by particular geological deposits and fossils, set in geographical and stratigraphical relationships.

The vastness of geological time can be disconcerting, and can cause conceptual problems. Most people, used to time marked out in hours and days and years, stretched to a generation on either side of them, can easily understand past events when related to those markers. Much of history, measurable in terms of months and years, is comprehensible in this way. To move, though, beyond written history is to move to a new scale, to one where individual years and individual generations are invisible, and the observable units of time – thousands and millions of years – bear no relationship to those we live in today.

However, to understand evolutionary processes it is essential to recognize the variable lengths of time over which they occur. This involves recognizing several different aspects of geological time. One is simply that periods of geological time are extremely long, beyond commonsense understanding, even when dealing with relatively recent periods. For example, even the last part of the last geological epoch – the

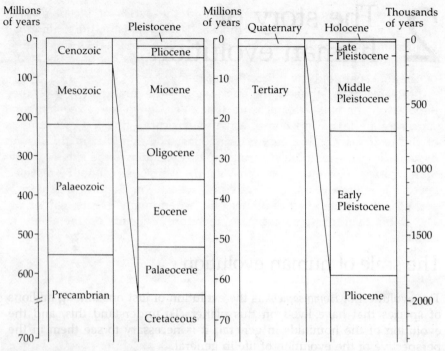

Figure 2.1 The geological timescale.

late Pleistocene – is a period of 115 000 years; that is, well over 50 times as long as recorded history, a period in which the equivalent 4600 generations of modern humans would have lived. The impact of these extensive periods becomes even more significant when earlier periods are incorporated – the Pleistocene as a whole, nearly 2 million years; the Pliocene, 3 million years; and the Miocene, 20 million years. At first sight, the vastness of time might defy explanation, for it might be thought impossible to imagine processes occurring at this scale. However, the paradox of the geological record is that although the lengths of time may be enormous, the processes of life still continue to operate on a day-to-day basis. In other words, the geological record may show patterns of long-term change and continuity, but biological processes operating on the scale of a single individual's lifetime still apply. It is this fact that enables us to grasp the scales involved in evolutionary processes.

This is not to deny, of course, that there may be processes occurring on a long-term scale. The point is that long-term processes do not override shorter-term ones. The frame of mind with which to approach the long stretches of the past is that there are a variety of processes occurring on several different timescales. There are the long-term processes of plate tectonics and continental drift, the 20 000–40 000– and 100 000–year cycles of orbital variation and hence global temperature variation, the

10 000–year cycle of an interglacial, and the cycles of lifespan of all species, which may vary from thousands of years for the Californian bristlecone pines, to fractions of a day for microscopic organisms (Imbrie & Imbrie 1979; Butzer 1982). The complexity of life is not the dominance of one timespan, but the integration of many.

Problems arise, though, in identifying these timespans, since they depend on the ability to measure time. Very often perceived temporal processes are less a function of actual biological or physical processes as of the resolution of the dating techniques. For example, in the distant past species arose with bewildering rapidity, relative to the length of time that occurred. However, very often dating techniques cannot be resolved beyond a million years. Consequently, what is rapid in one geological period is the entire span of a later one, where many events may occur. The ability to understand the past, therefore, depends on the ability to calibrate it.

Dating techniques

Dating techniques fall into two broad categories – *relative*, or those that determine whether objects and events are older or younger relative to each other, and *absolute*, where a date in real time (number of years) can be calculated (Oakley 1966). The development of dating techniques has been a story of absolute methods superceding relative ones.

Relative dating, though, still remains an important approach. The principal method of relative dating is stratigraphy or geological super-imposition (Fig. 2.2). For the most part, where a geological deposit is

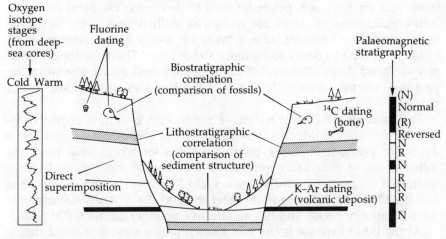

Figure 2.2 Schematic illustration of the principal methods of dating, correlation and calibration.

superimposed on another it represents a later or younger period. Stratigraphic analysis and correlation can be used to set up the *sequence* of events in the geological past. The other important technique in relative chronology is biostratigraphic correlation. In this case, the fossil remains of past animals and plants are used to order geological deposits. Strata that contain the same species or similar assemblages of species may, within an evolutionary context, be assumed to be contemporary. Similarities and differences between fossil sites can be used to construct a relative chronology. The underlying assumption of this method is that fossils that are morphologically similar would have been alive at the same time, and therefore deposits with the same type of fossils must have been laid down approximately contemporaneously. Where the evolutionary sequences of fossil lineages are known, biostratigraphy can be used to construct extensive chronologies, which may be correlated from site to site over wide areas.

Some scientific techniques have been developed to heighten the accuracy of relative dating methods. The best-known example is that of fluorine dating (Oakley & Montagu 1949). Fossils are known to absorb fluorine and other elements from their depositional environment, and therefore levels of these elements should indicate the contemporaneity and relative ages of the specimens. However, as fluorine levels vary enormously from one area to another, the technique has only local applicability.

For the most part scientific techniques have been used to provide absolute dates. The principle underlying most absolute dating techniques is that of radioactive decay (Tite 1972). Certain elements occur in unstable forms (isotopes), that decay into other elements (stable isotopes). This radioactive decay occurs at known rates, allowing the ratios between the stable and unstable isotopes to be used to determine the dates of events in the past. Rates of decay are measured in 'half-lives' – the length of time, which is a constant, that it takes for half a given quantity of an unstable isotope to decay to its more stable form. These 'isotopic clocks' provide good dates whenever it can be established at what point in the past they started 'ticking'. For each of the best-known methods, this is the case.

The most useful dating technique for human evolution is *potassium–argon*. Potassium (K) decays into argon (Ar) at a known rate (half-life = 1.3×10^9 years; Birch 1951); only where it is known at what point the initial levels of potassium were set is this a valid method, and consequently it is appropriate for volcanic rocks. However, given its very long half-life, $^{40}K/^{40}Ar$ dating (and its sister method $^{40}Ar/^{39}Ar$) is suitable only for very ancient rocks, and has an effective younger limit 500 000 years.

At the other extreme is the best-known radiometric or isotopic dating technique – *radiocarbon* (^{14}C) dating. All living matter absorbs an unstable carbon isotope (^{14}C) from the atmosphere where it occurs at low levels. At death, though, this absorption stops, and as ^{14}C is unstable it breaks down to nitrogen. Again, the rate of decay is known (half-life = 5730 years (Tite 1972: 88)) and so the ratio of the unstable to stable carbon isotopes (^{14}C/^{12}C) may be used to determine the date of death. Radiocarbon dating uses fossil material, and so depends on the presence of uncontaminated organic material. Furthermore, its short half-life means that it is seldom accurate beyond 40 000 years, although recent developments using an atomic accelerator may extend this back to 100 000 years ago (Gillespie, Gowlett et al. 1984).

In between the accurate ranges of radiocarbon and potassium–argon dating lie some lesser-known isotopic techniques (e.g. ^{234}U/^{230}Th) (see Bishop & Miller 1972). There remains, however, an important period between 500 000 and 40 000 years ago that is poorly dated. To some extent, other dating techniques may be used to fill this gap. *Thermoluminescence dating* (TL) uses the fact that uranium decaying in crystalline materials leaves electrons trapped in the crystal lattice to date material. By heating these materials the electrons are released as light, which can be measured and an age calculated on the basis of the rate of emission. *Electron spin resonance* (ESR) measures the same phenomenon, but without the destruction of the specimens. *Fission track dating* is also based on the decay of uranium, and in this case measures the length of time over which decay has occurred by counting the number of 'tracks' these emissions leave on the surfaces of minerals and glasses (Fleischer & Hart 1972). Although all these methods have the potential for filling the chronological gap between the two major techniques, they have still not been widely applied.

One further method that underpins the measurement of geological time is that of *palaeomagnetism*. The direction of the Earth's magnetic field has not remained stable during the past, but has intermittently reversed (Stacey 1969). These polarity reversals are often recorded in the stratigraphic record. Sequences of palaeomagnetic data can help in stratigraphic correlation, and individual observations can act as a limited test on other dating methods.

Palaeomagnetism is really one of a series of techniques that do not supply actual dates but act as a means of making correlations between areas. A similar technique of frequent use today is *stable oxygen isotope analysis* of microfossils collected from deep-sea cores. Analysis of the ratio of two stable isotopes of oxygen (^{16}O/^{18}O) has led to the construction of a temperature curve, using material cored from the deep sea. These curves have now been recognized from many different parts of the world, and have been subdivided into a series of stages (Shackleton & Opdyke 1976). Some correlation of these with terrestrial stratigraphy has been established, particularly in the loess regions of Europe (Kukla 1975). From the application of these and other techniques has come the chronological framework of human evolution.

Chronological framework of human evolution

A long procession of fossils has come and gone as the earliest evidence of human evolution, or the proverbial 'missing link'. Many of these fossils have now been discounted as belonging to other groups of animals. For example, a Miocene ape called *Pliopithecus* was once thought to be an early hominid on the grounds that it had a flat (orthognathous) face – a hominid characteristic. This is now recognized to have been a case of parallel evolution among related lineages. The others have been incorporated into various parts of the human evolutionary story.

Evolution is a continuous process, with no natural breaks, and so there can be no single starting point for human evolution. Chronological scale can only be measured in a taxonomic framework. Taxonomy is the classification of objects and phenomena, and in this case of plants and animals. The system of classification used in biology is known as Linnean taxonomy, and was developed by the Swedish naturalist Karl Linné in the eighteenth century. Using the degree of similarity and dissimilarity between the morphology of organisms, a nested hierarchical classification can be constructed which groups animals into larger and larger units. Consequently, the chronological scale of human evolution depends on the taxonomic scale.

Considerable controversy exists about the dates of the earliest appearance of the various taxonomic units (Andrews 1983; Ciochon 1983; Pilbeam 1984). Much of this controversy is derived from the methods used to reconstruct phylogenetic relationships (Sarich 1971; Goodman 1976; Eldredge & Cracraft 1980). The traditional approach is the analysis of fossil morphology, with the chronology of the evolutionary divergences calculated on the basis of chronometric measurements of geological deposits. For example, the recovery of fossils showing characteristics unique to the hominid family at 12 Ma would indicate that hominids and the apes had diverged significantly by at least this date.

An alternative approach is to use the so-called 'molecular clock' (Sarich & Wilson 1967; Friday 1981). This compares similarities and differences in the biochemistry of living species, and on the basis of the degree of similarity estimates the time since they diverged in their evolutionary history. Three basic sources of data are used: proteins, such as those contained in blood serums; 'parasitic' or viral genes associated with particular species; and actual mapping of the DNA. It is assumed that the rate of change in these is constant over long periods of time, and consequently that quantification of the differences will result in a means of calculating the age of evolutionary events. They must at some point, however, be calibrated with a well-established point in the fossil record, or else molecular clock-based phylogenies will provide only relative information.

When the molecular approach was first proposed by Sarich & Wilson (1967) it was widely criticized as it produced dates that were much later than those based on the fossil record. Now, though, there is much greater agreement between palaeontologists and biochemists for the date of the major events in primate and hominid evolution (Ciochon 1983; Goodman, Baba & Darga 1983; Pilbeam 1984). Consensus has come from revisions in the molecular dates, from better dating of the fossil record, and, most importantly of all, from the recognition by palaeontologists that not all the fossils can be linked to modern forms, but instead represent patterns of diversity in the past not continued through to the present day. The result has been a more complex reading of the evolutionary history of the primates.

The primates are currently thought to have diverged from the early insectivores by about 70 Ma ago (see Fig. 2.3) (Szalay & Delson 1979; see papers in Ciochon and Corruccini 1983 for a full discussion of these recent interpretations). The early fossil record of the haplorhines and strepsir-hines is poorly known, but the ancestral group of the catarrhines are known to be distinct from the New World platyrrhines by at least 35 Ma ago. The date of the divergence between the ancestors of the apes and of the Old World monkeys is poorly marked in the fossil record, but is probably at about 23 Ma ago. The African and Asian branches of the hominoids probably diverged at about 12 Ma ago. The molecular biolo-gists place the divergence of the hominids from the other African apes at about 6 Ma ago, and the best evidence for the earliest appearance of hominids in the fossil record is at about 5 Ma ago from Tabarin (Hill 1985) and Lothagam (Patterson, Behrensmeyer & Sill 1970) in Kenya (Fig. 2.4).

Between 5 and 1.2 Ma ago hominids can be divided into two major groups – the australopithecines and the genus *Homo* (Howell 1978). The

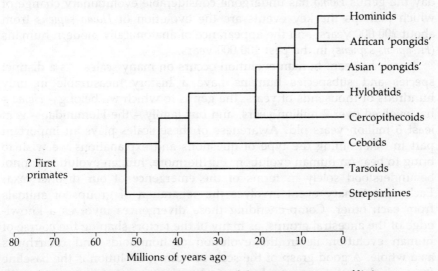

Figure 2.3 Evolutionary relationships of the major groups of living primates (see Szalay & Delson 1979; Pilbeam 1984).

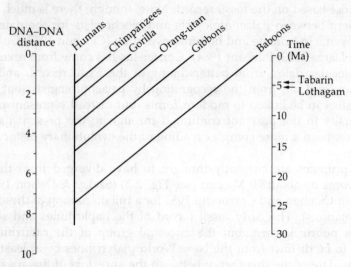

Figure 2.4 DNA-DNA hybridization distances for some groups of catarrhines. The scale on the right-hand side shows estimated times of divergence in millions of years, and the dates of the earliest known hominid fossils (based on Sibley & Ahlquist 1984; from Pilbeam 1986).

former represent the earliest known hominids, and the latter seem to make their appearance at about 2 Ma ago. From that date to the present day the genus *Homo* has undergone considerable evolutionary change of which perhaps the key events are the evolution of *Homo sapiens* from about 200 000 years, and the appearance of anatomically modern humans (*H.sapiens sapiens*) in the past 100 000 years.

As can be seen, human evolution occurs on many scales. As a distinct species and subspecies humans have a history measurable in only hundreds of thousands of years; the genus to which we belong – *Homo* – has evolved over 2 million years, and our family – the Hominidae – is at least 6 million years old. Awareness of these scales plays an important part in determining the type of questions and explanations we wish to bring to bear on human evolution. Furthermore, human evolution cannot be understood solely in terms of the emergence of our distinct taxa. Each evolutionary event involves the separation of groups of animals from each other. Comprehending these divergences involves a knowledge of the ancestral groups, as many of the factors shaping the course of human evolution lie in the evolution of hominoids and catarrhines as a whole. A good grasp of the scale of human evolution is the baseline from which evolutionary and ecological analysis must stem.

Fossil hominids

Hominid origins

The suggestion that the first hominids appear at the very end of the Miocene about 6 Ma ago contrasts both with earlier views that saw human evolution as principally a Pleistocene event, and also with more recent ideas that placed the divergence of the hominids and the apes (pongids) at no later than 15 Ma ago (see, for example, Pilbeam 1972). The basis for this latter interpretation was the assessment of *Ramapithecus* as a hominid or lying close to the origins of the hominids (Simons 1961; Pilbeam 1968). *Ramapithecus punjabicus* was first found in the 1930s in the Inidan subcontinent (Lewis 1934). Large numbers of specimens of *Ramapithecus* have since been recovered from Greece, China, Kenya and Turkey (Leakey 1967; Pilbeam 1968; Andrews & Tobien 1977), and closely related forms are also known from Hungary (Kretzoi 1975).

The reasons why these fossils were thought to be hominid lay in various dental characteristics, the only well-known anatomical features (Conroy & Pilbeam 1975). *Ramapithecus* had a reduced canine, thickened tooth enamel, enlarged premolar and molar teeth and was originally thought to have had a parabolic dental arcade. All these features occur among more recent hominids, and were considered to be diagnostic of the family. On the basis of this diagnosis hominid origins could be traced back to the middle Miocene at least (Fig. 2.5). Miocene hominoids were therefore interpreted in terms of a long separation of the living forms of ape.

This view of hominid origins has, however, come increasingly under attack. Partly this has been a response to the application of molecular biology to evolutionary systematics, partly to a great improvement in the quantity and quality of Miocene fossil hominids, and partly to a reconsideration of the various attributes found in *Ramapithecus* that were thought to be uniquely hominid. For example, thick tooth enamel has proved to be a complex trait that occurs not only in humans but also in the orang-utan (Kay 1981). Other Miocene hominids also displayed these characteristics, including *Gigantopithecus* and *Sivapithecus* (Kay 1981; Gannt 1983); Boyde & Martin (1984) have recently shown that the patterns of enamel development in the higher primates are extremely complex. Consequently, as more fossil evidence for Miocene hominoids accumulated it became clear that what were thought to be distinctive hominid traits were in fact part of a much more general pattern of hominoid evolution. As Pilbeam (1984; and see Ciochon and Corruccini 1983 for a full review) has cogently argued, *Ramapithecus* is best treated as an integral part of a Miocene pattern of evolutionary divergence, than tentatively linked to a much later event.

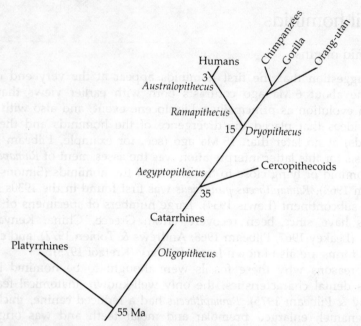

Figure 2.5 'Classic' model of the evolutionary pattern of the catarrhines, showing an early divergence of the hominids from the other apes, and *Ramapithecus* as a direct ancestor of later hominids.

With *Ramapithecus* rejected as a hominid it became one of an exclusive club of abandoned human ancestors, each of which possessed what was thought to be a unique hominid feature. However, in each case further analysis showed that many such features are not necessarily unique to the hominids, but reflect shared adaptive problems and solutions.

The interpretation of hominoid evolution that is most compatible with both the fossil and biochemical evidence would see events of the Miocene centring on an early African divergence of the hominoids, spreading out from there to other parts of the Old World, and only at the very end of this period giving rise to hominids. Consequently, the specimens and samples that have been assigned to such taxa as *Kenyapithecus, Sivapithecus, Ouranopithecus*, etc. (see Table 2.1) are not necessarily related to later and living hominoids and hominids, but truly Miocene evolutionary phenomena. This conclusion has important implications that will be discussed more fully in Chapter 7.

Pliocene hominids

As stated above (see page 21), it is not until about 5 Ma ago that hominid fossils become relatively common (see Fig. 2.6 for the locations of the sites

Table 2.1 Characteristics, and chronological and geographical range of the major groups of Miocene hominoid

Genus	Geographical distribution*	Chronological range (Ma ago)	Comments
Pliopithecus	WSEP; ECEP	15–9	A small primitive European form, often associated with gibbons, but probably a case of parallel evolution
Dryopithecus	WSEP	12.5–9	A larger European primitive hominoid, probably arboreal and forest-dwelling
Sivapithecus	ECEP; SPP; SiP; EAP?	15–7	A widepread and variable Miocene ape with some adaptations to more open environment and woodland; possibly ancestral to the orang-utan
Ramapithecus	SPP; SiP; ECEP?	+11–7	Previously considered to be the earliest hominid, but now recognized as an Asian ape closely related (if not a sexual dimorph) of *Sivapithecus*
Gigantopithecus	SiP	9.5–7	The largest known hominoid, probably terrestrial, with very large specialized back teeth; survived to middle Pleistocene
Ouranopithecus	SPP	12–10	A large hominoid from Greece, possibly ancestral to all living larger hominoids
Kenyapithecus	EAP; SPP	14–12	A larger African hominoid, previously linked to *Ramapithecus* but probably a separate group and possibly ancestral to later African hominoids

Table 2.1   (contd)

Genus	Geographical distribution*	Chronological range (Ma ago)	Comments
Proconsul	EAP	22–12	A very long-lasting group of African apes, the earlier forms possibly ancestral to all living hominoids; arboreal and forest-dwelling with a unique locomotor system
Limnopithecus	EAP	22–12	A smaller African hominoid

* Geographical distribution is based on Bernor's (1983) zoogeographic zones: WSEP, Western and Southern European provinces; ECEP, Eastern and Central European province; SPP, Sub-Paratethyan Province; SiP, Siwalik Province. See text for discussion and principal sources.

mentioned in the text). The earliest sites are those of Tabarin near Lake Baringo in Kenya, where Hill (1985) recently reported the discovery of a possible hominid fossil jaw dated to 4.9 Ma ago, and Lothagam, on the west side of Lake Turkana, but the best known and richest are the region of Hadar in Ethiopia and Laetoli in Tanzania.

From Laetoli have come large numbers of teeth and jaw fragments, as well as footprints of a bipedal primate thought to be a hominid (M. D. Leakey, Hay et al. 1976; M. D. Leakey 1978). At Hadar, Johanson and his co-workers found the now-notorious 'Lucy', a small partial skeleton, as well as many other fossils including a group of hominids that were apparently all killed at the same time by a flash flood (see *American Journal of Physical Anthropology* 1982, vol. 57(4)). The former site has a date of 3.6 Ma, the latter one of about 2.9 Ma.

Although they are very variable, Johanson & White (1979) argued that all the specimens belonged to a single species *Australopithecus afarensis* (Fig. 2.8). This species was characterized by a dental arcade that is long, narrow and straight-sided, with enlarged postcanine teeth, as would be expected for a hominid, but also having relatively large incisors and a canine larger than that known for other hominids. The face, particularly the alveolar (tooth-bearing) region, is protruding (prognathous). The brain case is small, with marked muscular attachments and pronounced postorbital waisting. *Australopithecus afarensis* thus has characteristics that would be expected for a very early hominid. Postcranially perhaps the most significant fact about this species is that it is clearly capable of bipedalism, although certain features such as curved phalanges (toe bones) might also indicate some arboreal heritage (Jungers & Stern 1983;

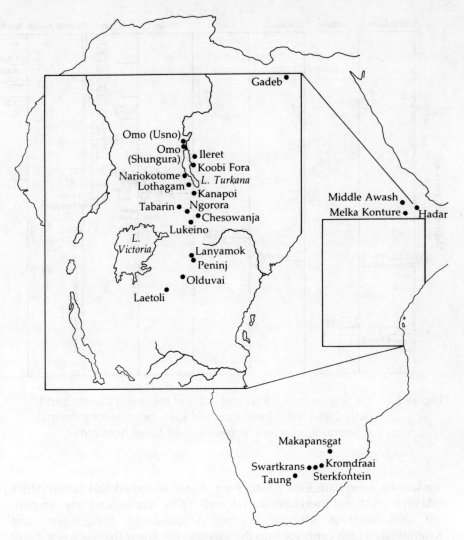

Figure 2.6 Sites of important early hominids (australopithecines, *Homo habilis* and early *H. erectus*) in eastern and southern Africa.

Stern & Susman 1983). A further notable aspect of *A. afarensis* is its marked variation in size, which, it has been suggested, indicates a sexually dimorphic species (Johanson & White 1979; Johanson & Edey 1981), but which has also been interpreted as indicative of the presence of more than one species of hominid at this early stage.

By the middle of the Pliocene the fossil record of hominids becomes much richer. Although there are problems in dating the South African material (see page 17), fossil hominids from between 3.0 and 1.8 Ma ago

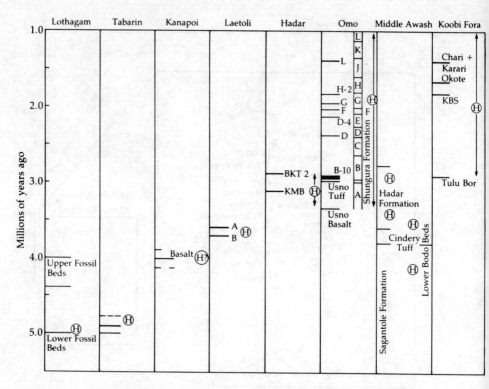

Figure 2.7 Geological formations and dates of the major Pliocene and early Pleistocene fossil hominid sites. See text for principal references. H refers to positions of fossil hominids.

are known from both East (Koobi Fora, Omo, Kanapoi) and South Africa (Makapansgat and Sterkfontein) (Howell 1978). These, and later important sites such as Olduvai, Peninj, Chesowanja, Swartkrans, and Kromdraai, which continue into the Pleistocene, show that between 2 and 1 Ma ago the hominids had diverged into several species, representing two distinct trends in human evolution.

The first of these trends is represented by the gracile and robust australopithecines. The gracile specimens have been assigned to *Australopithecus africanus* (Fig. 2.8), which Tobias (1980) has argued includes the earlier species *Australopithecus afarensis*, is a lightly built hominid, with a rounded, globular cranium, a prognathous, dish-shaped face, and enlarged molars and premolars. The canine is reduced relative to that found in *A. afarensis*. Somewhat later in time are more robust specimens of the australopithecines, referred to as *Australopithecus boisei* in East Africa, and as *Australopithecus robustus* in South Africa (Fig. 2.8). Some authors (Howell 1978) have suggested that there is a third species of robust

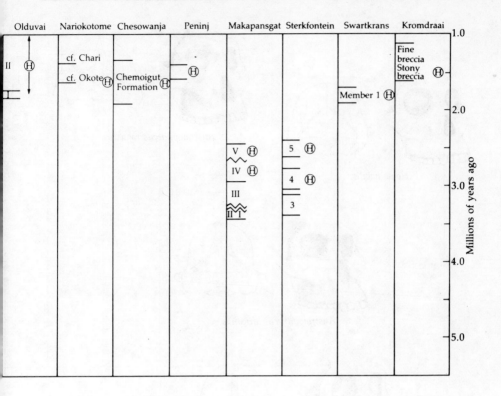

australopithecine, *Australopithecus crassidens*, in South Africa. All these hominids are very heavily built with marked crests and ridges for muscular attachments, and with very marked constriction of the skull behind the orbits. The face is large and often broad and square in the maxillary region. The teeth are the most distinctive feature of these taxa, with greatly enlarged molars and molarized premolars. The anterior dentition, the canines and incisors, is, in contrast, very reduced and crowded. The mandible, as would be expected for such large grinding teeth, is heavy and buttressed. As with all other known hominids, however, the robust australopithecines are adapted to habitual bipedalism. The other lineage is the genus *Homo*, first represented by *Homo habilis* (Fig. 2.8). Unlike the robust australopithecines, the early hominines (members of the genus *Homo* – see Table 1.2) are characterized by an enlarged cranial capacity, upwards of 650 cm^3. The teeth and jaws, while still larger than those of modern man, are nonetheless reduced relative to the australopithecines. *Homo habilis* has been found at various sites in East

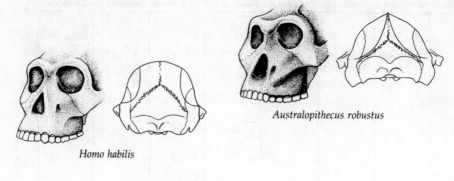

Australopithecus robustus

Homo habilis

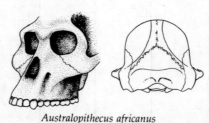

Australopithecus africanus

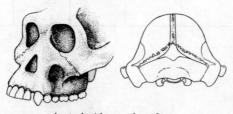

Australopithecus afarenfis

Figure 2.8   The earliest hominids (all drawn to the same scale): (a) *Australopithecus afarensis*; (b) *Australopithecus africanus*; (c) *Australopithecus robustus*; (d) *Homo habilis* (from White, Johanson & Kimbel 1983).

Africa – especially Olduvai and Koobi Fora – and is known also from South Africa.

Pleistocene hominids

At the beginning of the Pleistocene hominids were more diverse than at any time before or since, with the robust australopithecines and the early genus *Homo* both co-existing in Africa. However, two major events occur during the early Pleistocene. First, by 1.6 Ma ago *Homo habilis* has been replaced by *Homo erectus* (Howell 1978) and, second, the australopithecines became extinct. Excellent specimens of *Homo erectus* have been discovered on both the eastern (Koobi Fora) and western (Nariokotome) shores of Lake Turkana in Kenya at dates of about 1.6 Ma ago. These include an almost complete skeleton (KNM-WT 15000) of a *Homo erectus* subadult male, indicating the very heavy build of this species. The latest known australopithecine specimen is dated to a little over 1 million years.

Homo erectus was the first hominid to colonize beyond sub-Saharan Africa. Fossils of this species have been found in North Africa, the Middle East, China and Java, and related but probably later forms are known from Europe (Fig. 2.9). *Homo erectus* is characterized by an increased body

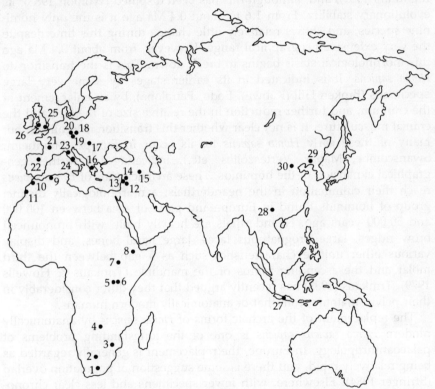

Figure 2.9   Sites of important later fossil hominids (later *Homo erectus* and early *Homo sapiens*): 1, Klasies River Mouth; 2, Saldanha (Florisbad); 3, Border Cave; 4, Kabwe (Broken Hill); 5, Olduvai and Laetoli; 6, Ndutu; 7, Omo; 8, Bodo; 9, Ternifine; 10, Salé; 11, Irhoud; 12, 'Ubeidiya; 13, Mount Carmel; 14, Qafzeh; 15, Shanidar; 16, Petralona; 17, Vérteszöllös; 18, Bilzingsleben; 19, Steinheim; 20, Mauer; 21, southwestern France late Pleistocene sites (including La Ferrassie and La Chapelle-aux-Saints); 22, Torralba/Ambrona; 23, Isernia; 24, Monte Circeo; 25, Swanscombe; 26, Pontnewydd; 27, Java early hominid sites; 28, Yingkou; 29, Lantian; 30, Zhoukoudian.

size; a thickening of the cranial bones and enlargement of the cranial vault; very large face and teeth compared with modern man; very marked supraorbital tori (brow ridges); and a long low cranium, with marked muscle attachment areas both along the parietals and the occipital. Postcranially, *Homo erectus* is very similar to modern man, although some workers (Day 1971; Day & Molleson 1973; Kennedy 1984) have identified several features of the femur and the pelvis that may differ significantly.

It has long been recognized that perhaps the most significant characteristic of *Homo erectus* is its persistence through time (Pilbeam 1975; Rightmire 1981), and, although this has been disputed (Wolpoff 1983), its evolutionary stability. From 1.6 to about 0.4 Ma ago it is the only hominine species, and shows relatively little change during this time despite the very extensive geographical range. However, from about 0.4 Ma ago this morphological stasis begins to break down. This is the transition to *Homo sapiens*. It is indicated in its earlier stages by some very large specimens (Broken Hill (Kabwe), Bodo, Petralona), by an enlargement of the cranium, and further reduction in the relative size of the face and the cranial musculature. It is not clear whether this transition is localized, but many of these early *Homo sapiens* fossils occur in Europe (Steinheim, Swanscombe, Mauar, Verteszöllös, etc.), indicating yet further geographical expansion of the hominids. These archaic forms of *Homo sapiens* reach their culmination in the neanderthals, a morphologically distinct group of hominids found in Europe and parts of Asia between 100 000 and 50 000 years ago. Neanderthals are heavily built, with pronounced brow ridges, large prognathous faces, large nasal bones, and display various other unique characteristics such as a gap between the third molar and the ascending ramus of the mandible (Trinkaus & Howells 1979). Trinkaus (1983) has recently argued that they differ considerably in their pelvic anatomy from that of anatomically modern humans.

The replacement of the archaic forms of *Homo sapiens* by anatomically modern *Homo sapiens sapiens* is one of the longstanding problems of palaeoanthropology. In Europe, the replacement is generally regarded as being relatively rapid, and there is some suggestion of population overlap (Stringer 1984). Elsewhere, with fewer specimens and less clear chronology, such overlap cannot be demonstrated. Furthermore, specimens in Africa seem to indicate an earlier appearance of anatomically modern humans on this continent, suggesting that it is here that the origins of modern humans lie (Brauer 1984; Rightmire 1984), possibly as early as 100 000 years ago. Certainly by 30 000 years ago anatomically modern humans seem to be the only representative of the hominids throughout the world, although in Australia specimens from Kow Swamp as late as 10 000 years ago display some characteristics reminiscent of the archaic *sapiens* forms (Thorne & Macumber 1972). Our own subspecies is characterized by a generally much more gracile or lightly built frame, thinning of the bones of the cranial vault, raising and rounding of the cranium,

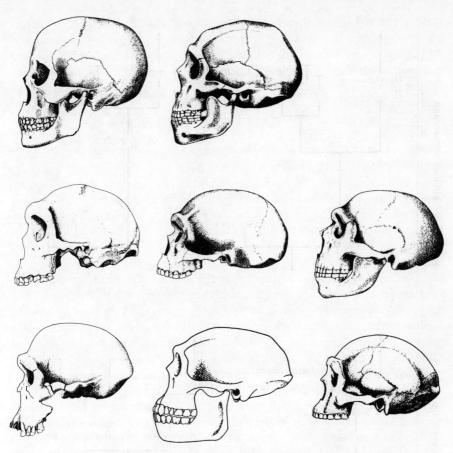

Figure 2.10   Later fossil hominids (all drawn to the same scale): (a) *Homo erectus* (1, KNM-ER 3733; 2, reconstruction of Java S4; 3, Zhoukoudian); (b) archaic *Homo sapiens* (1, Steinheim; 2, Kabwe; 3, Shanidar; 4, Monte Circeo); (c) *Homo sapiens sapiens*.

reduction in face and tooth size, and the development of a protruding chin button (Howell 1978).

Hominid phylogeny

The greatly improved fossil record, particularly in Africa, has enabled us to reconstruct the phylogeny of the hominids with some degree of accuracy. Gone is a simple unilineal pattern of ladder-like evolution towards modern forms, to be replaced by a more diverse and complex evolutionary history. However, even now, there is by no means full agreement about the precise details of this phylogeny (Figs. 2.11 and 2.12).

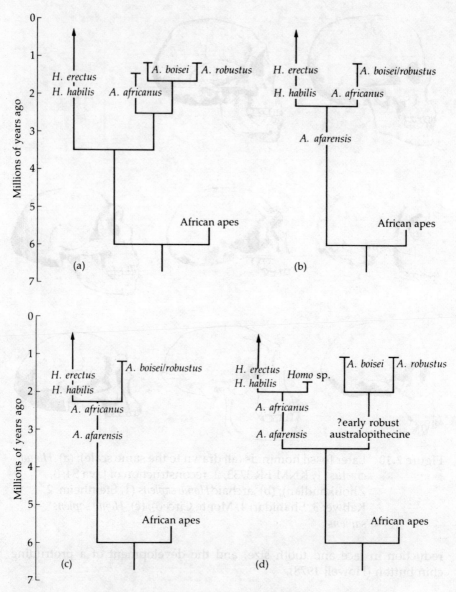

Figure 2.11   Alternative phylogenies for early hominid evolution:
(a) Walker & Leakey 1978; (b) Johanson & White 1979;
(c) Skelton, McHenry & Drawhorn 1986; (d) a model
showing early divergence of the robust australopithecines
and speciation within *Homo*.

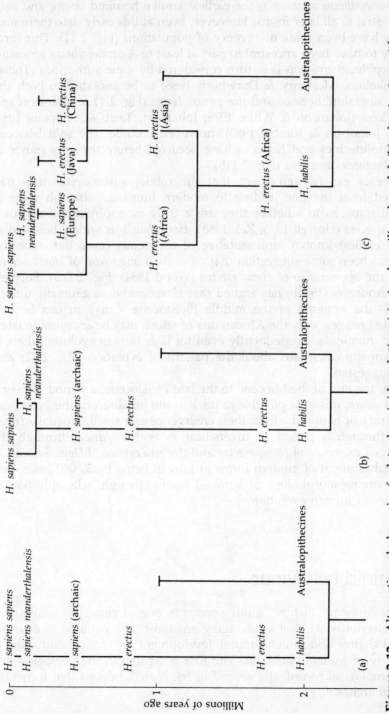

Figure 2.12 Alternative phylogenies for later hominid evolution: (a) simple unilineal model; (b) classic view with neanderthals as a side branch; (c) based on Andrews 1984a.

Australopithecus afarensis is the earliest known hominid taxon, and may be ancestral to all later forms. However, even at this early date there may already have been some divergence of populations (Fig. 2.11). This form is likely to have been ancestral in part at least to *Australopithecus africanus*. *Australopithecus africanus* is in turn considered by some authorities (Tobias 1980; Skelton, McHenry & Drawhorn 1986) to be ancestral to both the robust australopithecines and the genus *Homo* (Fig. 2.11c). Johanson and co-workers (Johanson & White 1979; Johanson, Taieb & Coppens 1982; White, Johanson & Kimbel 1983), however, consider the split between australopithecines and *Homo* to have occurred before the appearance of *Australopithecus africanus* (Fig. 2.11b).

There is general agreement that the robust australopithecines had diverged from the line leading to modern humans, although there is some dispute as to whether they are a truly monophyletic group or a single species (Howell 1978; Rak 1983). *Homo habilis* is widely believed to be the earliest known representative of the genus *Homo* but, recently, there has been some suggestion that more than one taxon of *Homo* occurs before the appearance of *Homo erectus* (Wood 1984) (Fig. 2.11d). Furthermore, Andrews (1984b) has argued that *Homo erectus* as generally understood – the hominid of the middle Pleistocene – may in fact be two separate lineages, only the African one of which may be ancestral to later, sapient, hominids. Consequently even for later human evolution there is not complete consensus about the pattern of evolution (Fig. 2.12) also been suggested.

From the end of the Miocene to the late Pleistocene, a period of over 5 million years, it is now possible to track in the fossil record the evolutionary history of hominids, from their emergence as a small, bipedal African form, through a period of diversification within Africa, through the prolonged existence of *Homo erectus* and the emergence of *Homo sapiens*, to the establishment of modern forms of human being by 30 000 years ago. The changing morphology of hominid fossils, though, tells only part of the story of human evolution.

Hominid behaviour

The evolutionary history of our species is one of changing adaptations and behaviours, as well as changing anatomy. The patterns of environmental change and of behavioural development are consequently part of the story of human evolution. The first is written in the geological and palaeontological record, the second in the material debris that forms the basis of archaeology.

Palaeoenvironments

The Earth's climate has by no means remained constant, but has fluctuat-
ed in relation to both internal and external factors. While the hominids
have been evolving there has been a general trend towards a cooler
climate (Fig. 2.13). During the Miocene and Pliocene this would have
resulted in the break up of the vast expanses of tropical rainforest and the
spread of drier and more seasonal tropical environments, as well as the
establishment of the more temperate environments that are a major part
of the world's biome today.

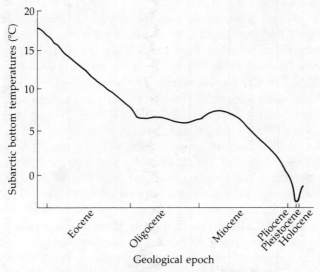

Figure 2.13   Later Cenozoic climatic trends – subarctic bottom
temperatures (based on Kennett 1977).

In the past 2 million years this has culminated in the ice ages, a period
during which the glacial sheets have expanded greatly and covered much
of the northern continental landmasses. At these times the temperatures
would have been much lower, the sea levels lower and hence many areas
connected by landbridges, and many parts of the tropics would have
been drier than today. Interspersed between the pulses of these glacial
advances were warmer periods, such as the one in which we live now.
During the Pleistocene there may have been as many as 20 such glacial–
interglacial cycles, possibly due to variations in the earth's orbit in
relation to the sun (Roberts 1984) (Fig 2.14).

These climatic and environmental changes undoubtedly played an
important part in hominid evolution. The increasingly dry, and hence
less-forested environments of the Miocene provided the context in which

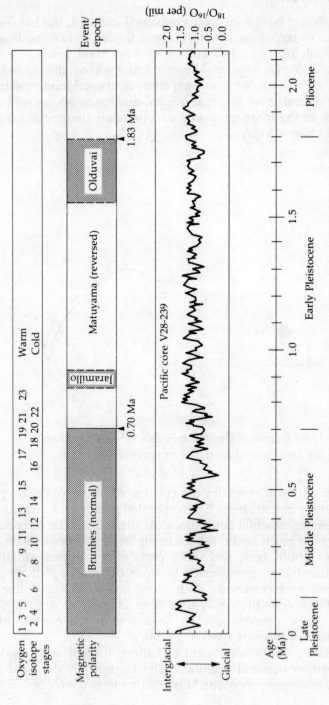

Figure 2.14 Pleistocene ocean temperatures, oxygen isotope stages, and geochronology of the Pleistocene (after Roberts 1984).

many species evolved in response to the world that was emerging. Hominids, among other terrestrial primates, were one of those groups of animals. Many of the characteristics of early hominids, particularly bipedalism, can be related to the requirements of these new environments.

Furthermore, the onset of the full glaciations of the Pleistocene at a time when hominids were beginning to expand beyond the limits of the tropical world, will have acted as both a driving force and a severe constraint on the behaviours and adaptations of early hominids. For example, the reduced sea levels of the glacial periods would have resulted in landbridges that no longer exist (Fig. 2.15); at the same time the lowered temperatures may have been a severe barrier to the spread of an animal whose origins lay in the tropics. By the end of the Pleistocene, though, hominids had colonized all the major habitats of the world, and only the remoter islands remained unoccupied.

Technology

A major difference between hominids and other primates is the degree to which they depend on artefacts for their subsistence activities, and the extent to which they are able to modify a wide range of the materials found in their environment to their own use.

Although chimpanzees use tools made of twigs and grass, for such purposes as 'termite fishing', they have not been observed using stone tools (van Lawick Goodall 1970). Hominids, on the other hand, have been manufacturing stone tools for at least 2.0 Ma; see Harris (1983) and Isaac (1984) for a recent review of this topic. At Koobi Fora (Kenya), Omo (Ethiopia) and Olduvai (Tanzania) simple modified stone tools have been recovered from dated geological deposits of at least 1.8 Ma old, and at Kada Gona in Ethiopia artefacts have been recovered from deposits that could date to between 2.5 and 2.7 Ma old (Roche 1980; Roche & Tiercelin 1977). Harris (1986) recently reported the discovery of stone tools dated to about 2.0 Ma old from the Semliki beds in Zaire, thus expanding the geographical distribution of these very early tools. It is usually assumed that branches and sticks were used by hominids for a period preceding the development of stone artefacts.

The stone tools that form the primary material of the early archaeological record have been classified in a variety of ways, to reflect systems of manufacture, stylistic differences and functional variability. One such system is that of J. G. D. Clark (1968), who recognizes five basic technological modes (Table 2.2). These modes cannot be treated either as chronological markers or as an evolutionary sequence; the simple technological modes recur consistently throughout prehistory, and the more complex ones are highly variable in their distribution in time and space.

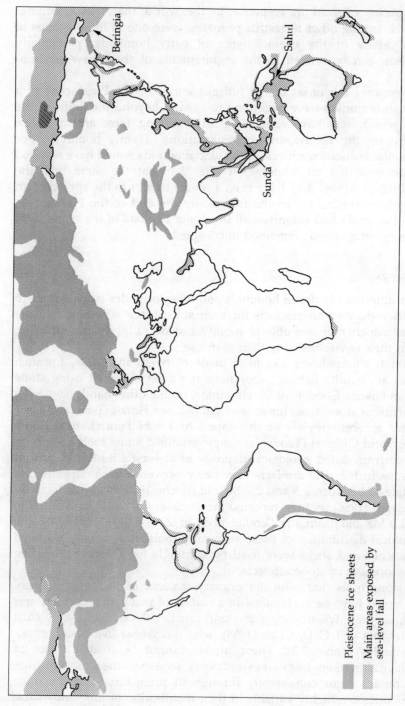

Figure 2.15 Distribution of Pleistocene ice sheets and coastal regions exposed by the associated fall in sea level (after Roberts 1984).

Table 2.2 Modes of stone toll manufacture in prehistory based on
J. G. D. Clark's (1968) technological modes

Technological mode	Characteristics	Assemblage terms	Distribution
Mode 1	Simple, direct percussion producing flakes and chopping tools	Oldowan	From early Pleistocene (especially Africa, but occurs continuously)
Mode 2	Production of large flakes, extensively retouched; handaxes	Acheulean (Chellean) (Abbevillian) (Karari)	Early and middle Pleistocene, extensively in Africa, Europe and parts of Asia
Mode 3	Systematic preparation of cores prior to striking	Mousterian Levallois (Middle Palaeolithic) (Middle Stone Age)	Early parts of late Pleistocene in Europe and Africa
Mode 4	Reduced striking platforms with blade production	e.g. Aurignacian Gravettian (Upper Palaeolithic)	Late Pleistocene onwards in many parts of the world, especially Europe; variable assemblages and distribution
Mode 5	Microlithic flake and blade production with retouch	e.g. Wilton Natufian Maglemosian (Mesolithic) (Later Stone Age)	Global post-Pleistocene distribution, with some late Pleistocene presence

However, these 'modes' represent the basic, albeit overlapping ways of manufacturing stone tools.

The most basic form of stone tool technology consists of striking flakes off stone cores yielding chopping tools and flakes that provide simple but effective cutting edges (Mode 1). The second technological system differs principally from Mode 1 in that it involves the removal of much larger flakes from the cores, followed by secondary retouching of the flakes. The predominant form this takes is the handaxe, which has characteristic secondary flaking on both sides. The development represented by Mode 3 involves the preparation of the cores before the detaching of the flakes. This provides flakes of a predetermined size and shape, and conseqenutly a more efficient use of raw material. Mode 3 overlaps considerably with Mode 4, which continues the pattern of core preparation, but produces instead long blades, rather than flakes, with reduced, punctiform platforms. Mode 5 also continues the process of miniaturization of stone tools, involving the production of large numbers of very small blades, which are often retouched.

It must be stressed that this is a technological, not typological or chronological classification, designed simply to describe stone tool technologies. Many archaeological assemblages display characteristics of more than one technological mode, and change can occur in more than one direction. Despite this complexity, though, distinctive patterns of variability do occur.

There is a broad chronological trend to the these technological modes (Fig. 2.16). The early and most of the middle Pleistocene are characterized by simple chopping tools, flakes, and handaxe industries, although the distribution of these last are limited to Africa, the Middle East and Western Europe. Towards the end of the middle Pleistocene prepared core industries make their appearance, largely in areas where handaxes had previously existed. From about 40 000 years ago, blade technologies occur in some parts of the world, especially Europe and the Middle East. Microliths are largely a post-Pleistocene phenomenon, although in sub-Saharan Africa they are present from about 40 000 years ago (Klein 1983). In all this, though, it should be remembered that some parts of the world, such as Southeast Asia, saw virtually no technological change throughout the Pleistocene.

The changing technology of the early hominids reflects several factors. Partly it reflects their greater manipulative skill. Partly, though, the increasing complexity of their toolmaking procedures reflects a change in hominid cognitive skills. As Gowlett (1984) has shown, the change from chopping tools and flakes through to core preparation involved an increase in the number of conceptual steps ahead that hominids were capable of making. In this case the pattern of technological development gives evidence not just on the physical and ecological constraints and potential of the hominids, but also their ability to conceive and plan actions beyond their immediate requirements. Indeed, recent work has suggested that the principal factor in determining the complexity in stone tool technology, and hence in patterning the archaeological record, is the amount of planning required for food procurement. Hence the occupation of more variable, seasonal and less-secure environments during pre-history resulted in increasing technological complexity (Binford 1980; Torrence 1983). This would also account for the pattern of increasing regionalization and temporal instability of hominid technology during the Pleistocene that Isaac (1972) has recognized.

Prehistoric hominid adaptation

Changing anatomy and technology undoubtedly formed the basis for a distinctly hominid way of life during the Pliocene and the Pleistocene. That way of life was shaped by the requirements of the environments in

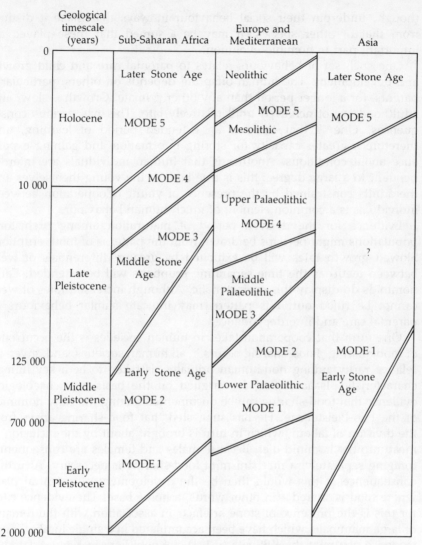

Figure 2.16   Classification of earlier phases of prehistory in relation to the geological timescale and technological modes (see Table 2.2) (modified from Isaac 1972: 384).

which hominids were living. Adaptive variation would also have occurred in their behaviour – their reproductive strategies, their social relations, and their foraging behaviour. Aspects of these can be reconstructed from fossil and archaeological evidence.

Living human populations display tremendous variety in social complexity, form and flexibility. Several fundamental characteristics, though, underpin their social behaviour in ways that make it distinct from that of other species. It may be assumed that these played an important part in hominid evolution.

One such set of behaviours relates to parental care and child growth and development. The human offspring depends on others, particularly parents, for a longer period than any other primate. Growth is slow, and adulthood is not achieved until relatively late. This has various consequences. One is that there is an extended period of learning, and therefore a greater capacity for storing information and gaining experience about conditions. Another is that human individuals are interdependent to a large degree; this is true both of the young themselves and the adults constrained by the presence of young. Cooperation between individuals is a common element of much human behaviour.

Evidence for the delayed period of maturation among prehistoric populations might perhaps be drawn from the patterns of tooth eruption. Slowed growth rates will be exhibited by greater differentials of wear between teeth, as the time separating eruptions will be extended. Early hominids do display this characteristic. Although increased rates of wear cannot be ruled out, this pattern may indicate similar behaviours of parental care and interdependence.

One form that cooperation takes in human societies is the occurrence of food-sharing. Food-sharing occurs in all human societies, and, given its relative rarity among non-human primates, is taken to be a key human characteristic. Isaac (1978a) has argued on the basis of archaeological evidence that food-sharing can be documented among the early hominids of the Plio-Pleistocene. He has suggested that food-sharing arises from the division of labour, which in turn is brought about by the inclusion of meat into the hominid diet. Because males and females are consequently foraging separately, a mechanism of food-sharing is necessary. A further consequence of this would then be the development of a central place where food is shared – in other words, a home base. The evidence cited for this is the presence of stone artefacts in association with the remains of large mammals, which have been accumulated in a single locality. Such evidence occurs at the KBS site (F_xJ_i 1) at Koobi Fora in Kenya, dated to 1.8 Ma, and at similar sites at Olduvai in Tanzania (M. D. Leakey 1972). According to this view, the establishment of a home base, the division of labour and food-sharing all occur early in hominid evolution.

Food-sharing is believed to depend on the presence of meat-eating. As a general rule, the anthropoid primates are herbivorous in their diets, with only a few species actively searching out animal sources of food (Harding 1981). Only for certain baboons (*Papio* spp.) and the chimpanzee have observations of hunting of mammals been made (DeVore & Washburn 1963; Goodall 1963; Harding & Teleki 1981). Modern humans, on the other hand, often incorporate large amounts of meat into their diet (Hill 1982). The development of hunting, it has been argued, represents a critical development in human evolution, demanding new skills and capabilities, and opening up new opportunities (Washburn & Lancaster 1968). It has, for example, been suggested that hunting requires higher levels of cooperation between individuals than does gathering of plant foods, and so it acted as a stimulus for the development of language and for bonds between males. Consequently, evidence for the early development of meat-eating, and the evolution of hunting skills and strategies would be important in the behavioural evolution of the hominids.

Evidence for meat-eating takes the form of animal bones found in association with stone artefacts, and of cut marks on these bones made by artefacts (Isaac & Crader 1981). As already suggested, the archaeological record shows such associations soon after 2 Ma ago, and many examples from the Pleistocene show that hominids have been involved with procurement of resources from animals for a long period of time. Certainly by the late Pleistocene, with the appearance of anatomically modern humans, archaeological sites with enormous quantities of animal bones testify to the carnivorous tendencies of hominids.

A further key characteristic of modern humans is the range of social relationships into which they can and do enter. Although this has led to some radical transformations from any basal primate social life, it must be based on one attribute that undoubtedly has a biological and evolutionary element. This attribute is the ability to recognize and distinguish between large numbers of individuals, and to adjust behaviour accordingly. This is achieved by the smiles, laughs and frowns that makes the human face such an effective communicator. The human face is unique in its variation, its tremendous control of facial expressions, and its ability to transmit a wide range of messages (Darwin 1871). The basis for this lies in the very complex set of muscles that give shape and expression to the human face, and it is this that provides the evidence for the evolutionary origins of much human emotion and behaviour. Without the ability to recognize large numbers of different individuals, the complex networks of kinship that structure human social life would not be possible.

However, despite the eloquence of the human face, the principal means of communication for humans is language. Again, this has an indisputable biological and evolutionary origin, as the human linguistic capacity is firmly built on the anatomy of the larynx, the dexterity of the tongue and lips, and the elaboration and enlargement of the brain. Language, the patterned use of sound as symbols, is mirrored in other means of human communication – music, art, writing – and indicates the fundamental basis of human behaviour. The ability to construct symbols in the head and in the material world that model past experience, present predicaments and future decisions, provides the foundations for modern human behaviour and culture. It must, too, have played an important part in the survival strategies of the early hominids.

Beyond narrative

Summary of human evolution

Hominids as a distinct family had emerged by the end of the Miocene at 5 Ma ago. The earliest hominids were small, bipedal and small brained, and possibly displayed considerable sexual dimorphism. Very rapidly, though, they diverged into separate lineages, best described as an adaptive radiation. One lineage led to the later australopithecines, a large toothed, small brained, large faced and frequently very robust group of animals that lived in Africa from possibly as long ago as 3.0 to 1.2 Ma ago. The other was larger brained, with less heavy musculature, and gave rise to the later species of *Homo* – *H.habilis*, *H.erectus* and *H.sapiens*. The African hominids, most probably *Homo habilis*, of the late Pliocene and the early Pleistocene, seem to have been responsible for the earliest development of stone tools, for the first utilization of animal resources on a scale comparable with modern humans, and perhaps with the foundations of human social life – language, cooperation and sharing – and thus the rise of the variable and complex social interactions that characterize our species today.

This outline of hominid evolution and prehistory has deliberately been kept simple, with many important issues glossed over and certain interpretations presented with greater certainty than the evidence might warrant. For example, the role of hunting, as opposed to gathering, in human evolution has been questioned over recent years, and there has also been a major debate in recent years about the extent to which the early and middle Pleistocene archaeological record provides evidence for the utilization of animal resources (Binford 1980, 1983; Isaac 1983; Shipman 1983; Potts 1984a). Experts would find in this many points they would wish to question. The purpose though has been to summarize briefly the broad outline of the current evidence in palaeoanthropology to those not familiar with it, and also to emphasize the narrative element in hominid evolution. Our evolutionary past can be treated as a story that can be traced among the fossils, in the archaeological records, and through the biology and ecoloy of our closest living relatives, the primates. It is a story in which the characters succeed one another with reasonable regularity, and in which the plot shows the inexorable adaptive success of being bipedal and large brained.

The fossils do not speak

Apart from its brevity and simplicity, though, this outline is incomplete because it is narrative rather than explanation. Although it identifies the principal events, and places them in a temporal and spatial context, it does little to *explain* human evolution. If there is a dominant explanatory framework it is one of hindsight – that is, it imposes a pattern on the past based on the present characteristics of the human species and condition. It is rather like reading a detective story when we already know who the murderer is. This knowledge undoubtedly colours our reading of the earlier parts of the book. For example, because intelligence and technology are major elements of our success today, it is often assumed that these were the most significant elements of our behaviour in the past. This idea certainly underlay many of the earlier assumptions about brain enlargement preceding other changes in human evolution (Reader 1981).

Perhaps the reason why hindsight is such a dominant framework stems from the belief that once placed in their chronological order, the fossils tell their own story. However, this is far from the case. Rather, the fossils, or indeed all other sources of information, depend for their significance on a theoretical framework. In other words, what is missing from this account of human evolution is the reason why any of these changes should have taken place, and the mechanisms through which they occurred. It is only hindsight that informs us, at this level, that larger brains should be a successful adaptation, or that bipedalism should have been an appropriate form of locomotion. What is needed is a theoretical framework that rather than placing early hominid characteristics in the context of our own later behaviour, compares them with the alternatives available to the early hominids at that time. This requires more than just listening to what we think the fossils say, but also considering what other fossils there might also have been.

To go beyond a narrative of human evolution towards an analysis that shows why hominid characteristics should have been successful requires us to take the fossil record, which can tell us what did happen in the past, and combine it with the expectations of evolutionary ecology, which can tell us what we can have expected to have happened in the past. By comparing the observed and the expected it should be possible to proceed beyond an understanding of human evolution based on hindsight, to one based on sound ecological ideas.

3 Evolutionary ecology

The evolutionary history of the hominids represents a unique pattern of biological change. The central point of this book, though, is that unique biological forms can be the product of ordinary biological processes and mechanisms, and that this applies to hominids as much as to any other group of animals. The general principles of evolution and ecology, therefore, are the appropriate theoretical framework for understanding human evolution. What is required is not the development of any special theories, but the rigorous application of general ones that have proved their power in the broader field of evolutionary biology. In this chapter some of the more important ideas of evolutionary ecology will be described – the relationship between evolution and ecology, the character of natural selection, the route to adaptation, and the extension of evolutionary principles to behaviour.

Evolution and ecology

Ecologists study the relationships between organisms and their environments, their purpose being to elucidate the principles governing these relationships. Such relationships, though, can be extremely variable. As Pianka (1978:2) points out, what constitutes an organism and an environment does not remain constant. What is an organism at one level is part of the environment at another. Pianka has suggested the term *organismic unit* as a means of avoiding this problem, and has identified several such units (Fig. 3.1). In ecology the unit of analysis can range from the individual organism through to the entire community made up of several species. Each level can be understood in terms of its interaction with the environment.

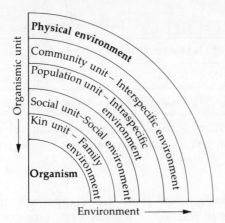

Figure 3.1 Nested character of the organismic unit and environment in ecology. Each unit constitutes part of the environment of the unit nested below.

Equally, the environment is also a variable concept. It comprises the basic physical characteristics, such as temperature, precipitation, soils, and so on, as well as biotic entities such as sympatric species that act as predators, competitors and food resources. Furthermore, it should be stressed that the environment of any organism also comprises other members of the same population and species, with which it will have genetic and social interactions. The environment, in this view, is not a narrow typological list of geographical and biotic factors, but everything – physical, biological and social – that impinges on an organismic unit. What is critical is less what the relationship is between as the mechanisms mediating that relationship.

Several categories of ecological relationship can be recognized. Many interactions between different organisms involve a flow of energy – that is, where one organism consumes part or all of another (herbivory, animal predation, parasitism, etc.). The character of energy, as described by the laws of thermodynamics, gives a structure to these energy-based relationships. This structure has been recognized by ecologists in such concepts as the trophic pyramid – the pattern of declining levels of population and energy as one proceeds up the food chain as a result of the inefficiency of energy transformation (Fig. 3.2) – and the ecosystem. Variations in the structure of energy relationships between organisms help account for the variations in the distribution of plants and animals. Other relationships are based on the flow of materials. These would include such phenomena as the carbon and nitrogen cycles, essential ingredients for life that move around an ecosystem along predictable routes.

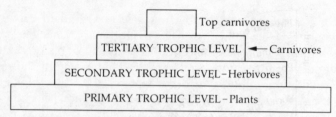

Figure 3.2   The trophic pyramid: loss of energy at each stage of
transformation gives a pyramidal shape to ecological
communities.

Less tangible but equally significant are competitive interactions between organismic units in relation to a shared resource such as food, mates or space. Competitive ability and competitor avoidance will be a key factor in determining the behaviour, distribution and abundance of plants and animals.

Beyond these basic relationships lie others such as social, spatial and genetic relationships, but the structure of the biological world that we can observe empirically is a product of the variation in these relationships. The science of ecology is the unravelling of the patterns in these relationships and the formulation of the principles governing them.

The principles of ecology are intimately bound to the theory of evolution because it is natural selection that in the long term shapes ecological relationships through differential reproductive success. It is this interaction that constitutes evolutionary ecology.

Natural selection

Differential reproduction

The neo-Darwinian theory of evolution by natural selection is central to modern biology. Biological evolution is a complex phenomenon, involving many processes, but the mechanism of natural selection lies at the heart of them. At its simplest, the theory of evolution states that those individuals that leave the most offspring, relative to other individuals, will be genetically better represented in subsequent generations, and consequently those generations will resemble more closely those reproductively successful individuals. The mechanism by which this process of differential reproductive success occurs is referred to as natural selection. Selection is nothing more nor less than differential survival of biological entities (Futuyma 1979).

Natural selection, then, is the mechanism that determines the form and frequency of individuals in each generation, and can thus be said both to maintain biological systems (stabilizing selection) and to drive them in new directions – in other words, evolutionary change. However, although natural selection is the central component of biological theory, it does not operate in isolation, and a full understanding of the process of biological evolution requires incorporation of the other biological processes that direct and constrain the operation of natural selection – that is, the context in which natural selection takes place.

Constraints on selection

The first constraint on selection is that it operates on the variation found in populations. It was the problem of why plants and animals varied, both within and between species, that Darwin was trying to explain, rather than to develop a theory of evolution. That is perhaps why the first two chapters of *The Origin of Species* are entitled 'Variation in Nature' and 'Variation Under Domestication', and why the term evolution does not actually appear in the book. Natural selection is the process whereby those varieties that survive and reproduce successfully relative to other varieties will become the dominant form in the population, or species within the community. Selection determines the range and frequency of variation found in biological systems.

Equally, though, selection can only operate when variation exists and is of adaptive significance. The power of selection, and consequently the direction and rate of evolution, is constrained by the extent and nature of the variation within the population. An understanding of differential reproduction depends on recognizing the range of variation of form, both behavioural and morphological, that exists.

Not all variation, though, will form the raw material of evolution, for another constraint is the genetic basis of life. Selection operates on the phenotype – that is, the actual morphological, physiological, biochemical and behavioural manifestation of an organism (Futuyma 1979:506). It is the fitness of the phenotype that determines survival and reproductive success. However, selection can operate only if there is a means by which the phenotypic characters can be inherited – that is, passed on to the offspring, and hence continued down through the generations. Without this attribute, phenotypic fitness would be of no evolutionary consequence. It was the absence of a mechanism by which characters could be inherited that led to the rejection of Lamarck's theory of evolution through acquired characteristics. In modern biological theory the rules governing inheritance are those discovered by Gregor Mendel. The genetic basis of life constrains the power of natural selection. Two genetic characteristics are of particular importance. The first is that the gene is unaffected by life history. Information can flow from the genotype to the phenotype, but not back again. And second, that it is the gene, incorporated in a haploid gamete, that is passed from parent to offspring. These two facts, combined in humans and most animals with the process of sexual reproduction, determine which individuals may benefit and suffer from the reproductive behaviour of other individuals. It is the gene that supplies the thread of continuity in evolution. The limited number of ways in which genes can be passed from one generation to another acts as a limitation on natural selection.

New genes appear in the population principally as a result of mutations. It is mutations that maintain and increase the level of genetic variation. They are thus another constraint on the power of natural selection. A mutation is an error in the replication of a gene during meiosis. Its presence may introduce a new phenotype (i.e. a new variant) that will compete with those already in the gene pool. Whereas other sources of novelty do occur (for example, gene flow between populations, recombination, heterozygosity), without mutation selection can only maintain the existing structure or form, or, where this is no longer viable, lead a population to extinction. Evolutionary analysis must therefore take into account the rate and nature of mutation, or, in other words, the source of the variation that forms the basis for natural selection. The consequences of this are important. One is that whereas the process of mutation is random (in terms of which gene may undergo an error in replication), the form of the mutation is not; that is, the type of phenotype produced by a mutation will depend on the nature of the original phenotype (Dawkins 1976). An amoeba cannot undergo a mutation that will provide human intelligence: its mutations will be essentially amoeboid. It is this that may give a gradualistic character to evolution. Another implication is that the consequences of a mutation may not all occur instantaneously or simultaneously. For example, a mutation that gives an increased capacity for learning may occur. Although this may have some immediate effect, its full impact may not happen for several generations and may depend on the particular types of information that are learnt.

A further factor affecting the operation of natural selection is that of competition. In developing his theory of evolution Darwin took the concept of competition from the nineteenth-century political economists in general, and from Malthus's demographic ideas in particular. The finite availability of resources in relation to the potentially high rate of reproduction and population increase provided Darwin with the excess of population over resources necessary for natural selection to work. Competition – interactions, direct or indirect, between individuals for a shared resource – is a precondition of natural selection. It is in the context of the short supply of resources that those variants best adapted to acquire them will have a reproductive and hence a selective advantage.

This leads on to the final constraint operating on natural selection and also takes us back to the central notion of reproductive differences. For a characteristic to come under the influence of natural selection it is necessary for that characteristic to have some affect on the chances of an individual reproducing successfully. Without some interaction between the nature of the phenotype and differences in reproductive success, natural selection cannot operate. Differences in phenotype that do not have a significant affect on the chances of survival of an individual will not play an important part in evolution.

In summary, the core of evolutionary theory is the principle of natural selection – that is, the differential reproductive success of biological entities. Strictly speaking, all other features of evolution are epiphenomenal. However, because natural selection must operate in the biological and physical world, other limits are set on it. It is these constraints, such as Mendelian inheritance, genetic variability, mutations, competition, etc., that give biological evolution its specific and observable character. It follows from this that an evolutionary approach is centred on understanding the operation of natural selection – its consequences for living matter and the context in which it works.

The unit of selection

A further, and crucial question, though, is on what does natural selection operate? What is the unit of selection? Considerable debate has taken place on this matter (Wynne-Edwards 1962; Williams 1966; Wilson 1975; Dawkins 1976, 1982a; D. S. Wilson 1980). In the pure Darwinian formulation the unit of selection is the individual. It is the individual that reproduces, and its morphology and behaviour determines its reproductive success. It follows from this that natural selection operates on the successes and failures of the individual. However, with the discovery of the particulate nature of genes and the process of meiosis it was clear that it is the gene, not the individual, that is passed down the generations, and therefore that the gene is really the unit of selection. According to Dawkins (1976), the individual is merely the perishable package in which genes travel. Given that genes are shared between individuals, according to their degree of relatedness (see Fig. 3.3), this means that the interests of the gene and of the individual may not always be the same. This may occur with closely related individuals, where the interests of the gene (which occurs in several individuals) are best served by the individual sacrificing something, especially its reproductive effort, in favour of its close kin. This has become known as kin selection, and has been formally developed by Hamilton (1964). Logically it places the unit of selection at the level of the gene rather than the individual, although for the most part the gene and the individual share the same reproductive interests.

The context in which their interests diverge, though, is that of altruism. Altruism is an act that increases another's reproductive fitness at the expense of the individual. If the individual is the unit of selection then it follows that the only phenomena that should evolve are those that benefit

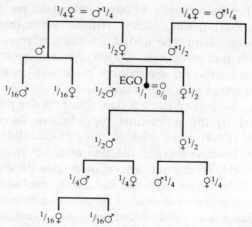

Figure 3.3 Degrees of genetic relatedness. The fractions show the proportion of genes individuals are expected to share on the basis of their relatedness. All figures represent genes shared with EGO.

the individual – that enhance its own reproductive success. A behaviour that reduces an individual's reproductive output, such as an altruistic act, cannot be selected for, as by definition it will occur less and not more frequently in each generation. When such behaviours occur the individual cannot be the unit of selection. It is here that the 'selfish gene' (Dawkins 1976) perspective is useful. Because individuals share their genes with their close relatives (Fig. 3.3), the reproductive success (survival of genes) of an individual must take into account the reproduction of its relatives, carrying a proportion of the same genes. This would then constitute an individual's *inclusive fitness*. Circumstances can occur – for instance involving parents and offspring, siblings, etc. – where fitness may be enhanced not by an individual itself reproducing, but by behaviours that increase the reproductive success of close kin, even at the expense of the individual.

Technically, then, the gene rather then the individual is the unit of selection. Dawkins has gone some way to clarifying the issue by distinguishing between *replicator survival* and *vehicle selection*.

There are two ways in which we can characterise natural selection. Both are correct; they simply focus on different aspects of the same process. Evolution results from the differential survival of *replicators*. Genes are replicators; organisms and groups of organisms are not replicators, they are vehicles in which replicators travel about. *Vehicle selection* is the process by which some vehicles are more successful than other vehicles in ensuring the survival of their replicators

(Dawkins 1982b:46).

Consequently, although it is important to recognize this distinction between individuals and genes, the two levels are not contradictory interpretations of the theory of natural selection, but rather complementary. Certainly, from the point of view of evolutionary ecology the individual, as the fully integrated and organized organism, represents the most interesting analytical unit, as it is the individual that must interact with the environment. There will be times, however, when the behaviour of the individual is only explicable in terms of its component genetic basis.

Such complementarity is not the case with the distinction between the individual and the group of organisms as the unit of selection. Here, in Dawkins's (1982b) terms, this is not the distinction between replicators and vehicles, but two competing vehicles of selection. Group selection is selection for characteristics that benefit the group of organisms as a whole at the expense of the individuals that carry those characteristics. This is altruism again, but altruism that cannot be accounted for by shared genes and kinship. It has been argued (Wynne-Edwards 1962; Wilson 1980) that species that behave in this way will exist in a more stable relationship with their resources, and consequently have greater chances of survival.

The problem with group selection, however, is that theoretically it should not be able to work. Imagine an organism that behaves in such a way as to decrease its own chances of survival, for example by giving an alarm call when it spots a predator, and so comes to the attention of that predator, but in so doing increases the survival chances of the group as a whole. Certainly, such groups will be at an advantage over those groups without such altruistic individuals that suffer higher rates of predation. However, this behaviour cannot be maintained, for, as was argued in relation to kin selection, each succeeding generation will have fewer and fewer altruistic, alarm-calling individuals, until eventually, as a result of their higher mortality rates, they will disappear. The equilibrium point would consequently be a group of non-alarm-calling individuals. In this case, group selection can be seen to be weaker than individual selection.

Individual selection is more powerful than group selection because it is individuals that reproduce and are the vehicles of the gene. Although in an unconstrained world selection could theoretically occur at any number of levels, because it is constrained by the rules of inheritance, selection of the individual is the only practical level. This remains true even when models based on structured groups are used. D. S. Wilson's (1980) model of group selection, while mathematically sound, is an example of individual selection operating in very constrained circumstances (Harvey 1985).

This consideration has important consequences for the analysis of patterns of evolutionary ecology. Principal among these is that adaptive advantages must be thought of in terms of individuals and not groups and species, unless there is an inclusive fitness-based alternative.

Individuals are the basic material of evolution, and so must be considered the analytical unit of adaptive behaviour.

Selection to adaptation

Adaptation

The effect of natural selection, the differential survival of biological entities, is to promote adaptation. Adaptation is a term in frequent use in ecology, but has several meanings or shades of emphasis (Dunbar 1982). First, there is adaptation as a *process* – that is, the process by which an organism adapts, changes or conforms to the constraints of its environment. Adaptation in this sense may be the product of natural selection over several generations, or may be a more short-term acquired or learnt response.

A second meaning of adaptation describes the *actual relationship* between an organism and its environment. In this sense the term adaptation shows, or attempts to describe, what characteristics of the organism are related to certain aspects of the environment. For example, thick fur is an adaptation of mammals in relation to the low temperature of the environment. Here it is important to stress that the term used in this way is only valid if both the adaptive feature of the organism and the environmental attribute to which the feature is related are specified. And the third use of the term adaptation is as a measure – a measure of the *degree* of conformity between organismic units and their environment. The reason adaptation should be considered as a measurement is because there are no adaptive absolutes; the perfect adaptation does not exist. An adaptation can be assessed only in a relative sense.

Several ecological implications flow from these shades of meaning. One of these is that adaptation can occur through a whole range of biological characteristics – biochemical, physiological, morphological and behavioural. They are all ways in which an animal conforms to the constraints of its environment. For example, an animal may adapt to high temperatures by decreasing blood viscosity (biochemical), by increased respiratory or perspiratory capacity (physiological), by enlargement of relative surface area (morphological), or by keeping in the shade and reduced activity (behavioural). Modern humans can extend still further the range of adaptive systems by inventing air conditioning. In considering an adaptive problem the relative costs and benefits of each adaptive mode should be considered.

A further implication is that adaptation can be a genetically based process occurring as a direct response to natural selection, or it may be a phenotypic response of an individual to some attribute of its environment during its lifetime. For example, chimpanzees as a species have adapted to a largely frugivorous diet over a period of several million years, as may be witnessed by the morphology of their teeth and stomach. This is an adaptation through natural selection. On the other hand, the population of chimpanzees now living in the Gombe Reserve in Tanzania learnt to acquire bananas from the researchers working there who provisioned them (van Lawick Goodall 1971). In this case they were adapting to a new resource through learning. The former example is a result of changing gene frequencies, the latter a phenotypic change involving no alteration of the genome. However, the distinction between these two types of adaptation is not clear cut. Phenotypic alterations are not solely behavioural. For example, humans undergo phenotypic changes in respiratory physiology at high altitudes with no effect on their genome. On the other hand, behavioural changes can be genetically based. Nor is it possible to detach either entirely from natural selection. Where learned behaviour is involved, the actual behaviour may not be under direct genetic control, but the capacity for these behaviours may be variable and may be linked to genetic differences. Consequently, behaviours are at least indirectly a product of natural selection. Although the pathways may vary, natural selection and adaptation are integrally linked together.

The other critical implication of this discussion of adaptation is that while there may be some confusion about genes or individuals as the unit of selection, there is no question that it is individuals and not groups or genes that adapt (Williams 1966), nor cultures or societies (Foley 1981). It may be descriptively accurate to say that red deer adapt by seasonal movements, or that the Nuer adapt by herding cattle, but these are statistical summaries indicating the behaviour of all, or a large proportion, of the population. Although these statements are descriptively essential, they are not based on any theoretical assumptions. This is especially true with hominids, where, because of the institutional and organizational complexity of their behaviour, it has frequently been assumed that cultures adapt. This, however, is not the case (Ellen 1982). Individuals create, use, pass on the institutions and forms of culture as a means of adapting to their social and biological environment. This perspective is more useful in that it allows the behaviour to be directly related to the individual whose reproductive success is of analytical concern, and it allows the variability in adaptive behaviour to be seen and analysed.

So far, adaptation has been defined in three senses, and it has been shown that it can occur in several modes, and with varying levels of direct relationship to natural selection, from direct genetic control to learning capabilities. However, the actual character of adaptation remains elusive.

Limits to perfection

One view of adaptation is that it describes the perfect relationship between an organism and its environment, or at least a tendency towards perfection (Cain 1964). This view, when taken as an ecological and evolutionary axiom, has led to an untestable application of Darwinian theory – whatever an animal does must be the best possible in its environment. The implication is that forms are not merely adaptive, but perfectly adaptive. The perfectability premise, or 'adaptationist programme' has been subject to considerable attack (Lewontin 1978; Gould & Lewontin 1979), an attack that has implied a greatly reduced analytical value for the concept of adaptation and the power of natural selection as a biological process. The critique of these authors hinged on three points: that many features of organisms are consequences of developmental constraints; that many characteristics are allometric – that is, byproducts of size rather than direct responses to the environment; and that the vast majority of genetic material is neutral, as is currently debated by the molecular biologists. More recently, Gould & Vrba (1983) coined the phrase 'exaptation' to describe characteristics that have not arisen as a result of their adaptive value.

However, their critique is directed towards two ideas that are not necessarily part of an adaptationist programme. The first of these is that natural selection is a free agent, of limitless scope and power. As was shown earlier (see page 51), this is not the case. Natural selection operates in the context of other biological processes such as development and allometry. It is not that these cannot be affected by natural selection, nor that they override selective pressures, but that natural selection is parsimonious in its operation, and may frequently operate through developmental genes. The second idea is that an adaptation, within a Darwinian framework, must be perfect. This, though, is at odds with the definition of adaptation with which this section opened (see page 56) – that adaptation is a measure of the conformity of organism and its environment, and the degree of conformity is continuous from fully adaptive to maladaptive. This range should be represented in the biological world.

Gould & Lewontin (1979) were correct to highlight the dangers of *assuming* the perfectability of adaptation, but incorrect to suggest that the improbability of completely perfect adaptation, and the methodological difficulties involved in studying adaptation, should undermine the logic of natural selection. In the same way that natural selection operates within certain constraints, so too does its product, adaptation. Various authors have attempted to list the limits of adaptation (Williams 1966; Curio 1973; Maynard Smith 1978; Oster & Wilson 1978; Dawkins 1982a), so that, as Dawkins (1982a:35) puts it, we might 'know what the theory of natural selection entitles us to expect'. The list here is based on Dawkins (1982a).

1. **Time lag between environmental conditions and the effect of selection**. Selection operates in the short term. Organisms are selected for the

immediate requirements of their environment. If environmental conditions change, then attributes previously adaptive may no longer be so. It may take several generations, though, depending on the intensity of selection, for the organism to achieve conformity with the environment again, if it ever does. Indeed, the environment may be inherently unstable such that full adaptation may constantly elude a species. Accordingly, adaptations must be considered in the context of the history of the environments in which they occur. Although selection may operate in the short-term, the study of adaptation should incorporate a longer term perspective.. Migration should also be taken into account here, as an animal may move into a new environment to which it is not fully adapted.

2.   **Historical constraints**. Selection may operate on the living organism only; it cannot start afresh with each generation, but must modify or sustain existing adaptations. Consequently, the evolution of new adaptations occurs in the context of old ones. A tendency towards perfection can consequently only be measured in relation to that which preceded it. For example, it is not particularly useful to ask in general whether bipedalism or quadrupedalism is the best system of locomotion. It is only useful to ask whether bipedalism was more efficient than the locomotor system from which it evolved. It is the overall effect of historical constraints that provides for evolutionary conservatism and adaptive imperfection.

3.   **Genetic variability.** In the same way that historical factors affect the direction of adaptive change, the availability of genetic variants will affect the occurrence of new adaptive traits. Better and even perfect adaptations may be imaginable, but they are only attainable if the genetic material exists.

4.   **Compromising factors**. Organisms do not come under a single selective pressure. Rather they are constantly subject to an almost infinite array of factors that affect their reproductive success in complex ways. Many of these selective pressures will conflict with each other. For example, it may be advantagous for an animal to maximize food intake, but time spent feeding is time that could also be spent on reproduction or parental care, maximization of which would also be of benefit. The outcome of these conflicts is a compromise, a best-fit solution that maximizes no single selective pressure but benefits overall fitness. This will consequently inhibit the perfection of any single adaptive feature. Another way of looking at this is to recognize that although each adaptation provides some benefit it will also incur costs, whether in terms of energy or time, or in terms of the consequences for another part of the adaptive strategy.

5.   **The unit of selection**. The discussion on the unit of selection present-

ed above has consequences for adaptation as well. As adaptation is a consequence of selection, it follows that adaptation must occur at certain levels. This in turn leads to the recognition that what might be adaptive at one level might be maladaptive at another. For example, it may be adaptive for an individual to maximize reproductive output, and hence to contribute as many individuals as possible to the next generation. However, if this strategy is pursued successfully by everyone in the population, then the result could be total environmental degradation and the extinction of the entire population. Although this is an extreme example, and other mechanisms are likely to come into effect prior to extinction, it illustrates the conflicts that can inhibit the development of a perfect adaptation.

6.   **Unpredictability**. Animals live in complex environments, exploiting resources that are patchily distributed in time and space. According to the principles of natural selection defined at the beginning of this chapter, animals should conform as closely as possible to the conditions of this environment. However, that environment is made up of other organisms, each also adapting to its environment. The adaptations of many of these organisms are at odds with each other (predators and prey, competitors, etc.). Furthermore, this community may itself be affected by external factors, such as climatic change. The net result of this is an inherently unstable system, in which the character of selection is constantly shifting, and hence preventing the process of adaptation becoming one of fine tuning and an inevitable drive towards perfection.

Adaptation is the ecological manifestation of natural selection. The constraints operating on it overlap with those acting on the evolutionary mechanism. Whereas adaptation is an 'expected outcome' of natural selection, perfection is not.

Adaptation as problem-solving

It is perhaps more realistic and useful to view adaptation as a problem-solving process (Maynard Smith 1978; Dunbar 1982). Adaptive features are means of solving, within the constraints discussed above, the problems an organism faces in its environment.

> It is self-evident that any living species has a valid set of solutions for certain basic ecological or biological problems. It must secure food to replenish its energy store, must have a place to live, and a method to reproduce ... Possession of a valid set of such solutions is called adaptedness.
>
>   (Dobzhansky 1974:323, quoted in Jochim 1981)

This view of adaptation is consistent with the realities of the biological world. It integrates adaptation and natural selection, and provides a practical framework for an evolutionary ecology approach. An environment poses problems of survival for an organism. Natural selection operates on the behaviour, morphology, physiology and biochemistry of an organism, through its reproductive success, to minimize or solve these problems. Potential solutions are constrained by all the factors described above, but the end product is adaptation. The goal of an evolutionary ecological analysis must therefore be to identify the problems faced by an organism, and to evaluate the solutions that selection may favour or reject.

The dangers of anthropomorphism

According to this view adaptation is a strategy of survival, the strategy being the set of actions or attributes that best solves environmental problems. Describing adaptation as a problem-solving strategy provides a useful framework for relating the characteristics of an organism (its adaptive features) to the properties of the environment (the problems).

Regrettably both 'strategy' and 'problem-solving' are terms that have anthropomorphic connotations. In general usage they imply both conscious decision-making and intent on the part of the individual. Neither of these is compatible with the view that natural selection is a blind force, and that adaptation is the outcome of the interaction of chance with general, and impersonal, biological forces. It would certainly be unreasonable to expect spiders to be 'consciously pursuing a strategy', or for deer to be 'trying to solve the problems of predator pressure'. Even with hominids it is indeed unacceptable to assume that they could, at any particular stage in their evolution, perceive an environmental problem, let alone consciously work out the appropriate solution. Even for modern humans, with their unrivalled cognitive and analytical abilities, while they may well be capable of both perceiving problems and consciously pursuing strategies, it can by no means be presumed that the goals towards which they see their strategies directed are the same as the 'goal' implicit in evolutionary biology – reproductive success or Darwinian fitness. That their strategies have reproductive consequences and so evolutionary implications is another matter.

This use of terms apparently implying intent and laden with human values has attracted considerable attention and criticism over the years (see, for example, Allen et al. 1976). It must be stated clearly, though, that terms such as strategy and problem-solving are valid within evolutionary biology because they represent good analogues of the way in which natural selection operates and adaptation occurs. They are, though, emphatically analogues and above all extremely useful shorthand terms

that can succinctly describe the net product of all the factors that contribute to evolution and have been discussed in this chapter.

This view of these concepts as analogues and shorthand has been well
illustrated for the term strategy and justified by Diamond (1977:296–7).

a strategy connotes three elements: the operation of thought processes,
a preconceived goal, and a weighing of alternative means of achieving
this goal in order to assess which means is most suitable. Recently
ecologists and biogeographers have found it profitable to discuss plant
and animal species as if they too adopted strategies. For instance a
modern ecologist unashamedly reasons, 'A bird species of unstable
habitats must adopt a strategy of rapid reproduction'. Or: 'A high ratio
of search time to pursuit time is an optimal foraging strategy for a
predator on large, hard-to-capture prey'.

Until recently, such anthropomorphic reasoning about plants and
animals was considered dangerous and naive. It is now clear that the
language of strategy is a profitable shorthand for describing both
evolutionary phenomena and behavioural phenomena. At the
evolutionary level species and individuals vary in their adaptations; the
adaptations of some species (or individuals) permit them to leave more
offspring than other species in a particular situation; the former species
therefore come to outnumber the latter in that situation. Thus one can
describe evolution as having goals, such as long-term survival or large
number of surviving offspring. The probability of achieving these goals
is a function of biological adaptations, which are *analogous* to the
alternative means of achieving goals. The weighing of alternative
strategies is made by natural selection rather than by thought
processes. When we say that 'a bird species of unstable habitats must
adopt a strategy of rapid reproduction', this is *shorthand* for something
like the following: 'Species and individuals vary in their reproductive
rates. The more unstable the habitat, the higher is the probability of
local extinction or death due to random factors. Also the smaller the
population the higher is the probability of local extinction due to
random factors. The higher the reproductive rate the briefer is the
period between the arrival of a few colonists at a vacant piece of habitat
and the achievement of a large population size saturating this habitat.
Extinction probabilities are higher during this interval than when a
large population is achieved. The longer this interval and the fewer the
pieces of suitable habitat at any moment, the higher is the likelihood
that a species may happen to disappear from all habitat pieces
simultaneously. Therefore in an unstable habitat natural selection leads
to preferential survival of species with higher reproductive rates'.

(italics added)

As long as the underlying logic is understood, and it is remembered
that terms such as 'problem-solving' and 'strategy' are being used in a

precise, technical and analogical manner, then they can be extremely useful concepts. Certainly problem-solving represents the principal framework for the analyses presented in the later chapters of this book, and the identification of strategies of survival are an important goal in these analyses. Each chapter attempts to identify ecological and environmental problems faced by early hominids and hominoids, and then tries, by exploring the potential range of responses through a broad comparative approach, to identify and account for the adaptive strategies pursued. Consequently, this restricted and non-anthropomorphic usage should be borne in mind.

Optimality

Viewing adaptations as a problem-solving approach has the advantage of employing a minimal number of assumptions. There is no assumption of stability, nor of units larger than the individual, and there is no expectation of perfection in nature. Certain assumptions, however, do underly it. These are congruent with what is referred to in evolutionary biology as *optimality principles*.

The principle of optimality in biology can be summarized as follows:

> Organisms within a population vary with respect to physiology, morphology, and behaviour. Because resources are limited – food, space, mates, etc. – selection will favour those organisms whose behaviour and morphology enhances their access to those resources, relative to other organisms, and hence increase their output relative to others in the population. Thus the product of natural selection operating on a variable population is an increased relative abundance of those individuals with behaviours that enhance access to resources. In other words, whose behaviour relative to those resources may be said to be optimal. Optimization is therefore an expected outcome of natural selection operating in a world where resources are finite and act as a limiting factor.
>
> (Foley 1985, based on Pyke, Pulliam & Charnov 1977)

From this it can be seen that adaptation is a tendency towards optimization of the fit between what an organism does and the environment in which it lives. Selection favours the 'optimal solution' to the problems faced by an organism. In the analysis of hominid evolution we are trying to identify why certain characteristics should have been optimal solutions to the specific survival problems of the early hominoids and hominids. Elsewhere (Foley 1985), I have discussed in detail the validity and value of optimality principles to anthropology. Much of this discussion concerned the limitations on the power, scope and applicability of optimality principles. These limitations parallel the discussion on the limits of natural selection and adaptation presented above. Other parts of that discussion dwelt on the question of how far modern humans are free from the constraints of natural selection, and hence beyond the scope of the principle of optimality (which rests on Darwinian assumptions). As hominoids and the very early hominids form the central focus for analysis in this book, that question is unlikely to be of great significance in the results presented here.

Two aspects of optimality models, though, are worth stressing. The first is the notion of the *phenotypic set*, and the second the use of *optimality assumptions* as the basis for making comparisons between alternative adaptations.

A strategy implies the selection of one among a series of alternatives for action. An analysis of strategy is analysis of choice. As we have seen, in evolutionary biology it is natural selection that 'makes the choice'. For the analysis to be useful, therefore, it is necessary to know what the range of alternatives is or was, rather than just the actual outcome. In evolutionary biology the range of alternatives is referred to as the phenotypic set (Maynard Smith 1978). The optimal phenotype is the one that selection favours, the one that persists through time. For example, in his analysis of the evolutionary significance of intraspecific contests, Maynard Smith (1976b) identified a range of alternative behaviours that constituted the phenotypic set, even though not all of them occurred in nature. It has to be remembered, for example, that evolution of ritualized fighting systems, in which the contestants minimize the risks of being seriously hurt, evolved in the context of much more damaging alternative behaviours. The viability and stability of any strategy must be assessed in the context of the alternative possible strategies – that is, the phenotypic set.

However, apart from noting that in this context 'optimal' can refer only to optimality in relation to the other alternatives incorporated within the phenotypic set, and not to behaviours in general, it should also be inferred from this that the quality of a strategic analysis depends on the adequacy of the phenotypic set. In trying to account for the evolution of adaptive traits among the early hominids it is essential that we consider the range of alternatives that may have been open to them. As by definition these have not evolved, and are almost certainly not present in the fossil record, this raises certain methodological difficulties. What we need to be able to do is to estimate what other options early hominids may have had available to them. This depends not on direct observation, but on careful use of ecological and ethological principles and on the use of comparative data. An evolutionary analysis is only as good as the range of alternative evolutionary pathways that have been considered (Foley 1985), and in this book an attempt has been made to place the hominid characteristics that did evolve in the context of those that might have done.

Optimality principles stress the comparative method – evaluating the similarities and differences between behaviours and anatomical features in terms of their costs and benefits and comparative survival value. What in practice they do is to identify what the problems facing an organism are, and then to suggest the optimal solution – the one among a range of alternatives that maximizes benefits and minimizes costs. This in a way amounts to making a prediction about what should evolve. It consequently provides a template of the 'perfect adaptation' against which we can measure what actually did occur. In effect this is a way of modelling the selective pressures operating on an organism. By comparing the actual outcome with the expected outcome, we have a means of assessing how accurately the selective pressures (environmental problems) operating on an organism have been identified. Optimality principles form the yardstick of measurement for adaptations and adaptive strategies. With their use we may not except to find hyperefficient hominids performing evolutionarily perfect decisions in the early Pleistocene with the efficiency of a team of time and motion consultants, but we do have a means of determining why certain evolutionary pathways should be followed.

Behavioural ecology

Although the concepts of problem-solving and strategy are appropriate analogues for all aspects of adaptation, it is perhaps within the field of behavioural ecology that they have the greatest intuitive relevance. The behaviour of animals, their social organization, foraging activities, reproductive behaviour, and reaction to predators, are as subject to natural selection as are their anatomical attributes. In ways that are more obvious than with structures, the behaviour of an animal is a strategy of survival. Furthermore, with complex higher organisms such as primates, behaviour, with its potential for enhanced flexibility, is more likely to be a direct response to the exigencies of the environment than structural features evolved through the generations by natural selection, and so may involve decision-making processes that bring the concept of strategy towards being more than just an analogue model.

Certainly many of the adaptive changes that have occurred in human evolution are behavioural ones – the development of meat-eating, central-place foraging, kin-based social systems, etc. Many of the analytical tasks facing palaeoanthropologists consequently lie within behavioural ecology.

Krebs & Davies (1981) define behavioural ecology as the study of the survival value of behaviour. In turn, they link the behaviour to the ecological conditions in which any animal lives, and they view behaviour as a response to the constraints and requirements of those ecological conditions. Behavioural ecology, then, is largely about the function of behaviours, that is the extent to which they enhance survival and reproduction. It is this that links behavioural ecology to evolutionary biology as a whole. The direct link between behaviour and ecology and evolution places the emphasis on functional causation rather then mechanistic causation (Tinbergen 1963; Krebs & Davies 1981).

For example, a population of primates may live in large social groups. The underlying causality for this, the reason why they do it, may be considered both functionally and mechanistically. The functional reason for living in groups may be that it gives an individual a greater chance of not being killed by a predator. This is its survival value. The mechanistic reason, though, lies in the ways in which individuals recognize and interact with each other and so form social bonds that hold them together. The functional explanation depends on evolutionary principles, such as the optimality principle discussed above, and on the ecological principles that govern the character of the environment in which any organism lives. In the analyses that will be developed in the later chapters of this book emphasis will largely be placed on the functional character of evolutionary biology.

Seeking the selective reasons for a character to evolve has long been central to evolutionary biology. Within the field of animal behaviour this has been brought to the fore firstly by the growth of sociobiology, and more recently by the increased application of optimality principles to evolutionary biology.

As a subdiscipline, sociobiology grew directly out of classical ethology in response to the development of a stricter application of Darwinian theory (Wilson 1975). This placed greater emphasis on the relationships between related individuals (kin selection), and the explanation of altruism. At the time of publication of Wilson's text much of the immediate response was to the applicability of the principles of behavioural ecology to humans and the nature of genetic determinism. This discussion often took place at a political and polemical level. Subsequent developments have seen the debate lose much of its bitterness as the arena of discussion shifted to detailed questions of scientific validity.

Many of those questions have already been dealt with in this chapter – the question of whether adaptation is an expected outcome of the operation of natural selection; the problem of the level at which adaptation occurs; and the problem of whether processes other than natural selection can account for adaptive patterns. There is no reason why the arguments that have been presented here should not apply equally to behaviour as to physiology. With behaviour, though, there is one question that raises various difficulties, and that is the relationship between learning and the genetic basis of behaviour.

It has already been seen that for a feature to be subject to selection it must have some effect on reproductive success and also have a genetic element. That behaviours have consequences for reproduction is almost axiomatic, but the level of genetic control is far more controversial, particularly with regard to higher animals and humans. At one extreme is the view that each behaviour is controlled by a single gene, operating direct control. For example, Rothenbuhler (1964) was able to show that where honeybees (*Apis mellifera*) were 'hygenic' (that is, they removed diseased larvae from the nest), this behaviour was under dual genetic control. Two types of behaviour were involved – uncapping the wax and throwing out the larvae. Through breeding experiments, Rothenbuhler (1964) demonstrated that these two behaviours were under separate genetic control. In this case, genetic control is very direct and very specific, with complex behaviours being built up through the addition of more genes to the set of behaviours.

At the other extreme is the view that behaviours are learned, and that genes have no control over them. This is often considered to be appropriate for much human action (see, for example, the discussion in Kaplan 1978). Learned behaviour has been documented frequently by examining the way in which behaviours of the same species may vary according to the precise conditions to which an individual is subjected. The classic example cited frequently in primatology is the spread of 'potato-washing' among a population of Japanese macaques (*Macaca fuscata*); this behaviour, involving washing sand off potatoes, was 'invented' by one individual, and then spread by imitation through the population (Kawai 1965).

Between these two extremes, however, lies a range of other possibilities. It is unlikely that learning plays a major part in the lives of short-generational animals that live in fixed and predictable environments. On the other hand, with large-bodied, social and complex animals such as many mammals it is unlikely that genetic control on its own would be sufficient to take into account the wide and varied range of conditions an individual is likely to encounter. Interactions between learning and genetic control are to be expected to occur. The best model for this is perhaps that of game-playing (Maynard Smith 1983). Even the simplest of games involves a large number of potential situations and actions or moves. It would be extremely tedious to tell an individual how to play any game by specifying every possible move under every possible circumstance. On the other hand, leaving the individual to discover how to play entirely by experimentation would be exasparatingly slow. The best way of learning a new game is to summarize the basic aim and relationships in terms of a few rules. With these rules any player is able to work out the best possibility for each situation. The relationship between learning and genes in the higher organisms, and in humans, is likely to be similar in nature. Genetics undoubtedly provides the basic set of rules by which behavioural strategies can be pursued. These rules, however, are not precise blueprints for behaviour, but criteria for making decisions. With them the individual is able to start 'playing the game', but can also learn from experiences gained during life (Passingham 1982; Layton & Foley in press).

This game-playing model satisfies the basic conditions for selection to operate (i.e., that there is some genetic component) while recognizing the flexibility that behaviour frequently has. What selection will operate on is not the actual behaviour itself but the rules by which that behaviour has been determined. Such a solution has the advantage that it avoids the difficulties of genetic determinism that has plagued the development of sociobiology without throwing away the notion that behaviour can play an important part in the evolution of an organism and its adaptations. This is particularly important in studies of hominid evolution, where undoubtedly we can say not only that behavioural adaptations have been crucial, but also that such behaviours are unlikely to be under simple and direct genetic control.

4 Pathways to the past

Unusually for a book about human evolution, the previous chapter has been conspicuous for the almost complete absence of reference to hominids and for its avoidance of discussion of problems relating to the fossil and archaeological record – the only direct evidence of prehistoric evolutionary states. This has been an intentional omission, for one of the central points of this book is that the patterns of human evolution must be tested against general evolutionary and ecological principles, not reconstructed from specific assumptions about the nature of the human species.

However, it is important that the principles outlined in the previous chapter can be tested and applied to the data that are available. For this, the full range of approaches available to palaeoanthropology must be used, and so this chapter will discuss some of the issues involved in reconstructing the past.

Palaeoanthropology

Palaeoanthropology can broadly be considered the fusion of two separate branches of anthropology: physical or biological anthropology, especially the study of fossil hominids, and archaeology, the study of human behaviour from hominid material remains. Despite their apparent common aim – the understanding of early hominids – these two disciplines historically have been divided both by subject matter and by theoretical orientation. In recent years, however, a more interdisciplinary approach to palaeoanthopology has grown up. This has largely been based on the expanding application of biological, especially ecological, concepts to the study of early hominids. Although common aims and

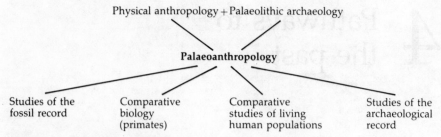

Figure 4.1   Schematic representation of the components of palaeoanthropology.

assumptions now underly much of the work in palaeoanthropology, distinctive approaches can nonetheless be identified (Fig. 4.1).

Evolution and fossils

Although the first attempts to construct a model of human evolution by Darwin (1871) and Haeckel (1876) were made prior to the discovery, and hence independently, of any hominid fossils, these material remains of early hominids have been the mainstay of studies of human evolution. One after the other, the early hominids of Europe, Southeast Asia, China and Africa have been the primary focus of debate (Reader 1981). Fossils are technically the mineralized remains of the tissues of plants and animals long dead. In practice, they are principally bones and teeth that have undergone various amounts of physical and chemical change since death. Information derived from fossils is primarily anatomical. Much of the early work on the anatomy of early hominid fossils was typological, using the characteristics of the bones as markers in human evolution, rather than as structures that aided or detracted from the probability of survival of the individuals concerned. This approach could be described as evolutionary, but it is evolution as phylogeny, or the reconstruction of taxonomic relationships, rather than evolution as the product of natural selection, the patterns of adaptations of the early hominids. Furthermore, the analytical framework was a straightforward linear one (Fig. 4.2) with apes at one end, modern humans at the other, and the fossils strung out along the line between them according to the number of human points (i.e. anatomical similarities with modern humans) that they could accumulate. Most debate concerned the addition and subtraction of points, and the subsequent promotion or demotion of the hominids on the line. Both neanderthals and australopithecines have suffered and benefited from many cabinet reshuffles in anthropological museums.

Two factors were perhaps most responsible for limiting the range of interpretation of fossil material. The first was chronological uncertainty and the need for the fossils themselves to be used as temporal markers.

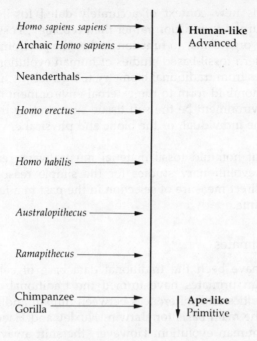

Figure 4.2   'Classic' unilineal model of human evolution, showing a
straightforward progression from ape to human forms.

Consequently, it became methodologically impossible for hominid
morphology to be seen to vary independently of time at anything but the
most superficial of levels. Research thus often merely confirmed existing
beliefs. The second factor was the assumption that human evolution was
unilinear. In the past, workers have let the present degree of divergence
in behaviour and morphology between modern humans and all other
species lead to the assumption that such divergence has always been the
case. The uniqueness of modern humans has promoted a belief in the
uniqueness of their ancestors. Whereas other taxa seemed to have
radiated into many forms from closely related ancestors, hominids were
thought to have evolved in a single series of ancestor–descendent relationships. The unilineal assumption and the single-species hypothesis
long inhibited palaeoanthropological analysis.

Recent developments have seen the release of both of these constraints. The development of the dating techniques discussed in Chapter
2 has meant that fossils can be dated independently of their morphology.
Although many fossils, such as the South African australopithecines,
remain poorly dated, it is now abundantly clear that different hominid
forms were living simultaneously (Howell 1978). Thus relationships
other than temporally dependent ancestor–descendent ones had to be

considered. In this new context of accurately dated fossils, analytical techniques have turned to function rather than typology. Fossils can now be related to other organisms, to function and to the environment, rather than to time. Modern fossil-based studies of human evolution now use a range of techniques from traditional biometry to microscopy and chemical analysis to relate hominid form to the external environment of the bones – whether that environment be the soft tissue surrounding the bone, the social context of the individual, or the biotic and physical environment of the population.

Direct studies of hominid fossil material must always remain at the centre of human evolutionary studies for the simple reason that they provide the only direct measure of selection in the past in a form that can be pinpointed in time.

Evolution and primates

Although fossils have been the traditional data base of early hominid studies, non-human primates have formed the traditional comparative framework. Similarities and differences between human and non-human primates formed the main basis for Darwin, Huxley and Haeckel in their classic studies of human evolution. However, the shift away from typology towards function described above has brought primatology further to the fore in palaeoanthropology. Models of human evolution now rely heavily on either direct analogy with primates, especially the baboon and chimpanzee (e.g. DeVore & Washburn 1963), or else on extrapolations of the general principles governing the variability in primate morphology and behaviour (e.g. Martin & May 1981). In particular, the expansion of field studies of primate behaviour in the past two decades has provided a far fuller picture of the possibilities of early hominid behaviour.

Originally, primatology in the service of palaeoanthropology took the form of 'fleshing out the bones' of the fossil material, an *ad hoc* application of frequently miscellaneous observations on primates. There was little theoretical basis for determining what was or was not relevant in primate behaviour or applicable to hominids. The non-human primates frequently became nothing more than a mirror in which palaeoanthropologists could find the reflection of their ideas about early hominids. The adoption of a broader comparative framework by primatologists (e.g. Clutton-Brock & Harvey 1977a, b), held together by an explicit use of evolutionary theory, has done much to improve the situation. Primatological extrapolations, it would now be argued, must be linked to selection. A behaviour, say food-sharing, if found among certain primates should not be incorporated into a model of early hominid behaviour unless the context in which it takes place, and thus makes it adaptive, is also incorporated. The recognition that behaviours are context-dependent has greatly clarified the role of primate comparisons in palaeoanthropology. Particularly critical here has been the development and more explicit use of theory in the field of animal behaviour (e.g. Wilson 1975; Dawkins 1976; Maynard Smith 1976a, b, 1983; Krebs & Davies 1981, 1984; King's College Sociobiology Group 1982).

Three basic approaches to the use of primates in early hominid studies can be identified. The first of these is the 'species model approach'. A primate species may be taken as a model for the early hominids, and, with a few modifications, applied in total. The main species used are the chimpanzee and the baboon (Jolly 1970; Dunbar 1976; Tanner 1981; Zihlman, Cronin et al. 1978; Johnson 1981; McHenry & Corruccini 1981; Zihlman & Lowenstein 1983). The justification for the species model is either phylogenetic similarity (in the case of the chimpanzee) or inferred environmental similarity (in the case of the baboon), or possibly both (in the case of some chimpanzee populations that live in the savanna). An alternative basis is the recognition of a key feature shared by the model primate species and the early hominid fossils. For example, Jolly (1970) argued that the gelada baboon shared with the early hominids, especially the australopithecines, reduced anterior teeth and enlarged posterior ones (Fig. 4.3). He showed that in the case of the gelada this was an adaptation to feeding on small objects, and in particular seed-eating. He inferred from this relationship that the early hominids might have had a similar diet. Although such models are enlightening, they suffer from the major

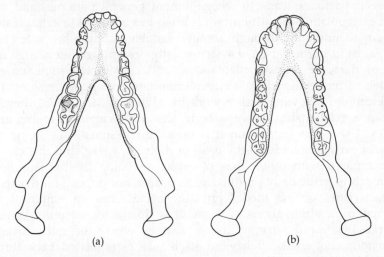

(a)   (b)

Figure 4.3   Relative tooth size in the two genera of living baboon drawn with posterior tooth rows at the same scale. The gelada (*Theropithecus*) (a) has relatively large molars and premolars, and small incisors and canines. In contrast, *Papio* (b) has relatively larger front teeth. Jolly (1970) has argued that the pattern seen in the gelada is a result of 'small object' feeding.

drawback that it is theoretically impossible for two species to be the same, otherwise they would not be two species. A model must take into account not only the similarities, but also the differences.

The second, perhaps more common, approach consists of an attribute analysis. This takes the form of listing human attributes and then finding – or not finding – their counterpart among the non-human primates (for example, types of cooperation such as altruism and food-sharing, meat-eating, language and communication). Their occurrence in non-human primates may be used to indicate the original context and function of certain characteristics of the hominids. Alternatively, their absence might indicate a key attribute that distinguishes man from the rest of the primates. Over the years many such key attributes have been suggested as a rubicon across which the ordinary primate cannot pass (tool use, hunting, language, etc.), but more detailed research has more often than not shown that the chimpanzee at least is capable of crossing such boundaries (e.g. Goodall 1963). The ephemerality of characteristics unique to modern humans in the face of mounting field observations of primates constitutes an inherent weakness of this approach. It may also be criticized for presenting 'just so' stories that allow for all possibilities. The occurrence of a hominid feature in other primates may be evidence for its presence among early hominids; its absence may be evidence of its signal importance among the early hominids.

The third approach is also comparative. Broad comparison of attributes between primates leads to recognition of general patterns, and rather than extrapolating the attributes it is often more fruitful to extrapolate the pattern to hominids through another variable. Clutton-Brock & Harvey (1977a, b) in particular have systematically drawn together a large quantity of data on primate adaptations, and constructed some powerful models of the relationships between important ecological variables. Thus, for example, following earlier work by Milton & May (1975) they have shown a relationship between body size and home-range size in primates. Using this correlation it is possible to estimate the home-range sizes of early hominids on the basis of their body size, and this can then be compared with other lines of evidence (Foley 1984b). This line of approach is particularly productive, as it does not depend on the specific characteristics of the model primate species, but on empirical rules derived from observations of them. It is thus a higher order of model (Clarke 1968), and a correct use of analogy where the rules governing behaviour, not to the behaviour itself, are extrapolated back through time.

A rather different use of primates in the service of hominid evolution is that of molecular or biochemical clocks. As explained in Chapter 2 (page 22), similarities and dissimilarities in biochemistry (proteins, viruses, immune reactions and DNA sequences) may be used to measure phylogenetic distance in the same way that gross anatomy can. This has been used extensively for primate evolution, and has had a major influence on current interpretations of the fossil record and human evolution (Sarich 1983; Pilbeam 1984). Two critical assumptions underly this technique. One is that similarities at a biochemical level indicate the sequence of evolutionary divergence of living taxa. For example, there are more immunological and biochemical differences between all the hominoids and the cercopithecoids than there are between species within each group (see Fig. 2.4). This indicates that hominoids and cercopithecoids diverged earlier than any of their constituent taxa. This assumption is now largely accepted. The other assumption is that the rate of biochemical changes is constant, because the characteristics under consideration have no adaptive value, so do not come under selective control and are therefore a function of the rate of mutation. If this is true, then the molecular differences may be calibrated, and used not just to determine the sequence of divergence, but the chronological pattern as well. Molecular and biochemical evolution can therefore be used as a clock. This assumption has been more widely criticized (Uzell & Pilbeam 1971). Many of the first divergence assessments, which gave late dates, have now been modified to take into account factors such as generation time (Sarich & Wilson 1973). As a guide to the sequence of evolutionary events, the molecular clocks are now widely used and accepted. However, they are unable to tell us anything about either past evolutionary states (Pilbeam 1984) or about lineages that have left no living descendents.

Living primates are an important source of information about early hominids, and both the principles and observations of ethology are increasingly incorporated as a key element of any study. As with any analogue model, though, it is vital that the true nature of the basis for the analogy is shown for its validity to be determined.

Living human populations

It may be argued that the product of hominid evolution is modern humans, and so the characteristics of contemporary populations may act as a guide to earlier phases of evolution. The principal source of such evidence is usually taken to be those humans who subsist through hunting and gathering. Hunting and gathering is an adaptation in which populations survive by exploiting resources as they occur in the wild and over the reproduction, behaviour and distribution of which humans exert little control (Foley 1984b). It is the similarity of this situation with that of the early hominids that provides the basis for comparison.

Arguments about the use of ethnographic analogy or models have frequently been rehearsed in the archaeological literature. Some of these have been at a rarified philosophical level, concerned with the nature of analogies in science as a whole (Binford 1981; Hodder 1982), and some have focused on the technical problems relating to the nature of archaeological data (Binford 1967; Yellen 1977). Further concern has been expressed about the historical particularity of surviving groups of hunter–gatherers (Lee & DeVore 1968: 4–5; Hayden 1981). Contemporary populations are confined solely to areas that are currently marginal to agriculture, and furthermore live not in a world of hunter–gatherers and non-human competitors, but in a world dominated by food-producers. Many of their behavioural and ecological features may reflect this fact.

When dealing with early hominids, though, a rather more fundamental problem arises, namely that whereas late Quaternary hunter–gatherers belong to the same subspecies as contemporary humans, the same cannot be said for pre-sapient hominids. Use of hunter-gatherers as a model for early hominids involves crossing taxonomic boundaries, and so is subject to many of the same limitations as non-human primate models. Consequently, procedures must be used that determine what is a valid analogy and whether such an analogy is robust enough to be extrapolated to different hominid taxa.

The usual procedure adopted is to seek out basic or universal characteristics of hunter–gatherers, establish their key role in human adaptation and behaviour, and then seek evidence for them in the fossil and archaeological record. Such key characteristics would include meat-eating, food-sharing, mobility, and so on. This is a procedure complementary to that used in primate analogies. In the same way, however, these can be self-fulfilling. For one thing, they do not really involve examining adaptive and selective alternatives, a key element of any evolutionary analysis. Discovery of characteristics analogous to those of modern hunter–gatherers in the past leads to the conclusion that the prehistoric populations were behaving in similar ways, without significant consideration being given to the alternative ways in which the same patterns could be generated (Hill 1984). The primary consequence of this has been to populate the past with hunter–gatherers who are substantially the same as their modern counterparts. This does not really take us any closer to solving the problem of understanding hominids who behave differently from both modern apes and modern people. Overuse of hunter–gatherer models results in the appearance of evolutionary and ecological stability in human prehistory. This has affected the focus of palaeoanthropological research of recent years. Attempts to identify the earliest hunter–gatherers in the fossil evidence of Plio-Pleistocene East Africa (Isaac 1978a, b) have led to a commonly held view that the hominids of the middle and late Pleistocene were fully fledged hunter–gatherers; this in turn has been an important support for the view that neanderthals do not differ significantly from modern humans (see especially Brace 1964; Brose & Wolpoff 1971). The current controversy about the interpretation of the Plio-Pleistocene archaeological material (Binford 1981, 1984; Bunn 1981; Gamble 1981; Isaac & Crader 1981; Potts & Shipman 1981; Isaac 1983; Potts 1984a) and the recent analyses of neanderthal fossils by Trinkaus (1982) has raised again the question of how prehistoric hominids, especially pre-sapient forms, differ from modern hunter–gatherers, and so possessed patterns of behaviour and organization for which there are no modern analogues.

Despite the problems associated with using modern hunter–gatherers as an aid to interpreting the past, they must remain an integral element of palaeoanthropology. Used correctly, they provide important insights as well as being one end of the continuum of evolutionary variability with which anthropologists must deal. As living populations of humans provide the only source of information on adaptation involving techno- logy and material items, they must remain central. Much of the evidence for prehistoric adaptation derives from material remains, and so it is important to understand the link between discarded material, technology and behaviour. This has formed the basis for ethnoarchaeology, in which hunter–gatherer studies have played a crucial part (Yellen 1977; Binford 1978a, b, 1979, 1980; R. Gould 1980). Furthermore, hunter–gatherers have long played an important part in discussions about the role of the environment in shaping human organization (Forde 1934; Lee & DeVore 1968), and so act as an important link between the more biologically based aspects of palaeoanthropology and other branches of anthropology.

The archaeology of early hominids

The archaeology of early hominids during the Pleistocene is the archae- ology of the Old Stone Age or the Palaeolithic. Ever since the first recognition that stone tools were indicators of past populations their distribution and morphology have been used as indicators of prehistoric behaviour. In their toolmaking abilities the hominids have their own palaeontological record – one independent of their bodies. From observa- tions of this record – observations about artefact morphology, spatial relationships and chronological patterning – come the evidence on which inferences about early hominid adaptation and behaviour are based.

Broadly speaking, two approaches have characterized archaeological studies of early hominids: *typological* and *behavioural*. Early work in Pleis- tocene archaeology was dominated by lithic typology. Assuming that artefact form reflected stylistic preference or technological skill and incli- nation, and that these in turn represented cultural groupings and hominid capabilities, then it was argued (usually implicitly) that typo- logical variation should show the spatial and chronological patterns of ethnic and cultural populations. These populations could in turn be ranked and ordered according to various evolutionary schema. The actual methods by which these patterns were reconstructed varied considerably, from the use of 'type artefacts' to sophisticated metrical and statistical analyses (Bordes 1961; Clarke 1968). The actual aims, though, were fairly uniform – the delineation in space and time of prehistoric cultures, and the analysis of these patterns in terms of migration, diffusion and internal evolution. New techniques have been developed but the basic aim remains that of cultural narrative (Isaac 1971a). Within these groups the adaptive behaviour was assumed to be largely constant.

A more explicit interest in hominid behaviour beyond or complementary to cultural narrative derived initially from extensions of lithic analysis during the 1960s. In the USSR Semenov (1964) developed a functional interpretation of stone artefacts through microwear analysis, while in the USA Binford & Binford (1966) reinterpreted traditional typological frequencies in terms of function rather than style. The import of these developments was that stone artefacts should be analysed principally in relation to their intended use, not as incidental bearers of cultural information. Stone tools helped hominids to survive, and so should be interpreted in the context of how well they achieved this aim. Apart from this change in direction in lithic analysis other developments occurred that placed behaviour as the central issue, and lithic analysis as one means in its investigation.

One such development was the increasing importance of environmental sciences in the interpretation of archaeological data. The context of the archaeological site, on a micro, local and regional scale (Vita-Finzi & Higgs 1972), and the organic remains found with stone tools became central aspects of archaeological analysis. With a much broader database it was possible to expand the range of questions asked to include some about the relationship between prehistoric populations and their environment – in other words, the evolutionary ecology of early hominids. Glynn Isaac and Lewis Binford and their co-workers in particular have developed and used a battery of techniques to answer specific questions about the behaviour of the early hominids, rather than letting the techniques determine the questions asked (Isaac 1971a, b, 1976, 1983; Isaac & Crader 1981; Binford 1981, 1984).

Studies in modern palaeoanthropology now incorporate these four basic approaches – fossils, primates, ethnography and archaeology. The eclectic use of a wide range of techniques, data and ideas, and a willingness to embrace interdisciplinary approaches, has provided the basis for the current lively status of research into hominid evolution.

The nature of the past

L. P. Hartley wrote that 'the past is a foreign country, they do things differently there'. For palaeoanthropologists, understanding that country is a matter of immediate concern, and so they have developed a range of ideas and concepts that enable them to travel there. Archaeologists and palaeontologists have devoted considerable time to the problems of how knowledge of the past is gained, and to the question of what observation of events in the past actually involves (see especially Binford 1977; 1981). All inferences about the history of our species depend on the adequacy of our knowledge about the processes by which information from the past comes to us. Consequently, the principles and methods used by palaeo-anthropologists to reveal the past need to be sketched out.

Direct and indirect observation

The study of the past and the present is often contrasted by stating that the former depends on indirect observation whereas the latter can be observed directly. Social anthropologists, ethologists and ecologists can all study populations and individuals alive today, and draw conclusions from their direct observations. Palaeoanthropologists, on the other hand, must observe the systems of the past indirectly, through the material relics – fossils, artefacts, etc. This might mean that knowledge in the 'actualistic sciences' is more certain than the 'palaeosciences'.

This contrast, though, is probably not as marked as might appear at first sight (Mellor 1974). All knowledge, whether of the present or the past, is based upon inferences (Binford 1981: 26): that is, structured deductions made on the basis of principles that link phenomena together; this is often in a causal manner. So when a social anthropologist states that a particular group of people have a certain social structure, this knowledge is based on principles such as 'what an informant says relates to what a society actually does' or that 'the frequency of inter-actions between individuals reflects social networks'. These principles are subject to scrutiny, control and further investigation, but they remain the inferences on which knowledge of the present is based.

Information about the past is also drawn from inferences based on similar principles. For example, a statement about the community structure at a particular period in the past may be based on an analysis of the relative frequencies of different species in a faunal sample. The principle underlying this inference is that the frequency of fossil speci-mens reflects the frequency of living animals in the past. The difference, then, between knowledge about the present and the past is not so much the difference between direct and indirect observation, but differences in the length of a chain of inference, and the strength of the links that make up that chain. It may well be that any knowledge about the past must be based on a longer, and less easily investigated, set of inferences than knowledge of the present, but the epistemology is essentially the same. In either case, advances in the discipline rest on the extent to which the chains of inference have been scrutinized and tested.

Principle of uniformitarianism

The central principle that underpins research into past events and processes is that of uniformitarianism. It is generally considered that Charles
Lyell's development of the principle of uniformitarianism in the *Principles
of Geology* (1830) formed the basis for modern geology, and the necessary
conceptual framework for Darwin and Wallace's theory of evolution. At
its simplest the principle of uniformitarianism states that events in the
past can be accounted for only by processes and mechanisms operating
today. As S. J. Gould (1977: 150–1) has pointed out, though, there are
four elements to the principle of uniformitarianism:

1. Scientific rules, principles and laws are uniform in space and time.
2. Processes that shape geological events are uniform through time.
3. The rate of geological change is uniform.
4. The character (configuration) of the Earth has been uniform through
    time.

Gould has argued that only the first two elements are acceptable today.
Enough is known about the moving continents and the changing biological communities of geological time to prove that the world has not
remained uniform throughout its history, and, although change cannot
be incorporated into a few massive and brief catastrophes like Noah's
flood, neither does it occur constantly and evenly. The first two notions
of uniformity, though, remain essential to all aspects of the sciences that
study the past.

The most important, and useful, aspect of the idea of uniformitarianism is that it is not the world that is uniform through time, but the
processes that shape it. Uniformitarianism is a powerful and essential
concept at the level of mechanism or process; at the level of observation it
is a strait-jacket. For example, it is possible today to study intensively a
species, say a chimpanzee, and to describe in detail its behaviour. This
contemporary study might be useful for interpreting the behaviour of
chimpanzees in the past, recovered from the fossil record. It would only
be valid, though, if it were the principles governing the behaviour of the
chimpanzee populations that were extrapolated back, not the behaviour
itself. In other words, it is not possible to say that because chimpanzees
live now in multi-male groups that they did so in the past. It would be
possible, though, to say they did if the conditions under which multi-
male groups are formed could be specified, derived from contemporary
obervations, and if those conditions could then be identified as having
occurred in the past.

This limited use of the principle of uniformitarianism, in which the
level of uniformitarian assumptions is carefully controlled, inextricably
ties together past and present. Both depend on inferences drawn from

observations, and both are based on the assumption that the principles governing the natural world do not change through time and space, even if the products of those principles do. The methods used to observe the past, therefore, must be firmly linked to the world we live in today. This is the only way in which we can extend our knowledge back into the past and yet not impose our own perceptions on to that past.

Linking the past and the present

Middle-range theory

Binford (1977, 1981) has referred to the principles that relate past to the present as *middle-range theory*. These are theories that link the observable aspects of the past to the processes that operate today, so that statements can be made about the dynamics of life in the past. Such bridging arguments have long been used in geology, palaeontology and archaeology, but have recently become more explicit and formal as it has become recognized that common sense alone is not sufficient to interpret the fossil record. Consequently experiments have been carried out on diverse phenomena, such as decay of bone (Behrensmeyer 1978), disarticulation of carcasses (Hill 1975), and polish on stone artefacts (Keeley 1978; Keeley & Toth 1981). What they all have in common is an attempt to key the material remains of the past into the conditions under which they were formed.

Binford (1981: 29) has summarized the case for an explicit use of middle-range theory as follows: 'All our statements about the past are inferences relative to observations made on the contemporary archaeological record' (i.e. observations made in the present on material that can be studied archaeologically or palaeontologically) and 'the accuracy of our inferences relative to observations made on the contemporary archaeological record' (i.e. observations made in the present on material that can be studied archaeologically or palaeontologically) and 'the accuracy of our the past and the present can be linked only if they are directly comparable. Observations on the present, then, must be made in a form that is similar to the way in which the past can also be observed (Fig. 4.4). In other words, there is no point, say in looking at the behaviour of an antelope today, to act as a model for the past, unless the observations are linked to some aspect that is observable in the fossil record – say, for example, body size or some anatomical element.

Middle-range theory, then, is that aspect of palaeoanthropology that examines and describes the processes by which information is transformed from the living world to the fossil world, and so enables us to make inferences from the fossil world to the living world of the past.

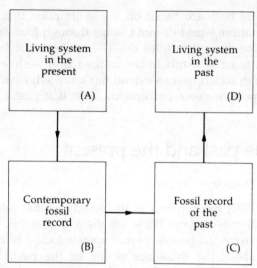

Figure 4.4   Linking the past and the present. The route of inference for knowledge about life in the past (D) depends upon observations of the fossil record (C), but interpreting this record depends on understanding the process of transformation during fossilization (D and C). This in turn depends on observations of contemporary fossil formation, or the way in which observable behaviour in the present would be visible in the fossil record.

Taphonomical processes

In practice, most elements of middle-range theory are concerned with how behaviour, whether of humans or other animals, is transformed into a material debris or preserved in the fossilized remains of animals. This is the field of taphonomy – the study of the processes of burial or the transformation from the biosphere to the lithosphere (Efremov 1940; Behrensmeyer & Hill 1980; Shipman 1983). To put this another way, taphonomy basically attempts to answer the question – how representative of life in the past is the fossil record?

Because no general theory of how the fossil and archaeological records form has yet been developed, no general answer can be given to such a question. The factors contributing to the structure of these processes are diverse, and research has concentrated on isolating the effects of individual components. There are thus good studies on the effect of scavenging (Hill 1978; Brain 1981), burial (Isaac 1967), habitat differences and size effects (Behrensmeyer & Dechant Boaz 1980), size (Behrensmeyer 1983), trampling (Gifford-Gonzales, Damrosch et al. 1985;

Behrensmeyer, Gordon & Yanagi 1986) and water action (Hanson 1980). Particular behavioural processes have also been investigated, such as butchering (Binford 1981), toothwear (Walker 1981), artefact polish (Keeley 1978), and settlement formation and decay (Yellen 1977). The overall nature, though, of research into taphonomical processes can best be seen as a series of contrasts.

Most important is the contrast between the behavioural components of the fossil record and the geological components. The fossil record is not solely the product of biological factors operating during the life of an animal, and nor is it solely a result of geological processes that occurred after death. Rather it is a blend of the two, and no analysis can afford to ignore one or the other. Research into the biases of the fossil record has consequently been concerned with factors of life (predepositional) and postmortem (postdepositional) factors. The former has been largely concentrated within archaeology (ethnoarchaeology), focused on the ways in which particular human behaviours determine the structure of the archaeological record. For example, Binford has shown (1978a) that the spatial distribution of artefacts in an Eskimo camp reflects different ways of discarding (tossing or dropping) material items, and that it is human behaviour that determines the pattern. On the other side, Behrensmeyer (1983) has carried out a long-term study of the processes of decay and destruction operating on a population of large mammals in East Africa, to discover how bones disappear after death.

A further contrast is that between taphonomical research into processes operating today on the contemporary fossil and archaeological record (neotaphonomy – actualistic studies), and direct studies of prehistoric contexts. The former, which are usually concerned with middle-range theory as described above, are directed towards constructing models of the process of fossilization that can then be applied to the fossil record. The latter, on the other hand, try to identify, in place, the representativeness of a particular fossil or archaeological assemblage. The former is represented by studies such as Hill's (1975) analysis of postmortem changes on a modern East African landscape, and his construction of a skeletal disarticulation model (Hill 1979), while the latter include Hay's (1976) detailed reconstruction of the environment at Olduvai, and Shipman's (1982) analysis of the faunal sample from the important middle Miocene site of Fort Ternan, the only site to have yielded hominoids in Africa during this period, including *Kenyapithecus*, once thought to be conspecific with *Ramapithecus* and therefore a putative hominid. By and large, studies in palaeotaphonomy represent the true end of taphonomical research, in that they result in statements about the nature of the past, but they in turn depend directly on research into processes going on today.

The final contrast derives from the differences between archaeology and palaeontology. Palaeontologists, dealing with a wide range of non-human organisms, have mostly been concerned with postdepositional effects, with functional anatomy, and with environmental aspects of adaptation. Archaeologists, while not ignoring these factors, have also had to recognize the importance of social and cultural factors in the formation of the archaeological record, as well as the fact that their information is derived not just from the bones of the organism itself, but from the material remains of their activities as well. Consequently, the range of neotaphonomical research in archaeology has been broader, involving many of the techniques and concepts of social anthropology as well as ecology.

Even though there are means of approaching the problems of the past without direct recourse to the fossil and archaeological record (for example, biochemical studies and hunter–gatherer analogies), these direct relics remain an essential and central aspect of the discipline. They represent a main pathway to the past, but their interpretation depends entirely on our understanding of the ways in which they have been formed and transformed. Developing our understanding of the past, therefore, depends on the continued pursuit of taphonomical research and the construction of middle-range theory.

Methods for studying the past

In the light of these considerations of how knowledge of the past can be gained, it is possible to propose a set of procedures that may act as a guide for investigating the evolutionary ecology of any group of animals, including hominids. The principal aim of these guidelines is to ensure that palaeoanthropological investigations start with sound behavioural and biological principles, and, in turn, that such behavioural theories are testable when applied to the past.

Theory and models

A point established at the end of the first chapter was that since data cannot tell their own story so theory is essential for probing the events of the past, and as a means of getting beyond the description of hominid evolution towards its analysis and explanation. In practice, this means that specific questions must be asked. The role of theory is to generate those questions. As will be elaborated in the following chapter, the theory of evolutionary ecology may be used to generate questions about hominid evolution. The key idea here is that theoretical considerations can lead directly to questions and predictions about the past. For example, ecological theory states that in tropical conditions primary production should vary with availability of moisture (Murphy 1974). This predicted pattern of variation may be used to define potential responses of animals. Predicted response could then be used for a model of adaptation that could be tested against the available data.

However, theory (that is, logical deductions and predictions from a few axioms) is not the sole source of questions about the past. Observations on the fossil record, or indeed on contemporary biological forms, can, when placed into the context of a theoretical framework, lead to the identification of important areas of research in the subject. For example, a bimodal distribution of some morphological characteristic present on fossil hominids might prompt specific questions about sexual dimorphism. These questions can then draw from the body of theory available on what is likely to promote or inhibit the degree of sexual dimorphism. In this case, observations lead to a consideration of the theories that might account for the observations. Use of data in this way is a scientific method based on 'pattern recognition' (Binford 1983:97).

Another pattern-recognition technique is to search for anomalies within the patterns (S. J. Gould 1980). Apparant anomalies between current explanations and the data may frequently be used to formulate specific questions about the data, and consequently new methods and explanations. The classic example of this in physical anthropology is the unmasking of the Piltdown forgery, where its increasingly anomalous position in human evolution led to the development of new methods of investigation. Again, though, the role of theory was crucial, because it was the discord between the theory or interpretation of human evolution and the characteristics of the Piltdown skull that led to the identification of the problem.

A general theory or explanatory framework, however, is inadequate on its own. It must be expressed in such a way as to make it directly comparable with the data available to test it. This is the role of the model, to act as the interface between theory and data. A model describes or predicts the structure and variation of phenomena derived from the principles of a theory. So for example, a theory may state that sexual dimorphism is 'caused' by inter-male rivalry, and that the conditions under which inter-male rivalry will be most significant will be where resource availability favours large-group foraging. The model that would be derived from this would be a description of the pattern of variability in sexual dimorphism – that is, marked differences between males and females where the environment has unevenly spaced resources and so large-group feeding, and minimal sexual dimorphism where resources are evenly spread. With this model the theory has been transformed into a form that can be directly compared with the available data – measures of sexual dimorphism and resource distribution.

With studies of the past, though, a second level of model building is required. This is because, as described above, the fossil and archaeological record is not solely the product of behavioural or predepositional factors, but also of geological or postdepositional factors. Consequently, the model of sexual dimorphism proposed here would have to be transformed into another form, suitable for testing in the past. This would involve considering how sexual dimorphism might be represented in fossils, and how environmental variation might be reconstructed for ecosystems long gone. This again emphasizes the role of middle-range theory and taphonomical research.

However, this ideal of how to proceed can be complicated by further factors. Because of the limiting nature of the way fossil and archaeological records form, different behavioural models may, when transformed into models that predict the structure of these records, be identical (Hill 1984). Regrettably, though, the transformation of behavioural models into their archaeological or palaeontological manifestations may result in equifinality – that is, different behaviours produce identical fossil records. Consequently, it is seldom sufficient to predict what the archaeological and palaeontological record will look like if one model is correct. Overlap between models must be considered, and points of difference actively pinpointed.

Four pathways to the past

Neither theory nor models on their own are sufficient in palaeoanthropology, for they would amount to imposing the present on the past. Because the theory must, initially at least, be drawn from our understanding of the world as we see it today, it is a reflection of contemporary structure and variability. To avoid having this structure simply reflected back in from the past, independent methods of determining what did actually happen are needed. Just as the fossils are mute without the framework of theory, so, too, the theory is self-confirming when not put to empirical tests. Four routes to such tests may be suggested:

1. **Inferential**. Inferences may be made about the pattern of fossilized material. A classic inference (although almost certainly an incorrect one) is that similarity in artefact morphology indicates similarity in the social or cultural context of the artefacts' manufacturers. This is the basis for cultural interpretations of the archaeological record. Where each link in the inferential chain (and there may be several) is carefully forged, and independently supported through actualistic and experimental studies, this is a powerful approach (see Binford & Sabloff (1982) for a critical review). The strength of an inference may be tested ethnographically, experimentally, or through simulation.

2. **Isolating techniques**. Most methods for finding out about the past attempt to draw conclusions from broad trends in the data. Binford (1981), though, has pioneered an alternative method that treats the broad pattern of the data with great scepticism and looks instead

specifically for small details that may seem comparatively insignificant but are in fact especially sensitive to behavioural variation, and consequently may be used to distinguish between hypotheses. Binford (1981) has suggested that butchery patterns are one example, and disarticulation of skeletons may be suggested as another (Hill 1975). A further extremely elegant example is Walker's (1981) analysis of toothwear using a scanning electron microscope.

3. **Probabalistic**. Not all methods are able to distinguish exactly between behaviours and hypotheses, but instead offer a statistical framework for assessing likelihoods. The mathematical basis for this is discussed by Pilbeam & Vaisnys (1975). In practice, it involves isolating processes that may have similar products and experimentally or theoretically attempting to assign probabilities to various outcomes. For this technique single occurrences are seldom of much use, and repeated patterns are necessary.

4. **Comparative biological**. It is to some extent possible to test ideas about the past without direct reference to the fossil record. The principal means in studies of early hominids is that of comparative biology. The pattern of interspecific and intraspecific variation among plants and animals can be used to correlate biological variables. Many such correlations have been worked out theoretically or empirically – for example, between body size and metabolic rate (Kleiber 1961). Where they are sound these correlations enable us to make direct statements about early hominids with only partial recourse to the details of the fossils. Even though it is necessary to examine the conditions under which any correlation is made, it is possible, where one or more variable can be determined for the past, to use the correlations to draw conclusions about organisms living in the past. A classic example of this approach has been the work on the use of protein biochemistry that is presently having such an impact on palaeoanthropology and the reconstruction of phylogenies (see page 20).

All of these categories of approach to the past are useful and are considered here. Each one may involve traditional methods such as artefact typology, or use more sophisticated scientific techniques. For all of them, though, a prerequisite is that they can accommodate the fact that fossilization processes are diverse. They must therefore be able to monitor behavioural patterns across a wide spectrum of species. It has now been amply demonstrated (see, for example, the literature on fossilization processes in East Africa, e.g. Behrensmeyer & Hill 1980; Shipman 1983) that the fossil and archaeological record of early hominids is the product of many processes, and few assumptions can be made in attempting to determine the relative importance of these processes.

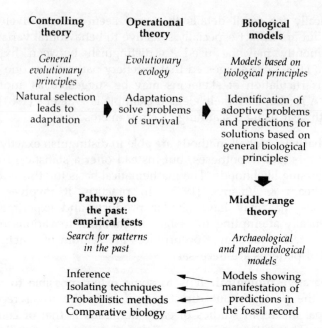

Figure 4.5   Pathways to the past: summary of the ways of investigating hominid evolution discussed in this chapter. See text for full discussion.

An example

These methods represent the interrelated ways in which problems in palaeoanthropology that can be identified or derived from theoretical propositions can be tackled and hypotheses tested (Fig. 4.5). They can be illustrated by an example that will be explored in much greater detail later in this book – the development of meat-eating among hominids.

The first stage is the identification of meat-eating as a significant palaeoanthropological problem. This is suggested by the different levels of carnivory found among the non-human primates and humans (K. Hill 1982), indicating that during hominid evolution some significant adaptive change occurred. Such a difference provides the basis for considering this to be an evolutionary problem.

In order to examine this palaeoanthropological issue, it is necessary to relate it to a body of theory. The relevant theory is an ecological one – that is, theory relating to trophic structure and to niche breadth. The problem of hominid meat-eating is really a special case of a more general set of ecological questions – under what conditions does an organism change its position in the trophic pyramid, from plant-eating to meat-eating? Under what conditions does an organism expand the range of resources utilized?

By phrasing the problem in these general terms it is possible to construct an ecological model based on general principles rather than the specific characteristics of one type of organism (in this case the hominids). This general model is based on adopting a broad comparative approach. For example, an animal expands its niche when the costs of exploiting a new resource are less than the average costs of resource exploitation in general (MacArthur & Pianka 1966). A model can then be constructed that describes the conditions under which this might occur – for example, depletion of existing resources, expansion of the new resource, development of a new procurement strategy, or reduction in competition. This would amount to a predictive statement about the conditions under which hominid meat-eating would have developed.

To test the prediction, though, the model needs to be formulated in terms of its 'fossil manifestation'. In other words, both the conditions of meat-eating and its actual practice should be identifiable in some data set. Such a requirement demands careful specification of environmental conditions, and the consequences of meat-eating. For example, if the conditions included reduction in the number of other carnivores or omnivores, and hence reduction in competition, then these species should undergo some change in frequency or diversity in the fossil record.

To pursue these expectations in the fossil record will require putting into practice the four principles by which knowledge of the past is gained (see page 86). Inferences, based on middle-range theory, can be made; for example, to state that a close spatial association between hominid artefacts and animal bones indicates processing of animal products. Isolating techniques can be used; for instance, the distribution of cut marks on animal bones in relation to meat (muscle) might be used to isolate those bones that had been processed exclusively by hominids from those where hominids succeeded other animals in a sequence of ulitization (Potts 1984a). Probability principles can also be used; for example, it would be possible to calculate the probability that animal bones and humanly modified artefacts will occur together given certain rates of animal mortality and artefact discard. And, finally, comparisons can be made between characteristics of living human populations and other animals, especially primates, to determine whether there are established physiological traits that indicate the antiquity of meat-eating (e.g. the anatomy of the digestive tract).

It should be noticed that in this example each of these principles uses the main approaches to palaeoanthropology described in this chapter – fossils, primates, living human populations and archaeology – indicating the need for a broad-based analytical methodology. Although this will not guarantee the solution of any palaeoanthropological problem, and in particular will often fall short of proof, it is a necessary prerequisite of analytical success.

Analytical palaeoecology

In this and the preceding chapters attempts were made to describe the appropriate framework for investigating patterns in hominid evolution. In the first chapter the current fossil and archaeological evidence for hominid evolution offered the first such framework – the actual data that must provide the basis for interpretation and analysis. It was suggested, though, that this evidence is insufficient on its own – that the fossil record cannot tell its own stories. Partly this is because of the form the evidence takes: it is either fragmented fossils or oblique living comparisons, making interpretation a far from straightforward procedure. And partly it results from the need for an appropriate theoretical framework that can link our observations of the past to the way in which we understand how biological and ecological systems work.

That framework was presented in Chapter 2. It was shown that the mechanisms and processes of evolution are linked to the principles of evolution through the central concept of adaptation. Of particular importance for what follows was the suggestion that adaptation is a problem-solving process – adaptations are the solutions to the problems of survival that have provided an individual with the greatest reproductive success. This was analogous to the pursuit of strategies by game-players. Identifying the problems faced by early hominids was suggested as an important initial goal in palaeoanthropology.

However, as this chapter has tried to show, although it is essential to start with sound evolutionary and ecological principles and modelling; means must be found to relate these to the data available. To put the principles into practice requires methods for investigating the past. What has been stressed here is that these methods are diverse, that there are a range of potential approaches, but that they must all be underpinned by sound uniformitarian principles and explicit use of middle-range theory.

The purpose of these chapters has been to show how palaeoanthropology can become more analytical by being brought within the framework of evolutionary ecology. The implications are far-reaching. If adaptations are the solutions to the problems an organism has faced, then we need to ask what problems the early hominids faced? We then need to place these problems into the context of general biological principles, so that hominid evolution can be treated in a broader comparative framework. The factors underlying potential solutions need to be identified and discussed, so that the reasons leading to particular 'hominid solutions' can be understood. And finally, these evolutionary and ecological models must then be related to the patterns of the fossil and archaeological record.

The remaining chapters of this book are devoted to this end. A series of broad biological and ecological problems that may have been signifi-

cant in hominid evolution – tropicality, body size, terrestriality, seasonality and interspecific competition – are identified and an attempt is made
to link them to the patterns in the evolutionary ecology of early hominids.
Each of these problems is shared with a wide range of other organisms,
and so fruitful comparisons can be made. In the end, what will constitute
human uniqueness is not any particular adaptations, but the combination
of them (Fig. 4.6).

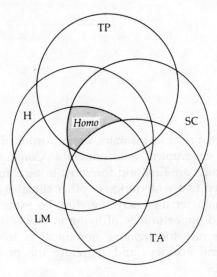

Figure 4.6 Venn diagram of human uniqueness and the human adaptive
strategy (shaded area) as the intersection of the biological
categories to which hominids belong. TP, terrestrial primates;
SC, savanna community; TA, tropical organisms; LM, large
mammals; H, hominids.

5 Hominids as tropical animals

Hominids are primates, and primates are an order of animals that have evolved and live in tropical environments. Consequently, it may be argued that hominids are first and foremost tropical organisms that have secondarily adapted to a wide range of other climates and environments. Many hominid characteristics may therefore be expected to derive from the constraints and opportunities of living in low latitudes. This chapter examines the grounds for treating hominids as tropical animals; the character of tropical ecology, and therefore the problems involved in living in the tropics.

Hominid evolution and the tropics

Three distinct lines of evidence can be cited for treating early hominids as products of a tropical environment – the current distribution of primates; the distribution of fossil non-human primates; and the distribution of fossil hominids through time.

Primate distribution

An examination of the geographical distribution of primates highlights their tropical character. Defining the tropics as the area lying between the Tropics of Cancer and Capricorn, most non-human primate species live within this area, and virtually no species occur beyond 25 degrees latitude in the north, and 30 degrees latitude in the south (Fig. 5.1). Aside from modern humans there are a few exceptions, confined to the genus *Macaca* (Napier & Napier 1967: 378). *Macaca mulatta* occurs as far north as Beijing in China, although the species may have been introduced by humans in

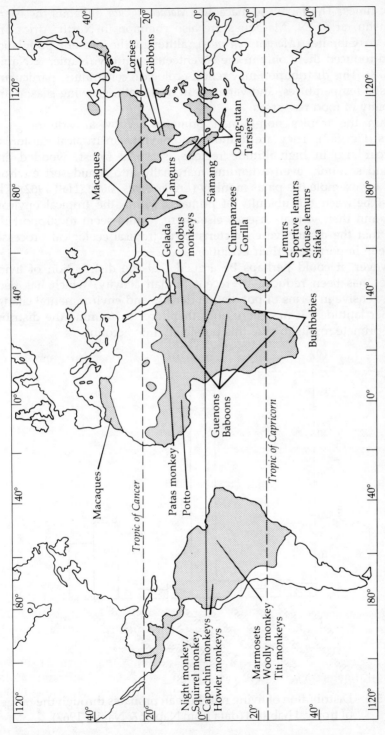

Figure 5.1 Distribution of living non-human primates (after Napier & Napier 1967).

historic times. The Japanese macaque, *Macaca fuscata*, inhabits the island of Honshu, at 41 °N. Macaques are also common in North Africa and extend to Gibralter (*Macaca sylvanus*), although the present population were introduced there only in the seventeenth century (Napier & Napier 1967: 378). This distribution may reflect ecological constraints, particularly decreased temperatures, and variation in daylength, growing season and availability of food resources.

Within the tropics non-human primates occupy a wide range of habitats (Fig. 5.2). They are found predominantly in tropical rainforest, but occur also in high-altitude regions, seasonal forest, wooded and grassland savanna, even extending marginally into semidesert environments, for example the patas monkey (*Erythrocebus patas*) (Hall 1962). The contrast between the ubiquity of primates within the tropical environments, and their virtual absence elsewhere, would seem to support the notion that the distinctive characteristics of tropical ecological processes have been important in their evolution.

However, it could perhaps be argued that the distribution of living primates has been reduced by recent human activity, which has been more extensive in terms of population density and environmental change in higher latitudes. It may be useful, therefore, to examine the distribution of primate fossils to take this possibility into account.

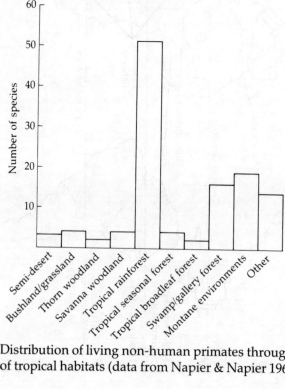

Figure 5.2   Distribution of living non-human primates through the range of tropical habitats (data from Napier & Napier 1967).

Fossil distribution

Fossil primates are by no means common, but they do occur in sufficient numbers to give some idea of their past distributions. Certainly, their prehistoric range is more extensive than that of today. As discussed in Chapter 2, the earliest primates can be traced back to the final Cretaceous (about 65 Ma ago) (Szalay & Delson 1979). Early Plesiadapiformes, a primitive form of primate, are found in North America and Europe from the late Cretaceous to the late Eocene. Strepsirhini, an extant suborder, are documented from the early Eocene onwards in North America, Europe, Asia and Africa. The suborder Haplorhini also appear in the early Eocene, and representatives are widely distributed across the continents. This extensive range is maintained for the Oligocene and into the Miocene. By 36 Ma ago, though, primates were extinct in North America. In Europe primates are common in the Miocene and into the Pliocene, but only *Macaca* is known for the Pleistocene. For the most part, the past 10 million years have seen primates confined to South and Central America, to Africa, and to the tropical regions of Asia.

This pattern is consistent with the tropicality of the order, for there have been significant climatic changes during this time. The early Cenozoic was a period considerably warmer than today, with a much more extensive distribution of tropical, especially forested, environments. The period from the middle Miocene onwards, in contrast, has seen a major decline in temperature as well as major changes in continental

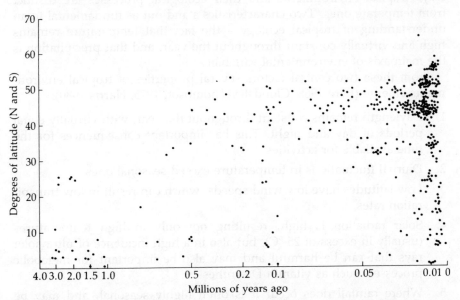

Figure 5.3 Distribution of fossil hominids in relation to latitude (data from Oakley, Campbell & Mollison 1977).

drift, resulting in a reduction in tropical habitat distribution (see page 107 for further details). Primate distribution has shrunk in accord with these climatic changes, supporting the contention that primates are severely limited by temperate environments.

Modern humans, and some of the early hominids, are the only primates to have escaped these confines. However, although their current distribution is global, the fossil evidence indicates only a gradual, relatively late colonization of high latitudes. Figure 5.3 plots the latitude of known fossil hominids against their approximate age. This indicates that before 1.0 Ma ago hominids were confined to the tropics and subtropics; that by this date the fringes of the temperate world were colonized; and that it was only in the late Pleistocene that hominids entered the high-latitude regions. The critical periods of hominid evolution, during which hominids diverged from the other hominids and developed their characteristics, such as bipedalism and tool-making, occurred within a tropical environment.

Patterns of tropical ecology

Factors affecting environmental structure

Given this tropical origin it is appropriate to enquire whether and in what ways tropical environments and their ecological processes are distinct from temperate ones. Two characteristics stand out as fundamental to an understanding of tropical ecology – the fact that temperature remains high and virtually constant throughout the year, and that precipitation is the main axis of environmental variability.

From these two central factors several properties of tropical environments emerge (Eyre 1968; Cloudsley-Thompson 1975; Harris 1980):

1. Daylength remains constant throughout the year, with virtually equal periods of day and night. This has important consequences for the time available for activities.
2. Diurnal fluctuations in temperature exceed seasonal ones.
3. Low latitudes have low wind speeds, which can result in low transpiration rates.
4. Solar radiation is high, resulting not only in high temperatures (usually in excess of 25 °C), but also in a high incidence of ultraviolet rays that can be harmful and may also be important for metabolic processes, such as vitamin D synthesis.
5. Where rainfall does occur it is often highly seasonal, and may be cyclonic and torrential. One result of this may be that mean annual

rainfall figures are not necessarily a good indicator of the availability of moisture.

6. Many tropical environments are characterized by a marked richness or diversity of plant and animal species. Whereas temperate environments are often dominated by many individuals of a few species, tropical ecosystems frequently contain small numbers of individuals from many species. This is particularly so with tropical rainforest.

7. Because temperature is not a sensitive variable other factors become important. In tropical environments there will often be a closer relationship between vegetation and soil type. Soil itself will vary locally according to geological factors.

8. Following on from this, tropical environments often exhibit a high degree of spatial variability in habitat type. Great stretches of habitat, such as those found in Eurasia and North America, are relatively rare in the tropics. Instead tropical environments may often be described as mosaic-like in their structure.

All these characteristics, distinctive to the tropics, can and do have major adaptive consequences for the plants and animals. Above all, though, it is rainfall that is critical. The structure and pattern of habitats in the tropics can broadly speaking be predicted by the variability in rainfall. Three interrelated attributes are important here. One is the total amount of rainfall, or the mean annual precipitation. From Fig. 5.4 it can be seen that habitats vary directly in relation to this value. Empirical work (Strugnell & Pigot 1978) and theoretical considerations (Murphy 1974; Rosensweig 1968) have shown that this may be explained in terms of increases in primary productivity, and the effect this has on habitat structure. With increasing rainfall, plant cover, biomass, plant production and secondary biomass will all increase (Fig. 5.5). Another attribute is the seasonal distribution of the rainfall. For productivity to increase moisture is required throughout the year, and so the longer the periods without rain, the poorer and simpler the plant communities. These habitats vary as much with the length of the dry season as they do with mean annual rainfall (see Fig. 5.4, which shows how these two variables are closely related). The final attribute is the predictability of the rain. Values for mean annual rainfall often conceal a high level of interannual variation. This may be critical, as it is often not the average amount of rainfall over a period of several years that is significant, but, in terms of animal adaptation and evolution, the frequency with which certain minimum levels are obtained.

Despite this complexity, mean annual rainfall is often cited as a determining variable. Although this is a simplification enforced by the paucity of detailed climatological data, particularly for the past, it is partially, justified because the three variables are closely interrelated

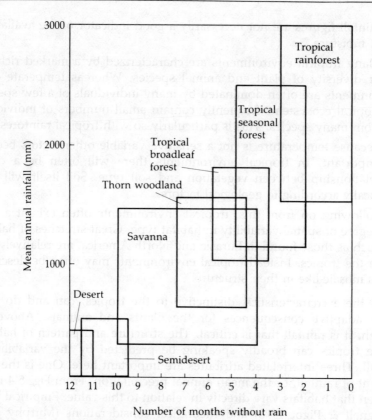

Figure 5.4 Tropical habitat variability in relation to mean annual rainfall
and seasonality (after Foley 1982).

(Harris 1980). With decreasing mean annual rainfall, seasonality will
increase and predictibility will decline. Arid environments are often
highly seasonal and subject to local and periodic variations in rainfall;
wetter environments usually have short or no dry seasons, with little
variation from year to year. As will be seen in Chapter 8, this seasonality
was significant in early hominid evolution.

Habitats

From these interrelated variables derives the habitat structure of the
tropics. At the wettest extreme lie the tropical rainforests, at the driest the
deserts. Gradation between these extremes is a continuum, which may be
classified in various ways, to various levels of detail. However, a broad
description of the major habitats is quite simple (Eyre 1968; Cloudsley-
Thompson 1975; Harris 1980).

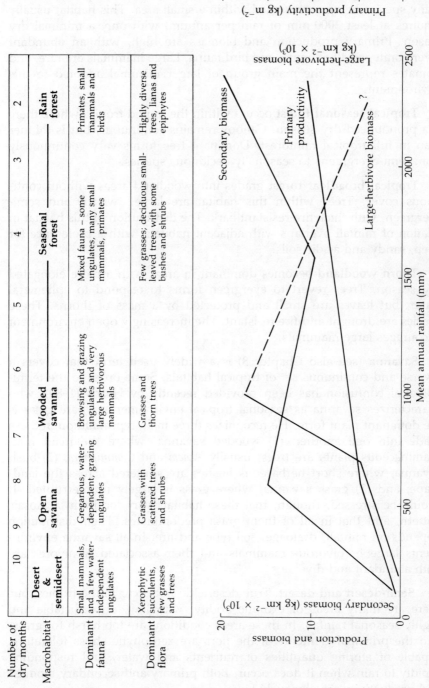

Figure 5.5 Ecological and energetic characteristics of tropical environments.

1. **Tropical rainforest** is forest with full and complete canopy, from three to five layers. Trees are tall, covered with lianas and epiphytes, with many species being represented within a small area. This habitat usually requires at least 3000 mm of rain per annum, with only a minimal dry season. Primary production and biomass are high, with an abundant invertebrate, small mammal and bird fauna. Large mammals are rare, and primates represent the main group of larger mammal adapted to this environment.

2. **Tropical seasonal forest** occurs within the humid tropics where there is a pronounced dry season. Canopy remains continuous, but is thinner than in full tropical rainforest. Dominant tree forms vary continuously from semi-evergreens to seasonally deciduous species.

3. **Tropical broadleaf forest** grades into woodland areas without continuous cover. Trees within this habitat are large, twisted and semi-evergreen, with thick fire-resistant bark. The distribution of this habitat in relation of rainfall overlaps with adjacent habitats, with a preference for deep, sandy and acidic soils.

4. **Thorn woodland** becomes dominant in areas with a more elongated dry season. Trees revert to evergreen forms to respond to ephemeral water, but leaves are small and protected by a mass of thorns. These species are drought and fire resistant. The increasingly open environment encourages large mammals.

5. **Savanna** (see also Chapter 8) is a widely used term that covers a diverse and continuous set of tropical habitats. Some order to the terminological confusion has been provided recently by Harris (1980), who characterizes savanna as seasonal tropical environments where grass is the dominant plant form. He recognizes three main types, although these grade into one another: (1) wooded savanna, where the main non-graminaceous plants are trees, usually *Acacia* and *Commiphora*; (2) bush savanna, where short herbaceous bushes are scattered across the landscape; and (3) grass savanna, where grass is largely uninterrupted. It should be stressed, though, that these habitats vary locally in a mosaic pattern, and that in all of them grass predominates. Their distribution depends on rainfall, drainage, soil type and fire. In all savanna environments large herbivorous mammals and their associated carnivores are both abundant and diverse.

6. **Semi-desert and desert.** True deserts do not occur in the tropics, but there are many areas of extreme aridity, with low, unpredictable and highly seasonal rainfall. In these areas conditions are too harsh for grass, and the principal elements of the flora are xerophytic stress tolerators, capable of storing quantities of nutrients and water, and responding rapidly to rain when it does occur. Both primary and secondary biomass and productivity are obviously low.

7. **Montane environments** do not fit neatly into any classification of tropical habitats, as, because of the stress caused by declining temperatures with increasing altitude, the habitats can mimic temperate and arctic forms.

It has been possible to show that hominids belong to an order with a tropical origin and evolution, and consequently with tropical adaptations. With this in mind, it has also been possible to identify the distinctive characteristics of tropical environments and ecology. These derived from the prime importance of moisture as the factor controlling environmental variability, and from which the structure of the tropical habitat forms derived.

It now remains to examine how these considerations may have shaped hominid evolution.

Early hominids in a tropical environment

Thermoregulation

From the foregoing it is clear that adaptation to equatorial environments will involve coping with high temperatures. This might be identified, therefore, as one of the adaptive problems reflected in hominid evolution. This contention is supported by the fact that the thermoregulatory mechanisms of humans are remarkable. Modern humans, as mammals, are homeotherms, that is they maintain a constant and high body temperature through internal heat production and control. For most mammals the core temperature is insulated from the environment by a coat of fur or hair that acts as a layer of insulation (McNab 1974). This is true for most members of the order Primates. Modern humans, though, are distinctive in lacking any significant body hair, and in their dependence on sweating as a means of regulating body temperature (Eichna, Bean et al. 1945). Unlike most mammals they have only a limited capacity for panting, but, despite having the same density and size of sweat glands as other primates, their rate of sweat secretion is higher than that of any known mammal. Modern humans, as travellers on underground trains know, can sweat 2 or more litres per hour for short periods of time, and maintain a rate of 1 litre per hour over longer periods (Weiner & Hellman 1960; Ladell 1964).

The fact that during their evolution hominids have modified their thermoregulatory system so drastically, and achieved such high levels of efficiency, suggests that selection as aresult of thermal stress was considerable. It is necessary, therefore, to identify the conditions under which thermal stress occurs and the possible solutions to such stress.

Ambient temperatures in tropical environments are often in the region of 30 °C, but actual heat stress may vary mostly in relation to solar radiation, which in turn varies with habitat. Solar radiation is highest in deserts, reaching levels of 200 cal m^{-2} h^{-1}. In savanna environments a typical figure would be 100 cal m^{-2} h^{-1} (Ingram & Mount 1975; Mount 1979). Stress would also be further affected by reflectance, humidity and wind. Thermoregulatory patterns would also be influenced by activity in relation to daily temperature fluctuations.

Which of these conditions is likely to apply to the early hominids? As far as is known, hominids did not inhabit deserts until the late Pleistocene or Holocene (see later, page 262). For the African early hominid localities, palaeoenvironmental evidence suggests that Peninj in East Africa was the driest environment, but even this was probably grass savanna (Isaac 1965, 1967, 1984). There is, however, consistent evidence to suggest that hominids were predominantly distributed within the savanna biome (see Chapter 8 for details). Solar radiation would therefore have been quite high. These environments generally have reduced wind activity and low humidity, the former increasing heat stress, the latter reducing it. In other words, although the early hominid environment was one of significant solar radiation, it does not seem to lie at the extremes considered necessary to result in such novel thermoregulation.

Activity patterns

It is to activity that many authors have turned to account for the causes of human thermoregulatory efficiency (Montagu 1964; Campbell 1974). Increased muscular activity in a hot environment can cause major problems. The most popular explanation for such stress has been the evolution of hunting (Campbell 1974). The intense activity associated with chasing animals around the savanna would seem to require new cooling mechanisms. This explanation, however, suffers from various drawbacks. Principal among these is the fact that sweating as a response to heat stress is usually delayed, and thus the benefits are unlikely to have been significant in the context of hunting (Newman 1970). Furthermore, none of the large carnivores appears to suffer from heat stress. Another difficulty lies in the fact that a consequence of sweating is a markedly increased level of water requirements, which would conflict with the need for more extensive ranging patterns necessary to operate at a higher trophic level (see later, page 130).

An alternative, activity based explanation lies not in what activity was being carried out, but when it was being carried out. Most species in tropical environments have distinct activity cycles, with a correlation between periods of minimal activity ('resting') and highest ambient temperatures, and, most significantly, highest levels of solar radiation (Fig. 5.6). High thermal stress might therefore be expected to occur among animals whose adaptation involves high levels of activity during the

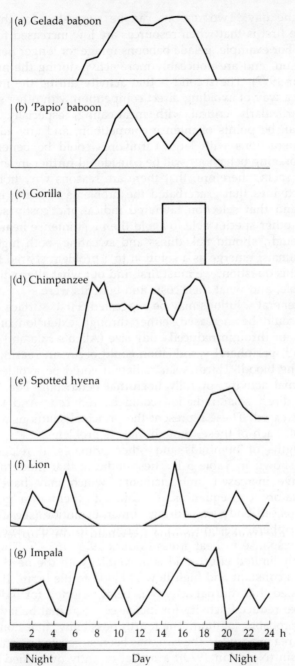

Figure 5.6   Daily activity patterns of various African mammals (from
(a) Dunbar 1977; (b) Altmann & Altmann 1970; (c) Fossey &
Harcourt 1977; (d) Wrangham 1977; (e) Kruuk 1972;
(f) Schaller 1972; (g) Jarman & Jarman 1973).

middle of the day. Two reasons can be suggested for this increased activity. The first is that when resources are low increased foraging time is required. For example, gelada baboons forage for longer periods during the dry season, and are noticeably more active during the middle of the day (Dunbar 1977). The second is that activity during the middle of the day may be a way of avoiding direct competition with other species. This may be particularly critical with meat-eating, especially scavenging. Carcasses can be points of intense competition, and any adaptation for reducing interactions with large carnivores could be beneficial. These aspects of foraging behaviour will be considered further in later chapters.

It would seem, therefore, that there are reasons why hominids were pursuing activities that exacerbated the problems of living in high temperatures, and that selection favoured radical and costly solutions not required by other species able to avoid the most intense heat.

Why, though, should nakedness and sweating, both highly unusual among mammals, emerge as a solution to a problem shared by them all? To answer this question, we must first find out what alternative solutions were available, and what their costs and benefits were.

Several general solutions may be suggested. First, surface area relative to volume could be increased, either through extension of distal limb proportions, or through reduced body size (Allen's rule and Bergmann's rule). Second, peripheral vasodilation could occur, increasing the rate of cooling of the blood. Third, solar radiation could be avoided, either by limited diurnal activity, or fully nocturnal behaviour. Fourth, the area exposed to direct solar radiation could be reduced. And last, panting could be increased. These represent the principal solutions available to a hot mammal. Each of these, though, has its problems.

Limb lengths of hominids and other primates in relation to body weight are shown in Table 5.1. These indicate that modern humans at least do have increased limb elements, which may have had some thermoregulatory consequences. In contrast, there is a general trend towards increased body size during human evolution (see Chapter 6 for details). Peripheral vasodilation is known to occur among modern humans in response to heat stress (Mount 1979: 165–7). This, however, can have only limited effect, and is in conflict with the need for humans to maintain a constant and high flow of blood to the brain. It has already been suggested that diurnal activity is being selected for independently, and therefore reduced activity (or increased nocturnal behaviour) would seem an improbable solution. The fourth possibility, that hominids could reduce the area exposed to the sun, has been suggested as an explanation for bipedalism (Newman 1970), a model recently quantified by Wheeler (1984). An erect man receives only two-thirds as much direct solar radiation as a quadruped, a ratio further enhanced when the sun is at its zenith. Although it is unlikely for heat stress to be sufficient to account entirely for the evolution of bipedalism, this may be an important

Table 5.1 Ratios of body weight to total limb length for some primate species

Species*	Limb length body weight[†] (× 100)
Mouse lemur (*Microcebus rufus*)	24.5
Greater dwarf lemur (*Cheirolagus major*)	25.5
Grey gentle lemur (*Hapolemur griseus*)	32.5
Ruffed lemur (*Verecia vaiegata*)	30.8
Woolly lemur (*Avahi laniger*)	39.1
Indri (*Indri indri*)	35.2
Dwarf bushbaby (*Galago demidoff*)	32.9
Angwantibo (*Arctocebus calabarensis*)	38.9
Potto (*Periodictus potto*)	29.4
Pygmy marmoset (*Cebuella pygmaea*)	27.3
Lion tamarin (*Leontopithecus rosalia*)	30.2
Squirrel monkey (*Saimiri sciureus*)	32.2
Woolly monkey (*Lagothrix lagotricha*)	31.3
Olive colobus (*Colobus verus*)	31.7
Proboscis monkey (*Nasalis larvatus*)	33.3
Talapoin (*Micropithecus talapoin*)	31.4
Olive baboon (*Papio anubis*)	31.8
Lar gibbon (*Hylobates lar*)	50.0
Pygmy chimpanzee (*Pan paniscus*)	33.5
Gorilla (*Gorilla gorilla*)	26.9
Modern humans (*Homo sapiens sapiens*)	42.7

* Non-human primate species calculated from data in Jungers (1985: tables 1 and 2).

† The index used here is the sum of Jungers's forelimb index and hindlimb index, which equals: forelimb length + hindlimb length (mm)/body weight (g)$^{0.33}$.

secondary consideration. Furthermore, if, as has been argued here, increased thermal stress is a function of increased activity (not just increased ranging), many of those activities would involve bending, thus reducing the thermoregulatory benefits of bipedalism. The final possibility, that of panting – the principal system of thermoregulation among ungulates and carnivores – is one that could be used to bring about rapid cooling. It is a system, however, associated with short bursts of activity, followed by rapid cooling. To be maintained over prolonged periods requires some mechanism for coping with hyperventilation (Newman 1970).

It would thus seem that the alternatives to sweating, while appropriate for most conditions, are not appropriate for conditions of prolonged and enhanced activity during periods of high solar radiation. That this solution has been selected for among hominids suggest that these conditions prevailed at some time in early hominid evolution. The problem, though, of this system of thermoregulation, is that the costs involved are high. The price of high levels of sweating is increased water dependence. Modern humans can withstand only limited water loss (up to 10 per cent of body weight), and are unable to ingest large quantities of water (1 litre per 10 min, compared with 100 litres per 10 min for camels). The principal consequence of sweating is the need for hominids to keep close to water.

Water relations

It has already been stressed that the key problem of tropical ecology is water, both through levels of rainfall determining resource availability and through the availability of surface water for those species that require regular watering.

Several adaptive consequences may be seen to derive from this. First, hominids, if they were as water-dependent as modern humans and most primate species, will be limited to areas with permanent surface water. Within savanna environments these may be highly localized.

A problem that follows from this is that either local resources must be exploited fully and efficiently (in the face of competition from other water-dependent organisms), or long day ranging to exploit more widely scattered resources, with a return to central areas for water, must be developed. The non-focal foraging patterns within a home range of many species would not be appropriate. Long-distance day ranging would itself have significant consequences, not least in requiring increased daily activity, and changed locomotor requirements (see Chapter 7). In other words, a significant positive feedback loop would occur between thermal stress, ranging behaviour and water relations. As hominids become increasingly active during the day, they require more water. This increases the distances they have to cover each day, which in turn yet further increases both thermal stress and water requirements (Fig. 5.7).

A further complication here is the relationship between sweating and nakedness. It is often assumed that evaporative loss is enhanced by loss of hair. However, Newman (1970) has argued that nakedness is not required for efficient sweating, but that sweating is required if there is no hair cover. Consequently he has suggested that thermal stress was increased by lack of hair, which in turn stimulated selection for increased sweating efficiency. This in turn raises the question of why nakedness should have evolved in the first place. Wheeler (1985) has recently suggested that bipedalism is a necessary pre-adaptation for the loss of functional body hair; bipedalism reduces the area of the body that receives solar radiation, and consequently thermal stress. With the exception of the head and shoulders this would allow the bipedal body to dissipate heat through sweating and evaporation.

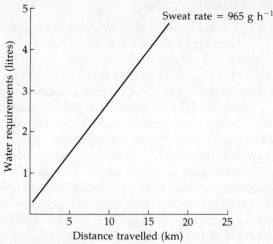

Figure 5.7   Relationship between distance travelled and water
requirements for modern humans; these requirements will
vary with body size (based on Mount 1979: table 7.1). Assumes
sweat loss rate of 965 g ^{1} at 35 C at 3 km ^{1} walking rate.

In summary, it would seem that for hominids in a tropical environment
the problems of heat and water are closely related. The novel nature of
the human thermoregulatory system suggests that hominids underwent
considerable selection in the tropics as a result of thermal stress; that this
thermal stress relates most specifically to activity requirements, most
probably in the context of extended or modified daily movement and
foraging and that reduced thermal stress could be bought only at the cost
of increased water dependence, with profound consequences for ranging
and foraging behaviour. It should be noted, though, that this model is in
fact independent of the type of resource exploited. Rather, it places
emphasis on the scheduling of daily activity, which, although difficult to
observe in the past, may nonetheless have been an important element of
the selective presures operating on hominids.

Palaeoenvironmental change

The problems of survival discussed above are largely divorced from any
specific historical context; they relate instead to the invariable laws of
thermodynamics. However, a further problem of living in tropical environments derives from the fact that these environments have not remained stable, but have undergone change during human prehistory.
These changes had a powerful effect on hominid evolution.

Global patterns of climatic change

The classic model of climatic and environmental change during hominid evolution was that formalized by Penck & Brückner (1909). On the basis of their work among the moraines of the Swiss Alps they described a process of gradual global cooling during the late Pliocene (Villafrancian) followed by four prolonged periods of intense glaciation, interspersed by shorter, warmer interglacials. Although modified in various ways during this century, this model has proved remarkably resistant despite the accumulation of evidence to the contrary. Although palaeoclimatologists have long recognized the much greater complexity of later Cenozoic climatic change, it has taken a long time for the implications for other branches of Quaternary science to be unravelled (Roberts 1984:25).

Current evidence suggests that since the early Cenozoic there has been a gradual decrease in temperature (Fig. 2.13). In the North Sea, the mean surface temperature was 16 °C in the Palaeocene, rising to about 30 °C in the Eocene, then falling to less than 10 °C in the early Oligocene (Buchardt 1978). During the Miocene temperatures rose again, to 15 °C, but this rise was followed by rapid drops in temperature during the Pliocene and Pleistocene. A similar picture is presented by Kennett (1977) for the sub-Antarctic region.

Associated with this period of temperature decline are marked changes in palaeogeography caused by continental drift. These included the southward shift of Australia and Antarctica and, most importantly, the closure of the eastern end of the Tethys Sea that had previously separated the African and Eurasian plates (Fig. 5.8). This had major consequences for the circulation of ocean currents and consequently for climatic patterns, possibly triggering off the change from stable, widespread, heavily forested tropical and subtropical environments to a much more unstable and seasonal set of habitats.

The onset of glaciation varies globally. Ice was building up in Antarctica by 10 Ma ago, but glaciation is more generally recorded between 4 and 3 Ma ago (Shackleton & Opdyke 1976; Mercer 1978; Roberts 1984). Mercer (1978) has suggested that large ice sheets built up in the Southern Hemisphere by 3.5 Ma ago, as opposed to 3.2 Ma ago in the Northern Hemisphere.

A full glacial climate developed during the past 3 million years. Earlier glaciations were probably less intense, but during the last million years these have become more frequent and severe. Since 800 000 years ago glacial–interglacial cycles seem to have occurred every 100 000 years, implying that in the middle and late Pleistocene there have been eight such oscillations (see Fig. 2.14) (Roberts 1984). Recognition of the cyclicity in climatic change during the Pleistocene has led to renewed interest in the astronomical theories of climatic changes pioneered by Milankovitch and Croll.

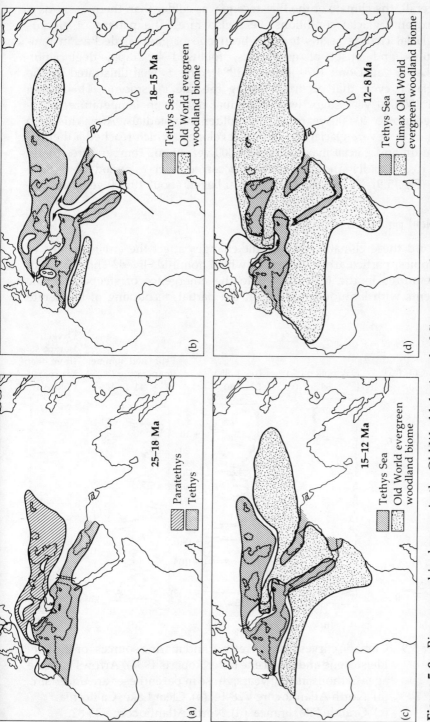

Figure 5.8 Biogeographic changes in the Old World during the Miocene. In the early part of the epoch (25–18 Ma) there was a continuous sea separating Africa from Eurasia. From then on a land bridge was present, and woodland became more widespread.

Overall, the climate of the Pleistocene was colder than the present day, but extreme glacial conditions were also rare. The pattern of glacial–interglacial change seems to have been one of gradual decline in temperatures and onset of glaciations, followed by rapid deglaciation (Broeker & van Donk 1970; Roberts 1984). This is well illustrated by the last glacial cycle that occurred during the late Pleistocene. This began about 100 000 years ago, with a gradual decline in temperature, interspersed up to 40 000 years ago by milder interstadials. After this time much more severe glacial conditions developed, which reached a thermal minimum and glacial maximum at 18 000 years ago. Temperatures thereafter rose rapidly and deglaciation occurred over a period of 6–8000 years (Fig. 5.9). The present interglacial began about 10 000 years ago.

Tropical palaeoenvironments

How did these climatic and tectonic changes affect the environments of the tropics, particularly in Africa, in which hominids lived? The decline of temperatures in the Miocene led to the emergence of steeper climatic gradients with latitude, resulting in the partial decoupling of temperate

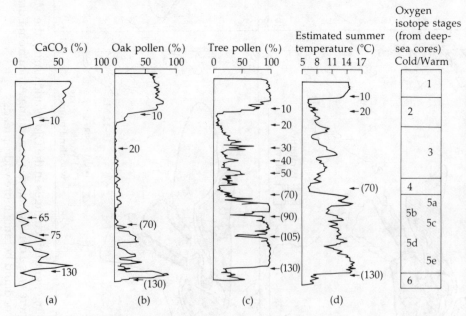

Figure 5.9 Climatic curves from terrestrial and marine sources for the late Pleistocene and Holocene (after Roberts 1984). Arrows indicate ages in thousands of years; those in parentheses are uncertain.
(a) North Atlantic core V28-14; (b) Clear Lake, California;
(c) Grande Pile, France; (d) North Atlantic core V23-82.

and tropical environments (Pearson 1978: 170). Temperatures in high latitudes decreased considerably, those in low latitudes much less.

The classic view of Miocene tropical and subtropical environments is that of large areas of unbroken forest. It is now clear that although this is an accurate description of the early Miocene (23.5–16.0 Ma ago) (Van Couvering & Van Couvering 1976), later periods were very different. In East Africa evidence for the late Miocene is limited, but Fort Ternan (14 Ma ago) and the localities from the Baringo basin in Kenya indicate that the forests were breaking up and being replaced by savanna mosaic environments (Van Couvering 1980; Shipman, et al. 1981; Hill, Drake, et al. 1985). The development of seasonal, savanna environments in Africa that are well attested in the Pleistocene appear to be a longer term development stretching back at least 10 million years.

The evidence from the Siwalik sediments of northern Pakistan (~8.0 Ma old) supports this picture. Badgeley & Behrensmeyer (1980) have argued that the hydrological and geomorphological context could not support full forest/woodland conditions on account of the seasonal variability, and that a mosaic of environments must have occurred at this time, from forest to open grassy areas.

Although evidence is lacking from other parts of the world, a picture seems to be emerging of long-term environmental change during the Miocene as a response to both tectonic and climatic shifts, resulting in a more open, seasonal, arid and variable tropical world.

By the Pliocene and Pleistocene this pattern had become established. For the period before about 25 000 years ago it is not possible to compile a comprehensive model of Pleistocene environments, because of the paucity of evidence, but isolated localities throughout the period indicate the establishment of full savanna conditions in eastern and· southern Africa and other parts of the tropical world (Bonnefille 1972, 1976; Hendey 1973; Klein 1974; Vrba 1974, 1975; Isaac 1984). They indicate that there is broad continuity of environment throughout the past 5 million years (see Chapter 8 for a more detailed discussion of this), but little is known about the relationship between climate and environment in the tropics.

Following the pioneering work of Solomon (1931) it was long thought that periods of glaciation in high latitudes correlated with 'pluvials'

Figure 5.10 African habitats: (a) present day; (b) late Miocene through to
(over) Pliocene; (c) under glacial conditions; (d) under interglacial
conditions (based on Bonnefille 1984; Roberts 1984). In (b)
numbers indicate early hominid localities: 1, Ethiopia; 2, Lake
Turkana basin; 3, Lake Baringo basin; 4, N. Tanzania/
S. Kenya; 5, Transvaal, S. Africa.

(a)

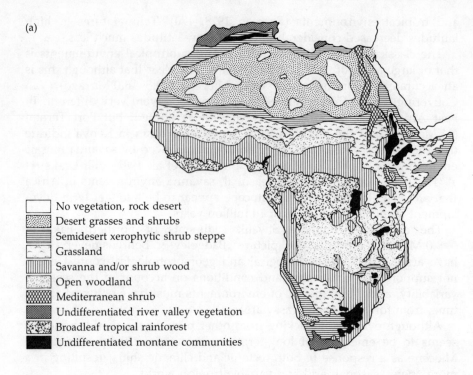

No vegetation, rock desert
Desert grasses and shrubs
Semidesert xerophytic shrub steppe
Grassland
Savanna and/or shrub wood
Open woodland
Mediterranean shrub
Undifferentiated river valley vegetation
Broadleaf tropical rainforest
Undifferentiated montane communities

(c)

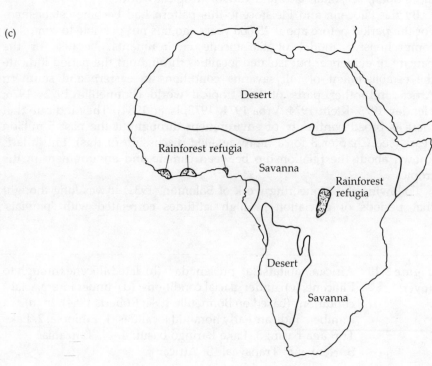

(b)

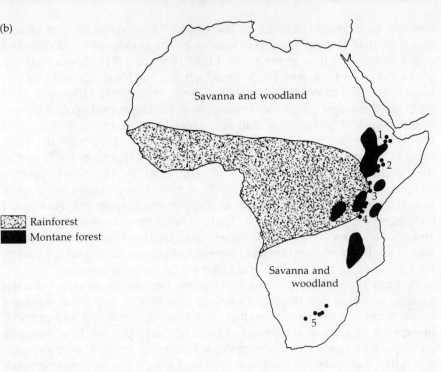

Savanna and woodland

Rainforest

Montane forest

Savanna and woodland

(d)

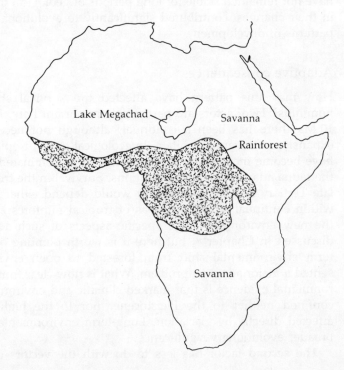

Lake Megachad

Savanna

Rainforest

Savanna

Savanna

(periods of increased rainfall) in the tropics. As a result, it was widely assumed that tropical rainforest was as or more extensively distributed in the Pleistocene than at the present time (Roberts 1984). Re-examination of the evidence from lake levels on which this model was based (Butzer, Isaac et al. 1972; Street & Grove 1975) has shown for East Africa and other parts of the tropics that the reverse is true. Depressed global temperatures resulted in lower rainfall and greater aridity in the tropics, and expansion of the tropical rainforest seem to be associated with the early parts of interglacials. It now seems (Flenley 1979; Hamilton 1982) that at the height of the glaciations tropical rainforests in Africa and America were radically reduced (Fig. 5.10). This new interpretation of tropical palaeoenvironments has helped to explain many patterns of tropical biogeography, as it is now clear that for long periods species of plants and animals were isolated in localized refugia. This alternating formation and breakdown of geographical barriers has played an important part in the formation of new species and other evolutionary changes.

Perhaps the most important conclusions that can be drawn from the current evidence for tropical environments is that the drier, savanna mosaics are not the recent product of anthropogenic firing and grazing, but are a long-term development in parts of the tropics, and are therefore an important part of the evolutionary history of tropical animals; and, secondly, that in terms of distribution and extent tropical environments have not remained stable for long periods of geological time, and so have, in their changes, contributed significantly to evolutionary and ecological patterns of development.

Adaptive consequences

How may this pattern have affected the survival strategies of early hominids? Two factors are particularly important here. First, for the past 10 Ma there has been a continual, although not necessarily constant, expansion of savanna habitats. In ecological terms, tropical environments have become increasingly seasonal, the flora dominated by grasses, and the fauna adapted to these conditions. Survival in the tropics through the late Tertiary and the Quaternary would depend either on specialization within continually reduced areas of tropical rainforest, or adaptation to the new environment. The specific aspects of such adaptation will be discussed in Chapter 8, but here it is worth pointing out that the long-term environmental shift from forested to open environments represented a major adaptive problem. What is now clear from the palaeoenvironmental evidence is that marked climatic and environmental change is confined neither to the Pleistocene, nor to the high-latitude regions affected directly by glaciation. Long-term environmental change was of broader evolutionary significance.

The second factor has less to do with the vectors of environmental change, than with the consequences of any change at all. The break up of the continuous belts of tropical rainforest, and their replacement by savanna environments has been important for creating isolated pockets, mosaic environments, and habitat boundaries or ecotones. Regardless of the specific character of these, significant evolutionary consequences flow from them. Isolated environments, such as islands of tropical rainforest in a sea of savanna, or vice versa, create small isolated populations, where selection can be specific and intense, and where genetic change can be both rapid and novel. Environmental change can thus be important in setting up the conditions for rapid evolutionary change and the appearance and maintenance of new forms.

The patterns of species distribution in relation to palaeoenvironmental change have been studied extensively in Africa and South America, particularly with respect to forest forms. The continual fragmentation of the African tropical rainforests, often confined to mountain refuges, has led to considerable allopatric speciation in a wide range of organisms (Moreau 1969; Laurent 1973; Hamilton 1982). Similar patterns have also been found for many of the fish species living in the tropical African lakes, alternatively linked and separated by fluctuations in rainfall during the Pleistocene (Beadle 1974; Greenwood 1974). The mechanism of speciation here, and it would apply to a wide range of organisms and environments, is that any form of environmental fragmentation is liable to lead to evolutionary novelty, through both drift and divergent selection (Mayr 1963).

Mosaic environments, and the boundaries between the habitats, may also be significant, for ecotones can often provide opportunities for exploitation above and beyond those of the actual habitats to which they form the boundary. These niches are ones to which animals capable of tolerating a wide range of habitats and environmental conditions (eurytopic), such as hominids, are particularly suited. And a final consideration is that palaeoenvironmental change can have the effect of destabilizing selection, opening up pathways to evolutionary change.

It can be argued that an environment that is variable in space and through time will promote evolutionary change. It is now clear that tropical Africa was such an environment during the later Cenozoic, and that hominids, and their precursors, would have been subject to selection in response to this. The overall trajectory of that change and variability was towards more open and seasonal environments. Given the tropical origin and character of the order Primates, rapid and radical evolutionary change could be expected to occur under conditions of environmental instability, as a solution to the problems of surviving in a spatially complex and dynamic environment.

The congruence between these general trends of tropical environmental change, evolutionary dynamics, and the emergence of hominids is shown in Table 5.2. Hominoids in the middle Miocene of Africa existed in

Table 5.2 Patterns of hominoid evolution in relation to tropical environmental change·

Geological period	Environmental dynamics	Population characteristics	Evolutionary patterns	Hominoid evolution
Middle Miocene	Stable rainforest: continuous and homogenous environment	Large heterogenous populations with low but continuous gene flow	Stabilizing selection: low speciation rates and slow evolutionary change	Early, mostly arboreal African hominoids
Late Miocene and Pliocene	Increasing aridity leading to seasonal and savanna conditions; mosaic environments; habitat fragmentation and formation of refugia/ ecological islands	Isolation of small populations leading to interrupted gene flow	Disruptive selection: genetic drift and local selection may lead to rapid evolutionary change and high speciation rates	Divergence of African hominoids; origin of hominids
Pliocene and Pleistocene	Increasing environmental instability and more rapid rates of environmental change	Small, local populations displaying variability and subject to fluctuating conditions	Disruptive selection and local population extinctions, plus population movements lead to discontinuities between overlapping and adjacent populations	Radiation of hominoids and hominids
Middle Miocene through to Pleistocene	Volcanic and tectonic activity in East Africa as a result of rift formation and spreading	Geographical factors further isolate populations	Reinforcement of disrupted gene flow and selection	Background to East African hominoid evolution

a largely undifferentiated environment, in large heterogenous populations with low but continuous levels of gene flow. Increased aridity would have led to an expansion of savanna environments and a general trend towards savanna adaptations (see Chapter 7). Because this increase of savanna would also have resulted in a more differentiated and variable environment, a combination of isolation and disruptive selection would have led to reduced gene flow and increasing divergence within hominoid populations. The more rapid rates of environmental change associated with the later Tertiary and early Quaternary would have reinforced this situation by the occurrence of local extinctions leading to major genetic and adaptive gaps between populations. The volcanic and tectonic activity that took place in East Africa, especially the emergence of major geographic barriers (e.g. lava flows), would have yet further enhanced the trend towards adaptive and phylogenetic divergence of the hominoids. In other words, the environmental dynamics of Africa over the past 10 Ma provided the right conditions, both in terms of the necessary environments and in terms of appropriate biogeographic conditions, for the radical evolutionary changes associated with the hominids during this period. Within these general environmental conditions, though, lie more specific characteristics of the hominids that played a significant part in their evolutionary ecology. One of these is that early hominids were large mammals.

6 Hominids as large mammals

Very often, in science as well as in everyday life, it is the most obvious things that get overlooked. The size of animals is a case in point. Elephants are self-evidently big, and mice necessarily small. As each animal species tends to come in only one size, the reasons underlying that size, and its relationship to other aspects of its behaviour, physiology and adaptation are often overlooked. However, modern studies are beginning to show that size is an integral cause and consequence of adaptation (Kleiber 1961; Huxley 1972; Jarman 1974; Clutton-Brock & Harvey 1977b; Eisenberg 1981; Harvey & Clutton-Brock 1981; R. D. Martin 1981; MacMahon & Bonner 1983; Peters 1983). The size of an organism is not just the end product of selection and adaptation, but is itself a significant factor in shaping evolution. Furthermore, and most significantly for this book, the relationship between body size and adaptation is predictable (and in some cases quantifiable) owing to certain basic geometric and bioenergetic rules. From these rules biologists have been able to build a series of powerful models that can explain certain evolutionary patterns. The potential for palaeoanthropology is that these models may provide predictions with which hominid evolutionary and adaptive patterns can be compared.

In studies of hominid evolution size has played, until recently, a relatively small part. The only area where intensive research and debate has been pursued is in questions of brain size, and it has long been recognized that encephalization – brain enlargement – has had a significant role in our evolution. However, it is equally important to note not just that brain size has increased, but that so too has body size. The earliest hominids were remarkably small, sometimes less than 30 kg whereas some of the middle Pleistocene hominids were large and robustly built. These changes in size are important clues to understanding the pattern of human evolution.

What this chapter tries to show is that many unique aspects of the hominids and their evolution may in fact be derived from the consequences of being large and warm-blooded. This objective may be achieved by looking at the basic rules of allometry, by describing the changes in body size that occur in hominid evolution, by examining comparatively the correlates of large body size, and, finally, by analysing the extent to which hominid adaptation conforms to broader ecological expectations.

Size and evolution

Allometry

Allometry is the term given to describe the change in proportions brought about by changes in size (Reeve & Huxley, 1945:123). Allometric growth involves changes in shape as a result of differential rates of growth in body parts. The classic ideas of this field were developed by D'Arcy Thomson (1917) in his book *On Growth and Form*, where he showed that significant changes could be brought about in an organism by differential growth rates in different parts. As a result of this, changes could be expected in morphology simply as a function of size, and, equally, changes in morphology could often best be achieved through size alterations.

Subsequent work has largely been concerned with quantifying and explaining the pattern of this relationship. Julian Huxley (1924) was the first to show that the formula

$$y = Bx^k$$

could be used to describe as a general law the constant ratio between different growth rates of specific parts of an organism. y is the biological characteristic that is unknown, but it can be predicted from B, which is body mass or some other measurement of size, and x and k which are constants, empirically derived for a particular population, species or other taxon (Peters 1983: 1). In other words, many biological attributes scale with body size, which can thus serve as a predictor if the scaling coefficient (based on x and k) are known. Since Huxley, many specific applications of this formula have been developed, dealing with such factors as brain size, metabolic rate, bone thicknesses, as well as a host of ecological relationships (see below).

The effect that size has on, for example, shape can be illustrated by considering some geometrical relationships. Basic geometry shows that, in the absence of changes in shape, a doubling in linear dimensions will result in a quadrupling of surface area (Fig. 6.1). Similarly, the volume will increase eightfold. For an animal, this means that to double in height

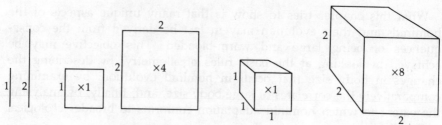

Figure 6.1   Diagram of the way in which changes in linear dimensions will result in allometric changes in two and three dimensions (surface area and volume).

without changing shape would mean sustaining eight times the amount of biological tissue. Not all allometric relationships follow these geometric rules, but they conform to the general principle that unit increases in size are not uniformly related to changes in other aspects of the organism. In the case of the doubling in height, we would expect an animal to alter in shape as it became larger to avoid the massive increase in body weight.

Mammalian evolution and size

These powerful relationships have been used to account for some major trends in evolution and adaptation. Within the mammals in particular patterns of evolutionary change involve changes in size – well illustrated by the evolution of the horse, whose Eocene ancestors were the size of a small dog (Romer 1959). The trend towards increased size is often referred to as Cope's law, and although it is far from true that all organisms evolve from small to large (see Marshall and Corruccini 1978 for a discussion of reversed trends), this is certainly a pattern that occurs widely (Bonner 1968). Explanations of this phenomenon have been sought in terms of the advantages of size to an organism trying to survive in a dangerous and competitive world – for example, increased predatory efficiency, increased predator avoidance, increased intelligence, increased thermoregulatory and metabolic efficiency, and increased longevity (Newell, 1949; Kurtèn 1953; Rensch 1959; Gould 1966; Bonner 1968; Stanley 1973). Recent work has confirmed some of these factors as important adaptive elements (Eisenberg 1981; Peters 1983), but Stanley (1973) adopted a more evolutionary stance. He argued that Cope's law was really a statistical and probabalistic generalization. He pointed out that selection will lead to an optimum body size, whether that be an increase or decrease. Selection tends preferentially towards enlargement because large body size is usually optimal for, and part of, a specialized organism, and such specializations seldom lead to further speciation and the formation of new taxa. New species, particularly the origin of higher taxa, usually derive from adaptively and morphologically generalized ancestors, and these characteristics are associated with small body size. Novel taxa will be small, and tend towards increasing size.

The evolution of the mammals stems from small-bodied ancestors, and has involved increases in body size. This is, however, not a universal trend. What happens in practice is that within any lineage there is a trend towards increased maximum and mean size, but minimum and possibly even modal size remains about the same as diversification occurs. Through time, therefore, larger species within a taxon will evolve, but this does not necessarily mean that the smaller end of the range will be lost. Stanley's (1973) theory explains an observable evolutionary pheno-menon, and predicts a high but not universal incidence of size increases. This can be observed to have happened many times among the mam-mals, such that although there has been an increase in mean size, modal size of mammals has remained essentially small (Fig. 6.2).

From this consideration of the evolutionary basis of size changes we may conclude that where new trends in evolution appear, they should occur among small-bodied populations, and that as evolutionary change

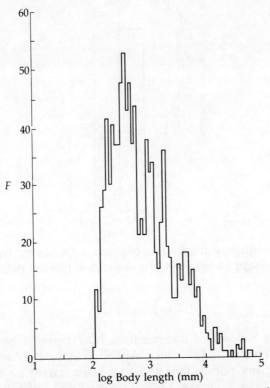

Figure 6.2 Frequency distribution of size classes of mammals (from Eisenberg 1981).

proceeds body size should increase among some taxa. It remains now to see whether hominids conform to this pattern, and then to consider what adaptive and selective factors might make a larger body size optimal.

Hominid body size

Eisenberg (1981) has shown that most mammals are less than 32 cm long (Fig. 6.2). With a height of about 170 cm modern humans are therefore about five or six times as large (in linear dimensions; much larger in volume and mass) than the 'modal mammal'. Humans are large mammals. Furthermore, within the primates, they belong among the largest extant species (Fig. 6.3). It is reasonable to conclude that hominids have been part of this general evolutionary tendency towards larger body size. It is apparent, therefore, that the selective factors that drive Cope's rule should apply to hominids, and help explain aspects of their evolution.

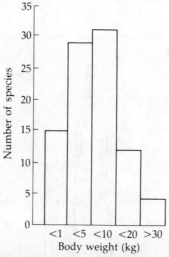

Figure 6.3   Frequency distribution of primate species by female body weight (data from Clutton-Brock & Harvey 1977a).

Estimating body size

However, the process of documenting how hominid body weight has evolved is strewn with difficulties. Although extensive data exist on body weights for living populations and to a lesser extent for living primates (see Clutton-Brock & Harvey 1977a; Jungers 1985), estimation of body size from fossil organisms can be hazardous. The extent of these problems is illustrated by the range of estimates that have been calculated for the australopithecines (Table 6.1) – *Australopithecus africanus* from 18 to 43 kg, and *Australopithecus robustus* from 36 to 80 kg (Steudel 1980; Grine 1981; McHenry 1982).

The principles underlying body weight estimates for fossils are relatively simple. Correlation and regression statistics are calculated for the relationship between living body weight and an anatomical characteristic that is observable on both modern and fossil individuals. The principal relationships that have been used for hominids and primates are:

1. **Vertebrae:** cross-sectional area of the last lumbar vertebra has a correlation of $r = 0.72$ with body weight in a sample of modern humans (McHenry 1975: 686–7). This means that fossil hominid body weight can be calculated from this measurement, using the following equation:

$$\log_{10} W = 0.6 \log_{10} V + 1.1$$

where W is body weight (in kilograms) and V is the cross-sectional area of the last lumbar vertebra (in square millimetres).

2. **Femora**: similarly, the size of the femoral head of modern humans correlates with body weight ($r = 0.68$) (McHenry 1976: 79–80).

$$W = 0.028 \text{ (head)} + 0.018 \text{ (neck)} + 0.013 \text{ (shaft area)} - 12.07$$

3. R. A. Martin (1980, 1981) has correlated ($r = 0.98$) body weight in mammals with the greatest width across the femoral head, and with the greatest width across the occipital condyles. He has used the latter to estimate body size of early hominids ($r = 0.98$):

$$W = 4.0 \times 10C$$

where W body weight (in grams) and C is the occipital condyle width (in millimetres).

4. Lovejoy & Heiple (1970) use femoral dimensions to estimate the stature of *Australopithecus africanus* and then extrapolate body weight from stature. Wolpoff (1973) adopts a similar technique for estimating the body weight of *Australopithecus*, using a ratio of 3.7 between height in centimetres and weight in kilograms. McHenry (1974) has also estimated stature and discusses weight, but does not calculate actual weights from them. Given the problems relating to changes in proportions of limbs, stature estimates are likely to be less useful than direct estimates of weight.

5. Steudel (1980) has pointed out that body weight/anatomical part regressions are based on weight at death. Few people are at their best in a mortuary so these body weights may not be representative of liveweights. As an alternative, she has used partial skeletal weight to calculate body size (Table 6.2). Partial skeletal weight is a measure of the major skeletal parts of the body (skull, mandible, both femurs, both humeri, pelvis,

Table 6.1 Estimates of body weights of early hominids

Specimen no.	Site	Taxon
Sts 5	Sterkfontein	*A. africanus*
Sts 14	Sterkfontein	*A. africanus*
Sts 14	Sterkfontein	*A. africanus*
Sts 73	Sterkfontein	*A. africanus*
—	Sterkfontein	*A. africanus*
Sk 3981	Swartkrans	*A. robustus*
Sk 82	Swartkrans	*A. robustus*
Sk 97	Swartkrans	*A. robustus*
KNM-ER 738	Koobi Fora	*Australopithecus* sp. (*boisei*)
KNM-ER 1503	Koobi Fora	*Australopithecus* sp. (*boisei*)
OH 5	Olduvai	*A. boisei*
KNM-ER 1472	Koobi Fora	*Homo* sp.
KNM-ER 1481	Koobi Fora	*Homo* sp.

Table 6.2 Estimates of partial skeletal weights of early hominids (from Steudal 1981) and relationship to living hominoids*

Specimen no.	Site	Taxon	Comparable with
Sts 17	Sterkfontein	*A. africanus*	Average orang-utan ♀
Sts 5	Sterkfontein	*A. africanus*	Small orang-utan ♀
SK 48	Swartkrans	*A. robustus*	Average/large orang-utan ♀
SK 11	Swartkrans	*A. robustus*	Small orang-utan ♀
SK 79	Swartkrans	*A. robustus*	Average orang-utan ♀
SK 52	Swartkrans	*A. robustus*	Average orang-utan ♀
SK 46	Swartkrans	*A. robustus*	Average orang-utan ♂
TM 1517a	Kromdraai	*A. robustus*	Average orang-utan ♂
KNM-ER 406	Koobi Fora	*A. boisei*	Large orang-utan ♂
Sts 19	Sterkfontein	*A. africanus*	Average orang-utan ♀
KNM-ER 736	Koobi Fora	?	Average orang-utan ♀
KNM-ER 738	Koobi Fora	?	Average orang-utan ♀
OH 20	Olduvai	*A. boisei*	Small orang-utan ♀
SK 82	Swartkrans	*A. robustus*	Small orang-utan ♀
SK 97	Swartkrans	*A. robustus*	Small orang-utan ♀

* The log partial skeletal weights of living hominoids are: *Pan* ♂ 2.50; *Pan* ♀ 2.45; *Gorilla* ♂ 2.66; *Gorilla* ♀ 2.47; *Pongo* ♂ 2.66; *Pongo* ♀ 2.47; *Homo* ♂ 2.64; *Homo* ♀ 2.56.

Table 6.1 (contd)

Estimated Body weight (kg)	Method	Source
25.4	Occipital condyle	R.A. Martin 1981
10.5–27.6	Vertebra	McHenry 1975
18–22	Femur → stature → weight	Lovejoy & Heiple 1970
43.0	Vertebra	McHenry 1976
37.3	Femur → stature → weight	Wolpoff 1973
10.7–36.1	Vertebra	McHenry 1975
49.8	Femur	McHenry 1976
52.7	Femur	McHenry 1976
43.1	Femur	McHenry 1976
49.1	Femur	McHenry 1976
52.4	Occipital condyle	R.A. Martin 1981
51.3	Femur	McHenry 1976
54.3	Femur	McHenry 1976

Table 6.2 (contd)

Log Partial skeletal weight estimates based on:			
Palate breadth	Byzygomatic breadth	Orbital width	Femoral circumference
2.39	2.5		
2.39		2.34	
2.44		2.45	
2.33			
2.4			
2.46			
2.46			
2.59	2.74		
2.54	2.94	2.77	
	2.5		
		2.81	2.47
			2.47
			2.64
			2.59
			2.64

sacrum and both scapulae). Although this does not give actual body weight, the combined weight of these bones is a useful measure of relative body size. She found that the most reliable interspecific predictors of partial skeletal weight were palate breadth (r = 0.96), bizygomatic breadth (r = 0.98), orbital width (r = 0.97), and circumference of the femur just below the lesser trochantor (r = 0.98).

Genet-Vargin (1966) and Robinson (1972) also estimate australopithecine weights, but do not provide details of their methods. Pilbeam & Gould (1974) use a variety of methods for their estimates (as specific specimens are not referred to, their data is excluded from Table 6.2). Stringer (1984) has used Steudel's technique for a variety of later hominids.

Body size of fossil hominid

In considering the adequacy of these estimates there seem to be strong reasons for using Steudel's method, rather than attempting to calcu-

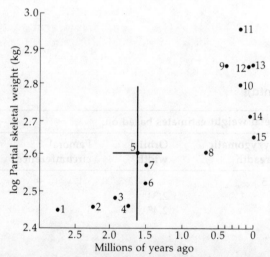

Figure 6.4   Plot of logarithmic partial skeletal weights of fossil hominids against geological age: 1, *Australopithecus afarensis*; 2, *A. africanus*; 3, *Homo habilis* (KNM-ER 1470); 4, early *Homo* (KNM-ER 1813); 5, mean and range for robust australopithecines; 6–8, *Homo erectus* (6, KNM-ER 3733; 7, KNM-ER 3883; 8, Java – Sangiran); 9–11, early *Homo sapiens* (9, Petralona; 10, Kabwe; 11, Bodo); 12, Middle Eastern neanderthal (Irhoud); 13,14, Western European neanderthals (13, La Ferrassie; 14, La Chapelle-aux-Saints); 15, anatomically modern human mean.

late a mean across several methods, as some authors have done. First, her method is based on interspecific regressions, rather than just modern humans. This makes them more appropriate for studying non-human hominids. Second, her regression values are much higher than those, say, those of McHenry. And, third, her use of partial skeletal weight seems to avoid the problems of distortion associated with death. The principal drawback with her method is that the derived data are in the form of partial skeletal weights, not actual weights, thus limiting their immediate usefulness for bioenergetic calculations. However, with these data it is possible to construct an approximate plot of the relationship between hominid body size and time (Fig. 6.4).

From this plot it can be seen that the earliest hominids, represented by the gracile australopithecines (*Australopithecus afarensis* and *A. africanus*), were small, although a slight and gradual increase in size can be noted around about 2 Ma ago. With the appearance of *Homo erectus*, though, there was a more rapid increase in body size between 2 and 1 Ma ago. This trend continued and reached its peak towards the end of the middle Pleistocene, with the specimens that are often considered to be transitional between *Homo erectus* and *Homo sapiens*. With the appearance of anatomically modern humans between 100 000 and 35 000 years ago there has been a decrease in body size, although it should be remembered that the variability in modern humans is considerable.

To interpret this pattern in terms of the general principles of evolutionary ecology requires an examination of the ecological consequences of body size.

Ecological correlates of body size

Metabolic relationships

Increases in size alter the relationships between different parts and functions of an organism. Perhaps the key consequence of this, as far as evolutionary patterns are concerned, is the relationship between energy and body size, crystallized in the classic Kleiber curve. Although it is obvious that larger animals require more energy than smaller ones, when relative rather than absolute quantities are considered, different relationships emerge. Figure 6.5 shows that as body size increases so the amount of energy required for basic metabolic maintenance per unit of body weight (measured in terms of oxygen consumed per unit time) decreases. From this relationship, a regression can be calculated to show that basal metabolic rate – the amount of energy necessary to maintain fundamental biological activity – directly depends on body size (Fig. 6.6), and that on a

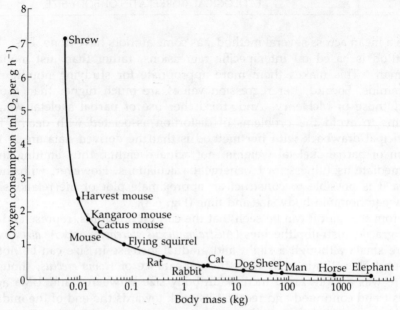

Figure 6.5 Kleiber's curve – the pattern of decreasing oxygen consumption per unit weight with increasing body size (from Schmidt-Nielsen 1975).

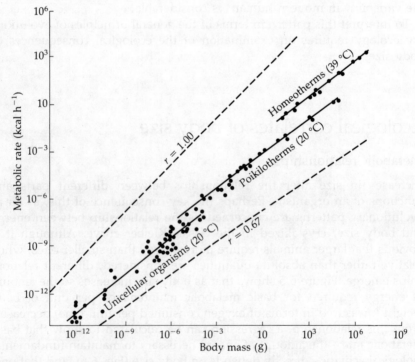

Figure 6.6 Relationship between body size and basal metabolic rate for various classes of animal (from Schmidt-Nielsen 1975).

logarithmic scale increases of one unit of body mass require only a 0.75 unit increase in metabolic rate. This may be described by the equation:

$$M = KW^{0.75}$$

where M is the basal metabolic rate (in kilocalories per hour), W is body mass (in grams) and K is a constant.

In a recent review, Peters (1983) has examined comprehensively the data and models that have been published on this problem, and has pointed out (pp. 45–6) that although they all support the 0.75 relationship, nonetheless it is statistically not universally true; in practice the relationship can vary. According to Peters (1983: fig. 4.1) the mean exponent is 0.738, the mode 0.74, and the standard deviation 0.11. The underlying reason for this consistent relationship is still not fully understood. It was originally suggested that the scaling relates to heat loss associated with surface/volume ratios of 0.67, but this is no longer acceptable with a 0.75 scaling (Kleiber 1961; Peters 1983).

Consequences of size increase

Whatever the cause, the ecological and evolutionary consequences are significant – with every increase in body size there is an increase in absolute food requirements, but a decrease in relative food requirements. This means that as body size increases so an organism's relationship to its resources will change, and so too will the selective pressures operating on it. The way in which such changes will occur should be predictable because their energetic basis is known. It is possible to correlate changes in body size with ecological as well as physiological attributes. These correlations can now be examined to provide a basis for understanding the ecological and evolutionary aspects of changes in hominid body size. All discussion here refers solely to mammals.

1.   Increased body size may broaden the dietary niche. A small mammal requires a large proportion of its body weight in energy each day to sustain metabolism (Tables 6.3 and 6.4). As energy requirements increase more slowly than size, a larger mammal requires less energy per unit of body weight per day. The ecological implication of this is that a small mammal will be confined to energy-rich foods or condemned to constant feeding, whereas larger mammals can afford to subsist off lower quality foods. It would thus be expected that some large mammals will have a broader dietary niche, incorporating more low-quality foods, although others may well subsist on high-quality foods. This generalization is confirmed by the dominance of large mammals among the low-quality herbivores (Eisenberg 1981: 271–4), and by Clutton-Brock & Harvey's (1977b) analysis of the relationship between food type and body size among non-human primates.

Table 6.3   Idealized examples of the relationship
between body weight and metabolic
requirements of mammals

Body mass (W) (g)	Basal metabolic rate (M) (kcal per day)	M/W ($\times 100$)
10	2.04	20.4
100	11.7	11.7
1 000	67.6	6.67
10 000	389.0	3.89
100 000	2 238.7	2.24
1 000 000	12 882.5	1.28

Table 6.4   Basal metabolic rates and metabolic efficiency of living and
fossil (*) primates according to body weight

Species	Body mass (W) (g)	Basal metabolic rate (M) (kcal per day)	M/W ($\times 100$)
Callithrix jacchus	241	22.9	9.5
Theropithecus gelada	9 830	384.1	3.9
Pan troglodytes	39 000	1 094	2.8
*Australopithecus africanus**	36 000	1 029	2.86
*Australopithecus robustus**	59 000	1 499.2	2.54
Homo sapiens sapiens	60 000	1 518	2.53

2.   Increased body size will increase the areas of annual (home) and day ranges. Although rising body mass will result in a fall in food requirements relative to size, there will be an increase in total or absolute requirements. A consequence will be that an organism should forage more widely. McNab (1963) and Harested & Bunnell (1979) have shown this to be empirically true for a wide range of mammals, and Milton & May (1975) and Clutton-Brock & Harvey (1977b) have also documented this for primates (Fig. 6.7). All these calculations are complicated, though, by differences between animals that live and forage in groups and those that are solitary, and by variation in environmental productivity. Thus, while broadly speaking there should be an increase in foraging area with size, it is unlikely to scale in a one to one relationship.

3.   Increased body size will lead to more mobility. Small mammals are more energetically constrained than large ones (and more subject to predation) so their mobility is limited. This greatly affects their adaptation. To survive, a small mammal must subsist on a resource type and

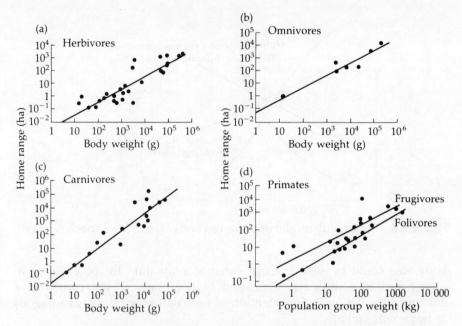

Figure 6.7   Relationship between body size and home range for various
classes of mammal ((a), (b) and (c) are from Harested &
Bunnell 1979; (d) is from Clutton-Brock & Harvey 1977b).

patch that can provide food indefinitely, or else provide food that can be
stored behaviourally or physiologically.

A large mammal is freer of these constraints because of greater mobility. It can move between patches, and therefore subsist off a higher
diversity of resources, and resources that are patchily distributed in time
and space. In particular, ephemeral resources can be opportunistically
exploited as just one part of a general foraging strategy.

4.   Increased body size will alter predator–prey relations. A predator is
limited (unless hunting in groups) to the size of the prey it can capture
(Bourlière 1963). Optimal prey size should maximize energy returns and
minimize the risks of injury (Fig. 6.8). Selection should therefore favour
increased body size among prey species, to reduce the risks of predation,
and among predator species to widen the 'prey menu'. According to the
life/dinner principle (in a hunting episode a rabbit is running for its life, a
fox just for a single meal!), prey size might be expected to increase more
rapidly than predator size.

5.   Increased body size will entail improved thermoregulatory efficiency
(decreased cooling efficiency or increased insulation and heat retention).
This aspect of increased body size has already been discussed extensively
in the previous chapter (see page 101). In terms of adaptation, increased

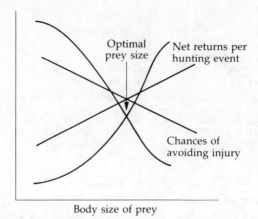

Body size of prey

Figure 6.8   Optimality model of preferred body size of prey species.

body size could be seen both to enhance adaptation to cooler environments and to complicate adaptation to hot ones, as the corollary of improved insulation is the retention of heat that may be disadvantagous in hot environments.

6.   Increased body size is usually associated with greater longevity. A large-bodied individual represents a considerable reproductive and energetic investment. Two implications flow from this. The first is that because growth is limited by intrinsic as well as extrinsic factors, the amount of time needed to reach full body size is necessarily greater. The second is that given the time and energy involved in the production of an individual, the more important it is that it survives a long time to maximize reproductive output. Taken together, these two factors will favour longevity, and indeed there is some evidence that in some large-bodied species longevity maybe an aspect of sexual selection. Body size does correlate positively with longevity for mammals (Eisenberg 1981: 310ff.), but it should be noted that two distinct reproductive trends are observable among mammals. The first is towards the production of a few precocial young (i.e. well developed and quite independent), the other for a large number of altricial offspring (i.e. very immature and dependent on the parents for survival) in each litter. These divergent strategies play an important determining part in longevity and survival rates, with the former tending towards a greater lifespan. Primates generally speaking give birth to precocial young, and Fig. 6.9 shows the relationship between mean body size of adults and recorded longevity for this order.

7.   Increased body size is usually associated with a slower reproductive rate. The extension of the lifespan associated with large body size in mammals incorporates all the life stages, including gestation and post-natal dependence. Consequently, the interval between reproductive

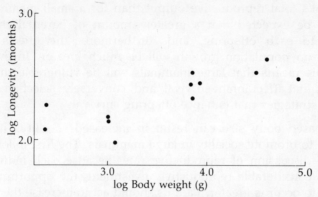

Figure 6.9   Relationship between mean and adult body size and recorded longevity for primates (data from Eisenberg 1981).

events tends to increase, and there will thus be a decrease in the overall reproductive rate of large-bodied animals (Fig. 6.10). To some extent this may be compensated for by a longer reproductive span, but the actual reproductive output of large mammals can be relatively low. The evolutionary and adaptive consequences of this are considerable. For large mammals, each offspring represents a greater proportion of an

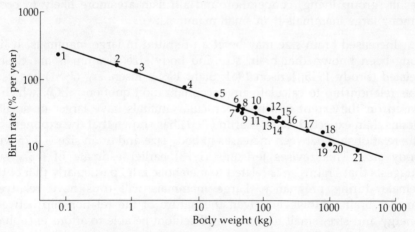

Figure 6.10   Relationship between body weight and birth rate for various African mammals: 1 and 2, elephant shrews; 3, mongoose; 4, dikdik; 5, Thomson's gazelle; 6, Grant's gazelle; 7, impala; 8, warthog; 9, kob; 10, hyena; 11, lechwe; 12, lion; 13, kongoni; 14, waterbuck; 15, wildebeest; 16, zebra; 17, buffalo; 18, giraffe; 19, rhinoceros; 20, hippopotamus; 21, elephant (from Western 1979).

individual's total reproductive output than for a small mammal. It may therefore be expected that a greater amount of parental care will be devoted to each offspring, and, furthermore, the effects of infant mortality on population growth will be much greater. In evolutionary terms, this means that large mammals will be vulnerable through any processes that affect infant survival, and, conversely, selection will favour adaptive strategies that enhance offspring survival.

8.   Increased body size can result in increased sociality. Two factors are likely to promote sociality in large mammals. The first follows directly from the discussion of reproductive rate. Because each individual represents a considerable reproductive investment, the opportunity for kin selection to occur is greater. Parents should act to increase the survival of each offspring, and laterally related kin should also behave altruistically towards each other. Large mammals should be selected for kin recognition, and differential behaviour towards kin as opposed to non-kin. Social behaviour would be the principal means of ensuring this. Kin-centred sociality is known to occur widely among the larger mammals (see Wilson 1975). The second factor derives from increased longevity. Long–lived animals are more likely to encounter the same individuals repeatedly during life. This opens up the opportunity for selection to favour those individuals that can react differentially to other individuals on the basis of previous experience. In this way some of the conditions specified by Trivers (1972) for the evolution of reciprocal altruism are fulfilled. As a result, group living, cooperation and altruism are more likely to occur among large mammals than small mammals.

9.   Increased brain size may be at a premium in large mammals. It has long been known that brain size and body size in animals are closely related (Brody 1945; Jerison 1961; Stahl 1965). Eisenberg (1981) has used this relationship to calculate an 'encephalization quotient' (EQ), which is based on the extent to which particular animals have larger or smaller brains than expected. R. D. Martin (1981) has shown that the exponent for the relationship between increases in body size and brain size is 0.75 with body size. This revises Jerison's (1973) earlier estimate of 0.67, and suggests that brain size is related to metabolic rate, particularly that of the female during pregnancy. Large mammals will thus have relatively smaller brains. However, given the nature of the relationship between energy and size, small mammals will seldom be able to afford encephalization quotients higher than normal. More importantly, perhaps, there would seldom be any advantage, given their brief lifespan. Large mammals, on the other hand, would be at a considerable advantage. Maintaining a large brain is extremely expensive (R. D. Martin 1981); the advantage provided by a large brain is the flexibility of response it allows. We have already seen that there are circumstances in the life of a large mammal where flexibility would be advantagous: the exploitation

of several resource types distributed patchily through time and space; the problem of repeated encounters with individuals, and the need to adapt behaviour to previous experience; and the need to differentiate kin. A further factor would be that long–lived organisms must cope with environmental changes. All these would be selective factors likely to lead to greater encephalization in larger mammals.

Many of the characteristics described above have been linked to a widely used model of evolutionary strategies – that of the $r - K$ selection continuum. Early work in theoretical ecology recognized that there is a general pattern of population growth, that could be described as a sigmoid curve (Fig. 6.11), and by the equation:

$$R = rN(1 - \frac{N}{K})$$

where R is the observed rate of increase at any one time; r is the maximum intrinsic rate of growth of the population or species; N is the number of organisms; and K is the number of individuals that may be supported by the environment (i.e. is broadly speaking what is meant by the term carrying capacity). In practice what this means is that the rate of growth of a population is determined by two factors. First, by its reproductive rate – that is, its inherent birth rate; and, second, by the environmental capacity to support that population. Which of these two factors plays a larger part depends on local conditions, particularly the existing size of

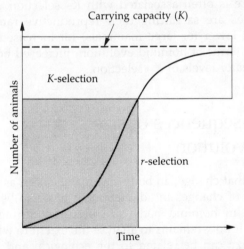

Figure 6.11 Relationship between population growth and r- and K-selection. While population levels are low relative to carrying capacity, the rate of growth is determined by population size and the intrinsic rate of reproduction. As the population approaches carrying capacity, competitive factors become more important.

the population (N). When the population is small, the rate of growth is largely a function of the intrinsic rate of growth (i.e. r is significant). When the population is larger, N becomes more important, and is increasingly affected by the carrying capacity (K), which will inhibit the rate of population growth. Consequently, at different times a single population may be said to be 'controlled' either by its r or by K.

From this very simple model has come a recognition of two basic evolutionary strategies. Where a species lives in an environment in which its population is well below carrying capacity, then it will be selected for its ability to reproduce rapidly. Because resources are at least temporarily abundant, reproductive rate will be more important than competitive ability in resource exploitation. Such a species may be described as r – selected. However, in an environment where populations are close to the carrying capacity, then a high reproductive rate will be less advantageous. More individuals cannot be 'fitted in', and so instead there will be selective advantage for those individuals able to compete effectively for what resources do exist. In this case, a species may be said to be K – selected.

Although it is widely recognized that these two strategies cannot be mutually exclusive, in general terms species are more or less r– and K– selected. The advantages of being one or the other depend on environmental circumstances, and these in turn lead to specific characteristics associated with each of these strategies (Table 6.5). It has been noted that increasing body size is often associated with K– selection. In becoming larger, many species are sacrificing their reproductive rate (which, as discussed above, is lower for large mammals) for increased competitive efficiency. Thus, in terms of hominid evolution, increased body size may be a function of greater levels of K– selection.

Adaptive consequences of size in hominid evolution

It has been shown that changes in body size may be seen as both a cause and a consequence of changes in adaptation. It has also been seen that significant changes in hominid body size occurred during the past 2 million years or so. It now remains to analyse the extent to which increase in hominid body size can be related to the ecological and evolutionary correlates discussed in the previous section. A summary of these correlates is shown in Table 6.6. Such an analysis requires an examination of the evidence for early hominid adaptation to see whether it conforms to the predictions, and a consideration of whether the environmental circumstances of the early hominids are likely to promote these adaptive changes.

Table 6.5 Correlates of r and K selection (from Pianka 1978)

	r-Selection	K-Selection
Climate	Variable and/or unpredictable; uncertain	Fairly constant and/or predictable; more certain
Mortality	Often catastrophic, non-directed, density independent	More directed, density dependent
Survivorship	High juvenile mortality	More constant mortality
Population size	Variable in time, non-equilibrium; usually well below carrying capacity of environment; unsaturated communities or portions thereof; ecological vacuums; recolonization each year	Fairly constant in time, equilibrium, at or near carrying capacity of the environment; saturated communities; no recolonization necessary
Intra- and interspecific competition	Variable, often lax	Usually keen
Selection favours	• Rapid development • High maximal rate of increase, r_{max} • Early reproduction • Small body size • Single reproduction • Many small offspring	• Slower development • Greater competitive ability • Delayed reproduction • Larger body size • Repeated reproduction • Fewer larger progeny
Length of life	Short, usually less than 1 year	Longer, usually more than 1 year
Leads to	Productivity	Efficiency

In pursuing these aims, first the foraging and then the social and reproductive behaviour of early hominids will be discussed.

Foraging behaviour

Three basic predictions can be made about foraging, assuming constant availability. First, there should be an increase in home-range area. Second, there should be an increase in the diversity of food types taken. And, third, either lower quality food should be incorporated into the diet, or there should be reduction in the amount of time spent foraging. Some of these have been discussed briefly elsewhere (Foley 1984b).

Table 6.6   Ecological consequences of increased body size (from Foley 1984b)

Size effects	Ecological implications
Increase in absolute metabolic costs	Greater food requirements; larger home range; lower population density
Decrease in relative metabolic costs	Ability to survive on low-quality food
Greater mobility	Ability to adapt to cooler climates and increased resources
Greater heat retention	Ability to adapt to cooler climates and increased activity; increased water dependence; heat stress in tropical environments
Increased strength/speed	Predator resistance/avoidance
Enlarged brain	Exploitation of complex resource patches; flexibility in behaviour; increased sociality; increased metabolic costs
Increased longevity	Increased reproductive span; increased developmental period
Longer prenatal period	Higher reproductive costs; lower birth rate; greater birth interval; precocial young

It is certainly clear that on the whole modern humans subsisting as hunter–gatherers have larger home ranges than do other primates. A comparison of home-range areas for modern hunter–gatherers and non-human primates shows that there may be several orders of magnitude difference (Fig. 6.12). To some extent, these very large home ranges are found among hunter-gatherers living in high-latitude environments, where they are the only primate, but even for tropical environments there is a significant difference.

To what extent, though, can this be accounted for by changes in body size? Milton & May (1975) have produced an equation to describe the relationship between primate body size and home-range area, taking into account the fact that primates live in groups.

$$\log_{10} HRt = 1.23 \log_{10} BW - 2.86$$

where HRt is the total home range (in hectares) and BW is the mean body weight of adults (in grams). Applying this equation to modern hunter-gatherers, the expected home-range area is between 8 and 10 km^2, far smaller than that observed (Fig. 6.13). The greatly increased home-range area of modern hunter–gatherers conforms to the expectations of increased body size, but greatly exceeds the amount expected.

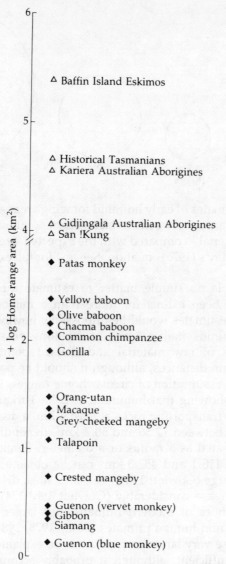

Figure 6.12 Comparison of home-range areas of non-human primates
(♦) and modern hunter–gatherers (∆).

Turning to the early hominids, it may be that their home-range area
was not so dramatically different from those of other primates. Using
Milton & May's equation, estimates of the home-range area of the early
hominids range from 3.71 km² for *Australopithecus afarensis* to 7.3 km² for
Homo erectus. How do these compare with the actual home-range area of
these species?

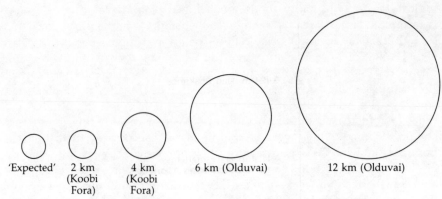

'Expected'   2 km   4 km   6 km (Olduvai)   12 km (Olduvai)
               (Koobi   (Koobi
               Fora)   Fora)

Figure 6.13   Estimates of early hominid foraging areas – based on
                  distances between artefact discard points and sources of raw
                  material – compared with the expected size based on Milton
                  & May's (1975) equation. See text for full explanation.

Obviously, it is no simple matter to estimate the home range of a
species that has been extinct for more than a million years. For most
organisms such estimates would be impossible; however, the toolmaking
capacity of hominids makes some calculations possible. The distance
between sources of raw material and discard points can be used to
calculate minimum distances, although it should be pointed out that they
are based on the assumption of circular home ranges. Isaac (1976:561) has
presented data showing that hominids at Lake Turkana during the Plio-
Pleistocene were transporting rocks at least 4 km, a distance that suggests
a home range of between 12.56 and 50.2 km^2, depending on whether the
4-km value is treated as a radius or a diameter. Similarly, a home-range
area of between 113.1 and 452.3 km^2 can be obtained from data drawn
from Olduvai Gorge (Gowlett 1984). For later sites, distances travelled for
raw material increase considerably (Gowlett 1984:174). These values are
all lower than those of modern humans, but larger than expected for
equivalent-sized non-human primates (Foley 1978, 1984b).

How may these very large foraging areas be explained? Certainly body
size alone is insufficient, although it probably accounts for part of the
variability. Another factor might be that some descriptions of hunter–
gatherer home range may include activities other than foraging, consequently making comparisons with non-human primates difficult. This
problem may also apply to the home-range estimates for early hominids
presented here based on distances of raw materials. Furthermore, much
of the primate data is drawn from populations living in relatively productive and, in particular, forested habitats. Open environments have
lower productivity, and thus a larger area has to be exploited to obtain
the required resources. The size of early hominid home ranges may
reflect the low availability of resources in savannas. They may also

indicate that poor-quality foods are being exploited (as expected), and therefore a larger area is required to sustain a population. Perhaps, though, this larger home range reflects a shift in trophic level at this or an earlier stage of human evolution. It is well known that omnivores and carnivores use larger home ranges than herbivores (Harested & Bunnell 1979, and see Fig. 6.7), because of the lower density of animal food sources. The relatively large home ranges of the early hominids may reflect the increased importance of meat in their diet. A final point that should be made, however, is that it is not necessarily true that all hominids utilized a large area for their foraging activities. It is quite possible that there may be considerable variation within the hominids, and that the techniques available to us can identify only the larger end of the home-range spectrum.

The second foraging prediction was that there should be a greater diversity of food types incorporated into the diet of a larger animal. This followed partly from their ability to move from patch to patch, and so to exploit ephemeral resources, and partly from the ability to utilize lower quality foods.

Some insight into this problem can initially be obtained by considering how hunter–gatherers and non-human primates use resources today. Peters & O'Brien (1981) have catalogued plant utilization for humans, chimpanzees and baboons on a continental scale for Africa. This shows that for Africa as a whole, chimpanzees use 168 genera, baboons 163 genera and humans 298. Although it must be remembered that these data will partly reflect the scale of distribution of the three primate genera as much as other ecological factors, they present the interesting suggestion that modern humans exploit a very wide range of plant food resources (but see Kortlandt 1984 for the alternative argument that it is chimpanzees that require a wide range of food types relative to other primates). Another approach is to look at the range of species used by various populations. Table 6.7 lists the number of plant species exploited by various groups of hunter–gatherers and other primates in Africa. Here it can be seen that hominids on the whole utilize a larger number of plant species than do other primates. Furthermore, when meat is included as an element of resource diversity, humans are carnivorous to an extent not found in other primates. Chimpanzees and baboons both predate on other species, but the rate of predation and the range of species predated are low by comparison with modern hominids (Teleki 1975; Harding & Teleki 1981) (Table 6.8).

Needless to say, evidence for the diversity of diet in the Plio-Pleistocene is rather harder to obtain. The two possible sources of information are fossil hominid remains and archaeological sites. The functional anatomy of teeth might at first sight appear the best source, but, regrettably, both morphology and wear indicate the predominant type of diet rather than its diversity. Thus, although we have Grine's

(1981) suggestion that the robust australopithecines were eating harder and smaller foodstuffs than were the gracile australopithecines, and Walker's (1981) view that the australopithecines were eating substantially the same frugivorous (fruit-based) diet as chimpanzees and orang-utans, we know little about relative diversity. Others have suggested that australopithecine teeth indicate specialization relative to other and later

Table 6.7 Number of plant species exploited by non-human primates and modern hunter–gatherers

Species/group	Number of Species	Source
Primates		
Yellow baboon		
(*Papio cynocephalus*)	14	Post 1981
Mantled howler monkey		
(*Alouatta palliata*)	15	Hladik 1981
Spider monkey		
(*Ateles geoffroyi*)	22	Hladik 1981
White-faced capuchin		
(*Cebus capucinas*)	40	Hladik 1981
Purple-faced langur		
(*Presbytis senex*)	12	Hladik 1981
Sacred langur		
(*Presbytis entellus*)	23	Hladik 1981
Common chimpanzee (Gombe)		
(*Pan troglodytes*)	207	Wrangham 1977
Common chimpanzee		Nishida & Uehara 1983
(*Pan troglodytes*)	330	(cited in Teleki 1981)
Common chimpanzee		
(*Pan troglodytes*)	141	Teleki 1981
Modern hunter–gatherers		
San (G/wi)	45	Silberbauer 1981
San (!Kung)	85	Lee 1968
San (#Kada)	79	Tanaka 1976
Western Australian Desert		
Aborigines	40	Gould 1969
North Queensland Aborigines	240	Roth 1901, quoted in Hayden 1981

Table 6.8 Hunting behaviour of non-human primates and modern hunter–gatherers (adapted from Hill 1982)

Forager	Meat foraged per hour (kg)	Meat foraged per consumer day (kg)	Average adult weight (kg)	Daily meat intake (kg)/body weight (kg $\times 10^{-3}$)	Percentage of daily calories provided by meat
Non-human primates					
Yellow baboon	0.006	0.036	35	0.1	3
Anubis baboon	0.002–0.004	0.016–0.032	25	0.06–0.13	2–5
Chimpanzee	—	0.027	35	0.08	3
Hunter–gatherers					
Ache (bow)	0.53	1.78	55	3.2	80
Ache (hands)	0.27	—	—	—	—
Yąnamamö (bow)	0.98	0.44	44	0.92	29
!Kung (bow)	0.60–0.66	0.325	44.7	0.73	20.5
G/wi (bow)	0.34	0.32	48.1	0.675	21.5
Mbuti (net hunters)	0.38	0.8	40	2.025	65
Mbuti (archers)	—	0.33	40	0.83	27
Bari	0.16–0.25	0.39	—	—	—
Anbarra	—	0.55	40	2.7	26

hominids, leading to the suggestion that the diet of australopithecines was less diverse than that of the genus *Homo* (Jolly 1970; Dunbar 1976).

The archaeological evidence provides little better information. Preservation is highly selective. Animal bones preserve better than plants, and some plants preserve better than others. The number of macroscopic plant remains found in association with early hominids is remarkably few (Isaac & Crader 1981; Isaac 1984) and so will tell us little about dietary diversity. The association of animal bones with human artefacts, and the occurrence of cut marks on the bones, indicates that early hominids were processing animal products (Bunn 1981; Potts and Shipman 1981; Isaac 1983; Potts 1984a), although the nature and extent of that processing are highly controversial (Binford 1981). However, the density of bones, and the diversity of species represented by bones with cut marks on them, perhaps suggest a range of animal exploitation in excess of that to be found among baboons and chimpanzees.

On the whole, therefore, we know virtually nothing about the diversity of diet of the early hominids. Body size would suggest an increase, but the only indication of this is possibly meat-eating. The third, and largely complementary prediction about foraging would be a shift to food resources of lower quality. The size of large mammals enables them to process bulky plant foods of relatively low nutrient quality (Eisenberg 1981). The best example of this among the primates is the gorilla. It is the largest extant primate, and is principally a folivore (leaf-eater). It is able to survive on this diet, despite the lack of a specialized dietary tract, because of the abundance of leaves and the amount that it is able to process. More broadly, Kay & Hylander (1978) have shown that folivorous mammals are generally larger than related frugivorous/insectivorous ones. A similar trend could be apparent among early hominids, associated with their increasing body size (Fig. 6.14). The contrasting strategies of increased meat-eating and utilization of plant foods of lower quality will be explored more fully in Chapter 8, where the ecological implications of increased body size can be integrated with the specific environmental conditions in which early hominids lived. Size is not a simple deterministic factor controlling foraging behaviour. Increased size closes certain adaptive options, but also opens new ones. Which of those new ones is taken will depend on other factors, and in particular, on the other selective factors operating on a population, or, in the terminology of this book, on the other environmental problems facing hominids.

Reproductive behaviour

The second category of behaviour where size may influence adaptation is that of reproduction, including social behaviour. Clearly, this distinction is arbitrary, for foraging affects reproduction and vice versa. In particular,

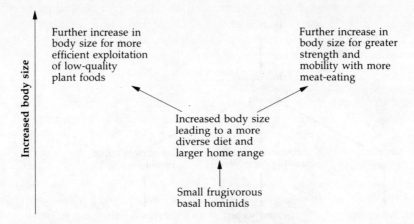

Figure 6.14   Model of foraging consequences for hominids with increasing body size.

it is likely that the advantages for foraging behaviour that result from increased body size will have less beneficial consequences for social and reproductive behaviour. An extreme argument, indeed, might be that the complexity of human social behaviour is the price that has had to be paid for foraging advantages!

The predictions that can be made on the basis of ecological correlates are shown in Table 6.6 (page 138). Two interrelated consequences are paramount. First, that through a combination of factors, reproductive output will decline, placing greater emphasis on the survival of each young. And, second, that selection should favour more complex social behaviour, partly as a result of increased care of offspring and partly as a result of increased longevity. Figure 6.15 summarizes the relationships between these variables.

Lovejoy (1981) has taken up this argument. He has suggested that the hominoids as a group have opted for large body size (compared to the cercopithecines), with consequent low rates of population growth. In order to remain viable they must either live in a hazard-free environment, with little predation or food shortage, or increase parental care. Lovejoy has argued that the African apes have pursued the former strategy, the hominids the latter. Chimpanzees, orang-utans and gorillas live in forested areas with little seasonality. Hominids, on the other hand, lived in seasonal environments with large numbers of predators, but off-set this by their increased parental care. It is intense parental care among humans, and by implication, among hominids, that is critical to human evolution. In order to increase parental care it is necessary for the mother to be released from at least some foraging activities. This in turn imposes

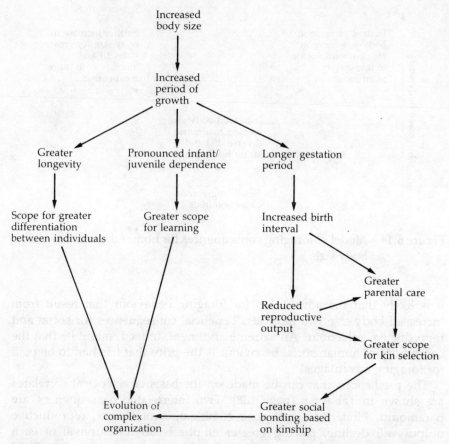

Figure 6.15 Suggested links between increased body size and the evolution of complex social behaviour.

two requirements on them. First, that the male provisions mother and offspring. And, second, that monogamous pair bonding is necessary to ensure that the male benefits from increased foraging effect. This is a pattern seen among many birds. In terms of human evolution, though, according to Lovejoy, two central human characteristics evolved to make this strategy possible – bipedalism, to enable food to be carried and transported to the young, and food-sharing among individuals regardless of whether they were directly involved in foraging. The outcome of this would be kin-based food-sharing at some ground nest within a social organization where paternity is recognized, as a response to the demographic problems posed by large body size. Thus human social behaviour may be accounted for by a combination of body size and environmental parameters.

Lovejoy's model broadly conforms to ecological and evolutionary

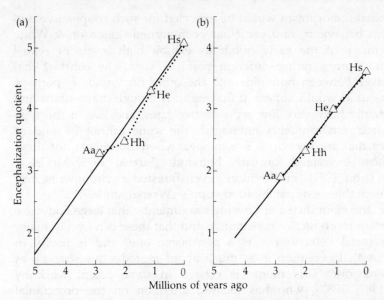

Figure 6.16   Relationship between brain size of fossil hominids (allowing for body size) and geological age. (a) The relationship using an estimate of EQ (encephalization quotient) based on body size/brain size relationships in mammals generally; (b) the relationship drawn from estimates based on catarrhine EQ (from Martin 1983). Abbreviations: Aa, *Australopithecus africanus*; Hh, *Homo habilis*; He, *Homo erectus*; Hs, *Homo sapiens*.

predictions (see page 129). The elements of cooperation that it predicts would be further enhanced by another line of argument. Longevity could be expected to increase with body size (see page 132). Associated with this is the expectation that individuals capable of differentiating between other individuals would be at a selective advantage, for they would be able to respond through experience to previous competitive and cooperative encounters. Thus selection would favour more complex and flexible social behaviour, where individuals would benefit and suffer for the consequences of their previous activities. Individuals able to optimize the amount of effort they put into cooperative behaviour would be at an advantage (Houston & Davies 1985).

Despite its apparent fit, Lovejoy's model can subjected to further scrutiny and criticism. Certainly, bipedalism, as Lovejoy's model would predict, appears early in hominid evolution. As discussed in Chapter 2 (see page 26), some form of habitual bipedalism is indicated by the track of footprints at Laetoli around 3.6 Ma old (Leakey 1978). The evidence for food-sharing and home bases is far more dubious (Binford 1981, 1984; Isaac & Crader 1981; Isaac 1983, 1984; Potts 1984b). Furthermore, low levels of sexual dimorphism would be expected for such cooperative and monogamous behaviour, and yet it has been argued (Johanson & White 1979) that many of the early hominids exhibit high levels of sexual dimorphism. From a rather different point of view, the contrast that Lovejoy makes between hominids and the other hominoids is perhaps not as clear-cut as would appear at first sight. Although orang-utans and gorillas certainly have very low reproductive rates, and live in the type of 'hazard-free' environments envisaged, the same cannot be said of chimpanzees that are known to live in savanna environments not dissimilar to those envisaged for early hominids (Suzuki 1975; McGrew, Baldwin & Tutin 1981). Furthermore, even forested environments may pose various problems of patchy food supply (Wrangham 1977).

However, the main thrust of Lovejoy's argument – that large body size imposes certain reproductive constraints, and that these can lead to major changes in social behaviour – is a persuasive one, and is useful in reminding us that evolution is as much about reproductive strategy as foraging behaviour. This theme is echoed in some recent work by Trinkaus (1981, 1983), who has focused attention on the postcranial differences between neanderthals and anatomically modern humans. These differences, it has been suggested, derive from conflicting selective pressures for the enlargement of the brain and body size and efficient bipedalism. As brain size increased, the problems of giving birth to a very large-brained infant led to restrictions in female locomotor efficiency and perhaps to high levels of infant mortality. With anatomically modern humans a switch seems to have taken place towards greater gracility, and perhaps also to a shorter gestation period and the birth of premature young. Once again, this would have placed considerable emphasis on the care of the young, a change which Trinkaus has suggested may have been important in the change of behaviour associated with the evolution of anatomically modern humans.

Body size, brain size and hominid adaptation

Aspects of both foraging behaviour and reproductive/social behaviour thus seem to be related to changes in hominid body size, the former in terms of advantages, the latter in terms of problems. The two are, though, linked by one feature critical in human evolution – the enlargement of the brain. The relationship between body size and brain size has already been discussed (see page 134). It was suggested that encephalization is extremely costly (R. D. Martin 1981), especially for the females, and will evolve only where the benefits exceed these high costs. For small mammals this will seldom occur, because of their relatively high metabolic rates. For large mammals encephalization will be advantagous

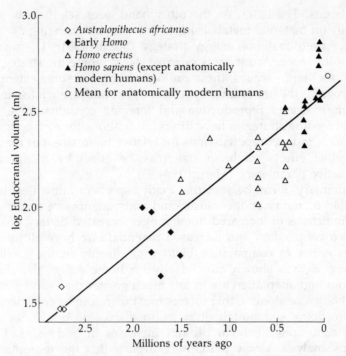

Figure 6.17   Relationship between brain size of fossil hominids and
geological age (after Stringer 1984).

where flexibility of response is required. We have seen here that for
foraging and for social behaviour a case can be made for both being
selected for among hominids, the first in relation to an increasingly
diverse and patchy diet, the second in relation to more complex social
relations. Thus enlargement of the brain would be expected from an early
period of human evolution. Martin (1983) has argued that this is the case,
and that early hominid brain size shows enlargement over what would be
expected for a Plio-Pleistocene ape (Fig. 6.16), and Stringer (1984) has
shown continuous brain expansion during hominid evolution (Fig. 6.17).

What should be pointed out, though, is that in highlighting all these
relationships no single line of causality can be identified. Martin (1984), in
his review of size relationships among the primates, has emphasized that
although good relationships exist between brain size, body size and
feeding behaviour among the primates, they can be interpreted in several
ways. Martin (1984: 92) has identified a 'foraging-strategy hypothesis' and
an 'energy-strategy hypothesis' as two alternative approaches to the
evolutionary and ecological aspects of size. The former hypothesis
suggests that it is the requirements of the foraging behaviour that will
drag brain size up to fit – unpredictable and patchy resources requiring

larger brains. The latter, on the other hand, sees selection as operating primarily on maternal metabolism, with brain size changing as 'a passive consequence of maternal energy strategy' (Martin 1984: 91) – small brains where a low-energy strategy is pursued, large where the strategy is high energy. As Martin argues, these can be combined to some extent in ways that recognize the importance of selection for brain size while allowing for the significance of reproductive and foraging considerations: '... differential feeding strategies have direct implications for metabolic turnover which have indirect repercussions for relative brain size, but that positive or negative effects on brain size may be offset by modifications of reproductive parameters' (Martin 1984:93).

In summary, it can be seen that many aspects of human evolution are explicable in terms of the causes and consequences of increased body size. Predictions of increased home range, increased dietary diversity, of increased cooperation and increased parental care have all found some support either in comparative biology or directly in the fossil record. However, as was shown most clearly for home range, the changes in behaviour and adaptation are in fact much greater than can be accounted for by body size alone. Other factors must therefore be considered.

Before doing so, though, it is worth discussing briefly the environmental conditions likely to prompt increases in body size. From the previous analysis it may perhaps be argued that the reproductive and social aspects are consequences of increased body size, but that the energy strategy in relation to resource utilization is the cause. We might thus expect to find the conditions likely to promote increased body size among the resources and environments in which early hominids lived.

Increased body size is most frequently a response to competitive conditions (Pianka 1978), for it is this that lies at the heart of K-selection (Fig. 6.11). The evolutionary ecology of the early hominids is thus a product of K-selection – high competitive ability, few offspring with low infant mortality. It cannot be said that particular habitats will result in K-selection for this is often specific to organisms and their adaptive characteristics. The critical factor is the level of competition and the stability of the competitive conditions. Where both of these are high, K-selected organisms are likely to occur. The levels and nature of competition in the environments in which the early hominids lived will be examined in Chapters 8 and 9, but before doing so it is necessary to examine in more detail a characteristic of hominids that has played an important part in their evolution – their terrestriality.

7 Hominids as terrestrial primates

There are few summaries of human evolution more succinct than 'we came down from the trees'. We are what we are because we are an arboreal animal that has taken up the challenge of a terrestrial way of life. This is often associated with a vague idea that somehow life is tougher on the ground. This is where the real evolutionary successes are, while the quiche-eaters of the biological world remained in the trees. Hominid success came from climbing down from the arboreal grandstand and entering the terrestrial arena of evolutionary conflict.

The argument that terrestriality is important in hominid evolution is an obvious and self-evident one. It derives from two simple and basic observations: one, that most primates, in contrast to humans, are arboreal, and the other, that among those primates that have adopted a terrestrial way of life, hominids have evolved one of the most extreme and specialized forms of locomotion – bipedalism. This degree of divergence from the evolutionary and adaptive patterns of our closest biological relatives would seem to be an adequate explanation for human uniqueness.

Regrettably, perhaps, hominid evolution is not that simple. Although primates are essentially an arboreal order, many species, living and extinct, have adapted to a more terrestrial life. Recent ecological and palaeontological work has demonstrated the significance of terrestriality in the evolution of some groups of primates. The ground-dwelling of hominids is part of, rather than counter to, a general primate evolutionary trend. Although this may undercut the view that the evolution of hominids is very different from that of primates, it does enable a fuller analysis of evolutionary patterns, one in which the consequences of ground-dwelling can be assessed, and the alternative solutions to the problems terrestriality poses can be compared.

The task of this chapter is to look at what terrestriality will involve for a primate: Why and how did primates became terrestrial, both in terms of the fossil record and evolutionary and ecological theory? What are the adaptive consequences of terrestriality? And what were the conditions under which the evolution of hominid terrestriality took place?

Primate evolution and terrestriality

The primates are generally regarded as an arboreal order. The primary defining characteristics given in Chapter 1 – grasping hands and feet, dependence on the visual senses, jumping and suspensory locomotor capabilities, etc. (see Fig. 1.1) – may be related to the problems of survival in a complex, three-dimensional arboreal environment. Furthermore, these characteristics occur among the earliest fossil primates of the Eocene, suggesting that trees may have been the preferred habitat of the primitive mammalian ancestors of primates, and that this became the specialized niche of primates as mammals underwent an adaptive radiation in the early Tertiary.

However, among living primates arboreality is far from universal. According to Clutton-Brock & Harvey (1977a), of 101 species (including modern humans) of primate, 23.8 per cent are terrestrial. These species, however, are not evenly distributed through the order, for only two prosimian and no platyrrhine species are terrestrial, whereas 42.9 per cent of catarrhines are terrestrial. As catarrhines are among the most recent evolutionary groups of primates, a trend towards terrestriality must be considered a key element of later primate evolution. When it is borne in mind that nearly half of the Old World anthropoid primates spend considerable amounts of time on the ground, the uniqueness of hominid terrestriality and its all-embracing explanatory power begins to diminish. What it is necessary to explain, then, is not just a hominid characteristic, but a catarrhine one.

Reasons for terrestriality

Why should members of an arboreal order change to ground-dwelling? Two basic reasons may be suggested (Foley 1984b). The first is based on ecological principles, the second on the history of the environment. The primary constraint on an arboreal way of life is body size. Freedom of movement, swiftness, access to many food types is best served by a small body size. As discussed in the previous chapter, small body size also has certain disadvantages. For a primate, however, the price of release from the high energy costs of a small body size is terrestriality. Consequently, if there is a trend towards increased size among primates, a trend towards increased terrestriality should also be expected. The relationship

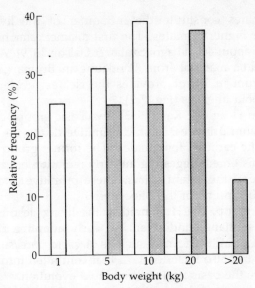

Figure 7.1   Relative frequency of arboreal (open) and terrestrial (shaded) primates by classes of body weight (data from Clutton-Brock & Harvey 1977a)

between body size and terrestriality among the primates can be seen in Fig. 7.1, where, although there are some large arboreal primates – for example, the orang-utan (but see below, page 160) – there is a general trend towards terrestriality with increased size.

On their own, though, the constraints on body size are insufficient to account for the development of terrestriality. A terrestrial way of life must also be viable and necessary in its own right. Appropriate terrestrial environments must be present. It has already been shown (see Chapter 5) that from the middle Miocene onwards climatic changes led to a less-forested tropical environment. This meant that there was competition between species over those areas of tropical forest remaining, and, more significantly, new and different environments available for colonization. The trends in primate evolution during the past 15 million years, within the Old World, reflect this palaeoenvironmental situation.

Primate evolution: the evidence

The fossil record provides the evidence for the evolution of terrestriality among primates. Although terrestriality may have evolved independently among the strepsirhines – for example, the ring-tailed lemur (*Lemur catta*) and some of the subfossil lemurs of Madagascar (Walker 1967) – interest here centres on the catarrhines.

The catarrhines constitute the infraorder of the living Old World anthropoids or higher primates. The first distinct catarrhines emerged in the Oligocene, about 40 Ma ago (Szalay & Delson 1979). Although there is some problematic material from Pondaung in Burma (Szalay & Delson 1979), the Fayum in Egypt provides the clearest evidence for the Old World anthropoid lineages (Fig. 7.2).

According to Fleagle & Kay (1983), two basic groups can be identified among the Fayum primates. First, a primitive taxon, the Parapithecidae, and, second, the earliest Hominoidea. The former group are numerically dominant at this time, suggesting an early radiation of catarrhines before the appearance of the extant forms. These primitive catarrhines became extinct by the beginning of the Miocene.

The second group, the Hominoidea, the living descendents of which are apes and humans, underwent an early adaptive radiation, which involved some primitive forms, such as *Aegyptopithecus*, *Pliopithecus* and *Propliopithecus*, but also included taxa that continued into the Miocene in forms that were the basis for later hominoid evolution.

The Miocene hominoids are numerous, complex and subject to greater taxonomic indecisiveness than is usual even in palaeoanthropology. Recent fieldwork, especially in the Siwaliks of Pakistan, and the application of new techniques and analytical methods, have had a revolutionary effect. Ten years ago there were basically three groups of Miocene

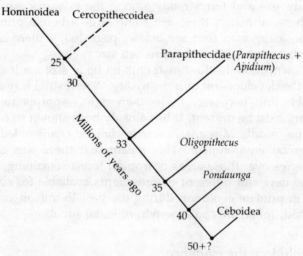

Figure 7.2   Simplified cladogram of the relationship between the higher
catarrhine taxa and the fossil evidence of early catarrhines.
Pondaunga is an Asian Eocene anthropoid primate.
Oligopithecus is an early anthropoid from the Oligocene
deposits at Fayum, Egypt (based on Szalay & Delson 1979;
Fleagle & Kay 1983).

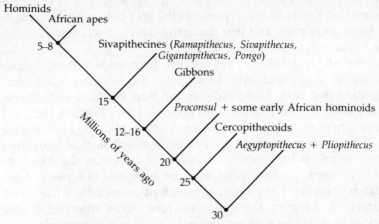

Figure 7.3   Simplified and tentative cladogram of late Oligocene and
Miocene catarrhines (based on Szalay & Delson 1979; Fleagle &
Kay 1983).

hominoid recognized in the literature – *Ramapithecus* as the first hominid,
the dryopithecines as the forerunners of the modern great apes, and the
ancestors of the gibbons. The present view is more complex (Fig. 7.3).
Following Pilbeam (Ciochon and Corruccini 1983, Ward & Pilbeam 1983;
Pilbeam 1984), it is possible to recognize several groups of Miocene large
hominoid.

On the one hand are the earlier forms found in Africa, perhaps
continuations of the earlier Oligocene radiations – *Proconsul* and *Limnopi-
thecus*. These are primitive, generalized arboreal frugivores, probably
living an arboreal life. They do not exhibit the specialized locomotor
adaptations of the later hominoids, but may represent the type of
hominoid that evolved subsequent to the split with the Old World
monkeys, the Cercopithecoidea.

The other group are more derived as well as being more widespread.
Although no longer appropriate, Pilbeam (1979) originally used the term
'ramamorph' to describe them – large primates with thick tooth enamel,
sometimes showing signs of adaptation to more seasonal and less-
forested environments. Their spread and evolution may well be related to
the expansion of hominoids, as well as of other animals, out of Africa
subsequent to the formation of a landbridge between Africa and Eurasia.
These species are common in the middle and later Miocene of south-
eastern Europe and Asia. The most common taxon is *Sivapithecus*. *Ramapithecus* is a part of this group, but Andrews (1983) and Pilbeam (in press)
suggest that the term *Ramapithecus* should be suppressed, and that the
specimens formerly placed within this taxon should be put into *Sivapithecus*. Other parts of this radiation include *Gigantopithecus* and

Ouranopithecus, as well as an African form, *Kenyapithecus*. It is increasingly accepted that this radiation represents the split between the living African and Asian great apes, and that the orang-utan is the extant descendant of these Miocene forms.

A current 'evolutionary tree' of the hominoids differs considerably from earlier interpretations. Among the major changes are, first, the recognition that early hominoids are far more complex and diverse than was originally thought. Simons & Pilbeam's (1965; Pilbeam 1969) attempts to hone down the taxonomic complexity of the Miocene Hominoidea have proved to be over-enthusiastic. For both morphological and biogeographical reasons, it has proved necessary to recognize significant biogeographic patterns, and so differences between the European, Asian and African hominoids. The pattern of increased diversity and the variation in the level of diversity through time raise some interesting ecological questions that will be pursued below in relation to terrestriality.

A second change in interpretation is that where previously there was an effort to relate, usually ancestrally, fossil forms to extant forms, there is a tendency now to treat them as adaptive forms in their own right, and only secondarily are they placed into the framework of their relationship with living species. This is a very important change. Miocene hominoids, as Pilbeam (1979) has argued, must be seen in the context of their contemporary environment, not merely as forerunners of later species. Emphasis should be on what a species is, not what they might have become. As suggested in Chapter 2 (see page 20), the impact of biochemical work has been important in this change of attitude, principally because the later divergence dates suggested by molecular and immunological evidence meant that many fossils simply could not be directly ancestral to living forms.

The other change in interpretation of the Miocene hominoids concerns their relationship to the other major branch of the catarrhines, the cercopithecoid monkeys. The classic view of the relationship between these two superfamilies is that the monkeys represent the more primitive and simpler grade of organization, while the hominoids (including ourselves, of course!) were more advanced and complex. This led to the expectations that early catarrhines should be more monkey-like than ape-like, and that the cercopithecoids should appear earlier in the fossil record.

This view has now been challenged. Fleagle & Kay (1983) have argued that relative to the hominoids many features of the cercopithecoids are derived, and that the hominoids are closer to the characteristics of the ancestral catarrhines. The suggestion, as indicated in Fig. 7.2, is that the monkeys branched away from the hominoids. Furthermore, the fossil record of the early cercopithecoids is extremely poor (Szalay & Delson 1979: 320–7), and there is no unequivocal evidence for the presence of monkeys before 20 Ma ago, the date for hominoid–cercopithecoid divergence preferred by the biochemists, and well after the catarrhine radiation known from the Fayum. This would also conform to the fact that the fossil record testifies to a late (late Miocene–Pliocene) radiation of the monkeys, in contrast to the early–middle Miocene one for the hominoids.

These three changes in interpretation – high diversity, only partial relationship to living forms, and the late evolution of the cercopithecoids – are all critical in considering the role that terrestriality played in the evolutionary ecology of the successive adaptive radiations that constitute the history of the anthropoids in the Old World (Fig. 7.4).

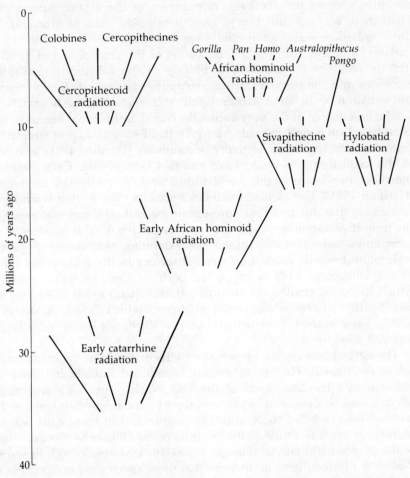

Figure 7.4 Adaptive radiations of the catarrhines (cf. Cronin 1983: fig. 4).

Catarrhine evolutionary ecology

From the perspective of evolutionary ecology the question raised by the pattern of evolution of the catarrhines is: What was the ecological basis of the various adaptive radiations identifiable in the fossil record? An answer to this question will enable us to place the hominids, the central focus of this book, within a more comparative framework.

Old World adaptive radiations

In Fig. 7.4, six adaptive radiations are shown but the actual number is rather arbitrary as it depends on the taxonomic level considered. First, there was an early catarrhine radiation in the Oligocene, consisting of primitive groups and the early forerunners of the extant superfamilies. Then there was the radiation of early hominoids, such as *Proconsul*. The third radiation was that of the sivapithecines; the fourth that of the gibbons, and the fifth, the diversification of the cercopithecoid monkeys (this is really two radiations, consisting of the folivorous (leaf-eating) colobines and the more terrestrial cercopithecines). And, finally, there is the radiation of the large African hominoids, including the hominids.

The emergence of the very early Old World anthropoids seems to have been based on a shift towards frugivory (fruit-eating). Living strepsirhine primates tend towards insectivory or omnivory (Harding 1981), and some of the fossil forms may also have had this type of diet. Catarrhines, on the other hand, are largely herbivorous, and, in particular, frugivorous (Harding 1981). The earliest fossil evidence from the Fayum would seem to indicate that this trend was present in the earliest forms and among all the primitive families of the group (Fleagle 1983). The success of the catarrhines was probably based on extending the range of primate adaptation towards diurnal, arboreal frugivory in the widespread forests of the Oligocene. This is supported both by the anatomical evidence, which indicates small slow-moving arboreal quadrupeds (Fleagle 1983), and by the palaeoenvironmental evidence, which Bown, Kraus et al. (1982) have shown convincingly (*contra* Kortlandt 1983) reflects true forested conditions.

The early Miocene was a period in which this basic catarrhine adaptation flourished. The early hominoids radiated initially in Africa and subsequently to other parts of the Old World. The early and middle Miocene can be described as the period when the hominoids were at their most widespread and successful. The adaptations of these early Miocene hominoids seem to continue the patterns of the Oligocene. Recent studies of the postcranial material (Fleagle & Kay 1983; Morbeck 1983; Rose 1983; Walker & Pickford 1983) all indicate that these species did not possess any of the locomotor specializations of the extant apes, but were rather generalized arboreal quadrupeds. Only the largest of them, *Proconsul*

Above-branch feeder

Below-branch feeder

Figure 7.5   Above-and below-branch feeding (see text for discussion).

major, shows any indications of terrestriality, and although others display some suspensory capabilities, none is a full brachiator. In view of Grand's (1972) hypothesis that suspensory abilities provide a more efficient means of moving between clumps of food, this may have had important foraging consequences. In a very detailed analysis, Aiello (1981) has shown that these Miocene arboreal quadrupeds can be further categorized according to whether they are *above*- or *below-branch* feeders (Fig. 7.5). Which category a species falls into depends to a large extent on body size, a factor that Aiello has shown is particularly important in the various adaptations of the Miocene Hominoidea. However, Fleagle (1984) has pointed out that although foraging behaviour and locomotion can be broadly linked, few good correlations between food category and specific locomotor pattern can be demonstrated.

Variation in body size, locomotor and feeding behaviour were ways in which the hominoid niche was partitioned among a wide range of species during the earlier parts of the Miocene. However, although several niches were available, they all occur within a single habitat – forested environments. The current evidence (Van Couvering & Van Couvering 1976; Andrews, Lord & Evans 1979; Pickford 1983) suggests that the landmasses of the tropics at this time were covered with large, continuous and undifferentiated expanses of tropical rainforest. These productive environments were the key to the early hominoid adaptive radiation that occurred between 20 and 12 Ma ago.

As has already been shown in Chapter 5, the climatic and geographic changes of the middle Miocene resulted in a more differentiated environment; the shrinking of tropical rainforests, and their replacement in many parts of the world by a more fragmented mosaic of habitats, in which woodland, bushland and grassland became increasingly common. These environmental changes had far-reaching effects on mammalian and catarrhine evolution. The ecological problem faced by the mid-Miocene catarrhines was how to adapt to reduced, often isolated forests, and more extensive seasonal wooded and bush environments. Both ecological principles and the continuing diversity of catarrhine forms throughout the later Cenozoic suggest that more than one response was possible, determined by the specific conditions in which the primates found themselves. In some cases, competition probably increased, because of dwindling availability of resources and contracted habitats. In others, extinction and isolation could have led to communities impoverished in species and among which competition was lax (MacArthur & Wilson 1967). The evolutionary patterns of the Old World anthropoids show the strategies selected for in response to these environmental conditions.

Alternative responses

What were these responses? The generalized, arboreal, quadrupedal apes, represented by the early hominoids such as *Proconsul*, began to reduce in diversity, distribution and numbers. In their place came more specialized apes capable either of more efficient use of their environment or able to survive in a wide range of new habitats. The sivapithecines represented one such response. *Ramapithecus*, *Sivapithecus* and *Gigantopithecus* are apes that all display characteristics associated with a harder, coarser and more seasonal diet. The principal evidence for this lies in the thickening of the tooth enamel (Pilbeam, Meyer et al. 1977; Ward & Pilbeam 1983). The associated environmental evidence also indicates that these apes were living in a more arid environment. And, furthermore, one of these lineages, *Gigantopithecus*, which survived on into the middle Pleistocene in China and possibly in other parts of Asia as well, was clearly, on the basis of its size, terrestrial. The only living representative of the sivapithecines is the orang-utan, now confined to a few areas of forest in Borneo and Sumatra. Although this is an arboreal animal today, its ancestral and collateral relatives may have been both more varied and possibly also more terrestrial in their habitat preference and locomotor behaviour (Andrews 1983). The extreme arboreality of the living orang-utan may indeed be a response to the arrival of hominids in Southeast Asia during the Pleistocene (McKinnon 1974). The postcranial adaptations of the sivapithecines are still poorly known. Rose and his co-workers (Raza, Barry et al. 1983; Rose 1983, 1984) have suggested that these middle and late Miocene hominoids did not possess the locomotor behaviours of the later and living hominoids, but rather they were capable of a wide range of movements and positions, probably centring on active climbing, but including also brachial suspension, quadrupedalism, quadrumanism and bipedalism.

A second response, that of more specialized use of the arboreal environment, is illustrated by the gibbons. The ancestry of this lineage is particularly obscure (Fleagle 1983). Although over the years many fossils have been attributed to the hylobatids, even from as far back as the Oligocene, this probably reflects their (cranial) similarity to the very early catarrhines. The current consensus, and the biochemical evidence, would seem to place the divergence of this branch of the hominoids at between 12 and 16.5 Ma ago (see Figs 2.4 and 7.3). These animals, of which there are some seven extant species living in Southeast Asia, are the aerial acrobats among the hominoids – extremely rapid brachiators living high in the canopies of the rainforests. In dietary terms they are primarily frugivores, and thus belong to the mainstream of primate feeding behaviours, but their locomotor behaviour gives them the ability to pursue this lifestyle in specialized and competitive circumstances (Chivers 1977).

The African apes show response lying half way between that of the sivapithecines and that of the gibbons. The chimpanzee and gorilla, like the gibbon, remained in their forested habitat. However, possibly like some of the sivapithecines, they have also adopted a more terrestrial way of life. The increased body size and knuckle-walking adaptations of the African apes are part of a more efficient use of the remaining areas of the forested environment. The gorilla in particular, with its leaf-eating specializations, has, through dependence on a low-value but ubiquitous resource, parallelled the gibbon in its degree of specialization. The chimpanzee, on the other hand, has maintained a more general pattern of resource specialization. This is reflected in its ability to exploit environments on the margins of forests. Indeed, one author has suggested that the chimpanzee was previously a more open-country and terrestrial animal, and, like the orang-utan, has secondarily adapted to the forest (Kortlandt 1972).

A response that did not occur until later is that of the other group of African hominoids, the hominids. Perhaps the hominids, and to some extent the chimpanzee, parallel in Africa some of the sivapithecines, such as *Gigantopithecus*, of the late Miocene of Asia in adopting a more terrestrial way of life in less-forested habitats of Africa. Although little is known about the behaviour and ecology of *Gigantopithecus*, these hominoids could claim to represent some of the most extreme terrestrial adaptations to the late Cenozoic environment found among the catarrhines, and converging on some of those of the hominids.

However, although many hominoids were able to respond to the new environmental conditions, from the middle Miocene onwards there was a decline in hominoid diversity and distribution. This contrasts markedly with the evolutionary fortunes of the other group of catarrhines, the cercopithecoid monkeys (Fig. 7.6). From the late Miocene onwards these monkeys became far more abundantly represented in the fossil record than the apes, a fact that might suggest that they were more capable of adapting to the drier and more restricted conditions than the hominoids. In particular, among the cercopithecoids a wide range of species, including

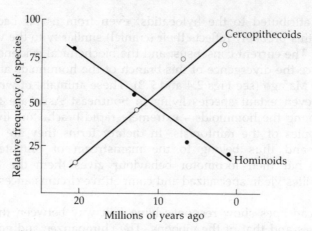

Figure 7.6   Relative diversity of cercopithecoids and hominoids during the later Cenozoic (from Andrews 1981).

Cercopithecus monkeys, baboons and macaques, adapted to semiterrestriality and occupation of the savanna where they survived on a diet of dry foliage and fruits, or, in some case, a trend towards full omnivory.

An ecological model of divergence

The period from 12 Ma onwards, therefore, has seen a widening of the catarrhine niches as a response to environmental change. From the perspective of evolutionary ecology, rather than phylogeny, a pattern of both divergence and parallelism can be traced in the fossil record (Fig. 7.7). In this model, an attempt has been made to plot the pathways followed by various primate groups in response to the changing selective conditions of the times in which they were living. From the earliest catarrhines there has been a pattern of divergence and parallel evolution, an interplay of habitat (forest, woodland and savanna), diet (frugivory, folivory and omnivory) and arboreal and terrestrial modes of life. Overall, there has been a trend towards a much greater degree of ground-dwelling, a trend that is reflected both in the evolution of the hominoids and the relative fortunes of the hominoids and cercopithecoids.

This pattern tells us both about the problems that these primates faced and about the processes by which organisms adapt. In particular it illustrates the point that the same basic problem – in this case increasingly open and seasonal environments – can elicit different responses through natural selection. Not all species will react in the same way to the same problem. The differences in response will depend on a variety of factors. To some extent, local conditions may vary – for example, the environmental changes in Eurasia may have been earlier and more drastic than those in Africa, leading to a more widespread adaptive radiation. Further

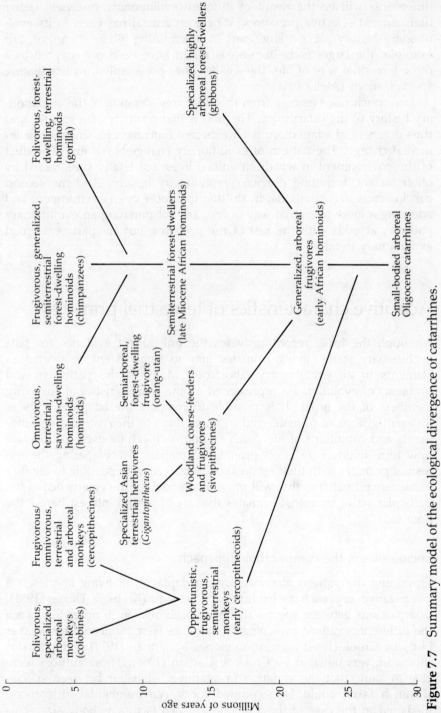

Figure 7.7 Summary model of the ecological divergence of catarrhines.

differences will be the result of different evolutionary histories, rather than current selective pressures. Where an animal has been in its evolutionary history plays a large part in determining where it can go. For example, the larger early hominoids might have been pre-adapted to a more terrestrial way of life, the smaller ones pre-adapted for brachiating specializations (Aiello 1981).

Two conclusions emerge from this brief consideration of the evolutionary history of the catarrhines. The first is that diversity of response, and thus diversity of adaptation, is an expected outcome of a single environmental change. The pattern of evolutionary change is not just a product of the environment in which an animal lives, but is also constrained by other factors, including previous evolutionary history. And the second conclusion is that hominids, in shifting to a more open environment and adopting a more terrestrial way of life, are not pursuing an evolutionary pathway at odds with the rest of the primates, but are part of a broad evolutionary trend.

Adaptive characteristics of terrestrial primates

Although the fossil record provides the only direct evidence for past evolutionary states, living primates may to some extent be treated as elements in an evolutionary laboratory. Many of the pathways and problems of evolution are represented by the characteristics of surviving members of the order. It is possible to compare the adaptive traits of different groups of primate, and to relate them to their varying environments and conditions of life. Such an approach can be used to elucidate how terrestriality may affect primate adaptation. By comparing the terrestrial primates with their arboreal cousins, it may be possible to identify some general patterns that will provide a model for the emergence of the particular set of terrestrial primates that are of central interest here – the hominids.

Socioecology: the comparative approach

Examining the pattern of variability in adaptation of living species is a comparative approach to evolutionary ecology (Krebs & Davies 1981). Comparisons between species that are closely related in order to discern the differences caused by ecological variables were pioneered for weaver birds by Crook (1964) and for antelopes by Jarman (1974). For primates this work was initiated by Crook & Gartlan (1966). These authors were able to show that the variation in adaptive behaviour between species within a taxon could be accounted for by environmental differences, mediated in the case of the antelope by such factors as body size. This approach has become a powerful means of testing ecological and evolutionary hypotheses, of identifying critical environmental factors, and for monitoring the responses of organisms.

This approach, however, is not without its critics and limitations. At its most general, there is a danger of formulating explanations *ad hoc* to account for any differences between species (Altmann 1974). When differences are found between two species, some environmental difference can nearly always be found to account for this, for no two environments are ever identical. In pursuing a comparative approach it is not sufficient just to identify environmental differences, but also to show how these differences can relate to adaptive traits.

A more practical difficulty lies in determining the taxonomic unit appropriate for comparison (Clutton-Brock & Harvey 1979; Krebs & Davies 1981). This is really a reformulation of Galton's problem (see Thomas 1978), which is concerned with the independence of data. If two species have the same adaptation, is this because they have the same ecological conditions or because they are both descendents of a common ancestor who had this characteristic? Resolution of this difficulty is critical if any form of quantification and statistical testing is to be used. Clutton-Brock & Harvey (1977a) have suggested that the appropriate level is that at which maximum variance occurs, and, for primates, this is the genus. However, for the more narrow taxonomic range of analysis here, where it is only the catarrhines that are being compared, the species is used to indicate trends in adaptive strategy.

Terrestrial primate socioecology

In several studies Clutton-Brock & Harvey (1977a,b; Harvey & Clutton-Brock 1981, 1985) have compiled and analysed data on the behavioural and ecological characteristics of primates. Their data base can be used to consider the differences between the arboreal and terrestrial catarrhines (Fig. 7.8, Table 7.1). These data suggest that although there is overlap between the two groups of animals, some ecological trends related to terrestriality occur. To use these trends to build models that give us expectations and predictions about early hominids, it is necessary to examine what selective agencies may have been responsible for these differences.

Figure 7.8 Comparison of the ecological characteristics of terrestrial and
(over)   arboreal catarrhines. The level of comparison is interspecific
                 (*mean). As Clutton-Brock & Harvey (1979) have argued,
                 comparison at this level is fraught with statistical difficulties,
                 but some trends can be seen. Data from Clutton-Brock &
                 Harvey (1977a).

(a) **Diet**

	Terrestrial	Arboreal
Frugivores	19	19
Folivores	3	15

(b) **Body weight**

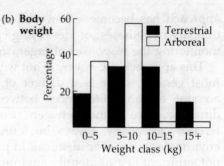

(c) **Sexual dimorphism**

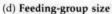

Terrestrial

Arboreal

1.0 1.1 1.2 1.3 1.4 1.5 1.6 1.7 1.8 1.9 2.0
Weight (♂/♀)

(d) **Feeding-group size**

Terrestrial

Arboreal

0   20   40   60   80   100 310   330
Number of individuals

(e) **Breeding-group size**

Terrestrial

Arboreal

0   20   40   60   80   100
Number of individuals

(f) **Population-group size**

Terrestrial

Arboreal

0   20   40   60   80   100   120
Number of individuals

(g) **Sex ratio of breeding group**

Terrestrial

Arboreal

1   2   3   4   5 7   13   14
Number of females per male

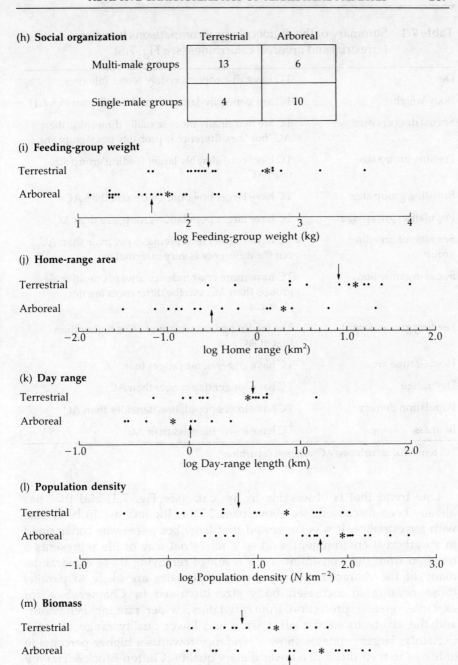

(h) **Social organization**

	Terrestrial	Arboreal
Multi-male groups	13	6
Single-male groups	4	10

(i) **Feeding-group weight**

Terrestrial

Arboreal

log Feeding-group weight (kg)

(j) **Home-range area**

Terrestrial

Arboreal

log Home range (km^2)

(k) **Day range**

Terrestrial

Arboreal

log Day-range length (km)

(l) **Population density**

Terrestrial

Arboreal

log Population density (N km^{-2})

(m) **Biomass**

Terrestrial

Arboreal

log Biomass (kg km^{-2})

Table 7.1   Summary of the socioecological comparisons between
terrestrial and arboreal catarrhines (see Fig. 7.8)

Diet	TC have disproportionately fewer folivores
Body weight	TC are generally larger than AC (see also Fig 7.1)
Sexual dimorphism	TC are marginally more sexually dimorphic than AC, but the difference is probably not significant
Feeding group size	TC have considerably larger feeding group sizes than AC
Breeding group size	TC have larger breeding group size than AC
Population group size	TC have larger population group size than AC
Sex ratio of breeding group	TC have slightly fewer females per male than AC, but the difference is very marginal
Social organization	TC have more of a tendency towards multi-male groups than AC, but the differences are not clear-cut
Feeding group weight	The feeding group weight of TC is higher than that of AC
Home-range area	TC have larger home ranges than AC
Day-range	TC have longer day ranges than AC
Population density	TC have lower population densities than AC
Biomass	TC have lower biomass than AC

TC, terrestrial catarrhines; AC, arboreal catarrhines.

One trend that is observable in the data (see Fig. 7.1) and that has already been discussed (see above page 152) is the increase in body size with terrestriality. It was suggested that large body size was constrained in an arboreal environment, and so a terrestrial way of life represents a freedom from this constraint. As a result of removing these constraints, many of the characteristics of terrestrial primates are likely to parallel those relating to increased body size discussed in Chapter 5 – for example, greater protection from predators, wider ranging behaviour, and the ability to subsist off a wide and lower quality range of food. Certainly, larger primates show a tendency towards a higher percentage of leaves in their diet and a lower dietary quality (Clutton-Brock & Harvey 1977b; Sailer, Gaulin et al. 1985). Furthermore, with greater body weight primates will have larger home ranges, and this can be seen for terrestrial catarrhines. The data presented here (see Fig. 7.8) show that day-range length will also be greater for terrestrial primates. As a consequence of this need for larger areas to support a single individual or a group of terrestrial primates, there is an associated tendency for terrestrial primates to have lower population densities (number of individuals per unit area) and biomass (body weight per unit area).

One reason for the greater home ranges found among the terrestrial primates might be that group size is larger among them. Traditionally, this has been related to antipredator behaviour (see van Schaik & van Hoof 1983), but other factors may also be responsible. First, many terrestrial primates often live in environments where distribution of resources is patchy, and Horn (1968) has suggested that where this occurs there should be a tendency towards increased group size to increase search efficiency. Another hypothesis is that larger group size will be selected for in patchy environments because of high levels of intergroup competition. Where two groups compete for the same patch, the larger group would have the competitive edge (Wrangham 1980).

Changes in social structure and reproductive and mating strategy may be expected to occur among terrestrial primates as a result of increased group size. Among primates sexual dimorphism is associated with male–male competition. This is high among multi-male groups and polygynous species, low in monogamous species. Where either polygyny or multi-male mating strategies occur males come into direct competition for access to females, and so differential increases in male body size will be selected for. As terrestrial primates tend to have larger group size, and thus only low levels of monogamy (which by definition involves small group size), then terrestrial primates may be expected to be more sexually dimorphic, than those primates that are predominately arboreal. Among terrestrial primates multi-male groups are more common than among arboreal ones.

Sexual dimorphism is related to another contributing factor, that of sex ratio (see Fig. 7.9). If sexual dimorphism is a product of inter-male rivalry,

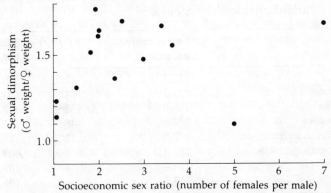

Figure 7.9   Relationship between degree of sexual dimorphism and sex ratios among catarrhines (adapted from Clutton-Brock & Harvey 1977b).

then this rivalry will be expected to occur in groups where males have to compete for a large number of females. This may be the case, but no relationship can be shown between socioeconomic sex ratio and social structure for the catarrhines (Clutton-Brock & Harvey 1977b).

These brief observations show that terrestriality poses common problems and opportunities, to which the various catarrhine species have found similar solutions. Although it is not possible to construct any simple line of causality, for example, from terrestriality to body size to sexual dimorphism, it is clear that a series of adaptive traits are closely and complexly related to each other and to terrestriality. The consequences of terrestriality are reflected in the morphology, behaviours and ecology of those primates that have 'come down from the trees'. In very broad terms, it is possible to say that a 'model' terrestrial catarrhine should show increased body size, increased sexual dimorphism, larger group size, and extensive ranging patterns at low population densities. This model might provide a useful context in which to examine hominid terrestriality.

Hominid terrestriality

To what extent, then do early hominids conform to or deviate from these expectations? Obviously, the limited nature of the fossil and archaeo-logical record makes it difficult to answer these questions in detail, but some observations can be made.

Table 7.2   Measures of percent sexual dimorphism in living hominoids and fossil hominids (from Frayer & Wolpoff 1985) based on various anatomical dimensions

	Lower canine breadth	n ($\male$/$\female$)	Molar (M_2) breadth
Pan paniscus	118.3	23/25	100.0
Pan troglodytes	123.3	84/90	103.7
Gorilla gorilla	138.0	153/95	107.0
Pongo pygmaeus	126.6	48/59	112.0
Australopithecus afarensis	127.5	11/5	111.2
Australopithecus africanus	117.3	9/6	109.1
Homo habilis	125.4	4/7	107.9
Homo erectus	113.6	6/15	106.0
European neanderthals	115.8	13/9	104.8
European early Upper Palaeolithic	109.8	7/6	105.5

Sexual dimorphism and mating patterns

We have already seen (Chapter 6) that hominids became larger during the course of their evolution. Some of this trend, at least, can no doubt be related to terrestriality. The degree of sexual dimorphism is rather more difficult to establish. Variability in fossil form due to sexual dimorphism is part of a continuum of variation caused by many factors, such as time, geography and taxonomic differences. Johanson & White (1979) have claimed that there is considerable sexual dimorphism within *Australopithecus afarensis*, the earliest recognizable hominid. If the specimens ascribed to this taxon do belong to a single species, then the earliest hominids are probably the most dimorphic of the family as a whole. Other members of the Hominidae also seem to show some sexual dimorphism (Table 7.2). Both the gracile and robust australopithecines are sufficiently variable for dimorphism to have been suggested. For the early representatives of the genus *Homo* there is probably too much taxonomic confusion to assign individual specimens to sexes (although it has been suggested that among the Koobi Fora specimens KNM-ER 1470 is a male and KNM-ER 1813 is a female). Sexual dimorphism has also been reported for *Homo erectus*, a species which includes some of the largest, most heavily built hominids known (see Fig. 6.4). With the evolution of anatomically modern humans there seems to have been a reduction in sexual dimorphism.

This pattern – that early hominids did display some degree of sexual dimorphism – suggests that the classic model of the early appearance of the pair bond, monogamy, in human evolution is incorrect, and instead that the early hominids possessed a social organization not dissimilar to that of other terrestrial primates – large group size and competition between males for access to females. Perhaps it is only with the appear-

Table 7.2 (contd)

n (♂/♀)	Femur length	n (♂/♀)	Mandible height	n (♂/♀)
24/33	101.2	10/10	100.0	12/17
124/124	104.9	38/58	108.7	22/20
170/170	120.9	84/54	123.8	47/22
69/73	115.0	32/29	117.0	12/16
6/10			118.4	5/5
7/3			119.6	4/4
4/8			126.9	5/10
10/22			119.6	10/17
12/10	108.1	4/1	115.5	7/8
7/8	108.4	5/3	115.3	8/8

ance of later hominids that this pattern was altered, and that either monogamy became predominant or age-structured and less directly competitive polygany, resulting in male–male competition expressed through characteristics other than size, became predominant.

Not surprisingly, going beyond observations of sexual dimorphism and attempting to discover anything about the social and reproductive behaviour of early hominids is extremely difficult. No direct fossil evidence provides information about this aspect of early hominid life, and reliable indirect inferences have yet to be developed. Some clues, however, may be provided by comparative anatomy. Harcourt, Harvey et al. (1981), following work initiated by Short (1979, 1980, 1981), have shown that among primates the size of genitalia varies with social system. At its simplest, species that live in multi-male groups have larger testes than those that live in single-male groups. The explanation for this is that in multi-male groups males will encounter more intense competition for access to females than in those populations where a single male has a monopoly of one or more females. A higher level of sperm production would be an advantage where copulatory periods may be brief and interrupted by other males. Martin & May (1981) have extended this analysis to include a discussion of possible mating patterns of early hominids (Fig. 7.10). They observed that testes size among modern humans falls within the levels expected for single-male breeding groups. This observation may be integrated with the discussion presented above on the presence of sexual dimorphism in hominids. As Martin & May suggest, and as is consistent with the fossil evidence, the 'original' mating system of early hominids would have been based on polygynous, single-male rather than multi-male groups. The level of sexual dimorphism in modern humans in size and form, and the higher levels of investment in male rather than female foetuses (Gibson & McKeown 1952) are both consistent with a polygynous mating system, the former because of inter-male rivalry (see above), and the latter because in polygynous systems the variance in male reproductive success is greater than that among females, and consequently it pays to put greater energetic effort into male rather than female offspring. It may therefore be put forward as a tentative hypothesis that early hominids may have had a single-male, polygynous reproductive system. This may contrast with earlier analyses, where cooperation between males was stressed and therefore it was expected that large-group, multi-male systems were likely to predominate. Modern reproductive systems are known to be highly variable. Polygyny does predominate among modern human societies (Ford & Beach 1952), but is clear that local conditions can modify social organization.

Regrettably testes are never fossilized, and so these hypotheses cannot be directly tested. However, a model of early hominid social organization consistent with the environmental constraints of the hominids and with general characteristics of the African hominoids can be developed.

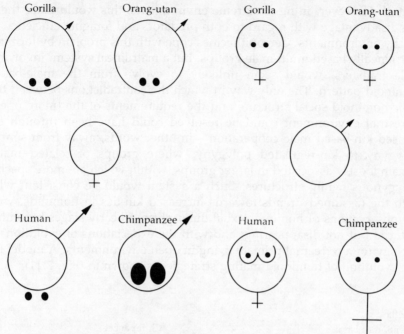

Figure 7.10 Genital size relative to body size among living large
hominoids. The top four outer circles show the sizes of males
relative to females, as well as the relative size of the testes and
erect penis. The lower four outer circles show female body
size, perineum and mammary glands relative to male body
size (from Martin & May 1981).

Gorillas live in polygynous groups where although more than one male
may occur, there is a clear system of dominance by a single male and thus
reproductive monopoly. The common chimpanzee, on the other hand,
lives in larger groups of associated males, with females moving about in a
semi-autonomous way within overlapping home ranges. Among African
hominoids, therefore, males form the core of the social groups. In contrast, cercopithecine males transfer between groups of related females,
which form the social core.

It is suggested that the basal African hominoids were largely polygynous, living in small groups in forested environments. Moving to a
more open environment would place tremendous strain on this system,
as males would be unable to defend larger territories and furthermore
there would be considerable selective pressure for larger group size as is
seen among other terrestrial primates. Among chimpanzees in a more
forested/woodland environment this has resulted in females maintaining
more independent social groups over which males have relatively little

control. However, in more extreme environments this would place them at a disadvantage with regard to both predators and foraging efficiency in patchy environments. Cercopithecines cope with this problem by forming matrilineally based multi-male groups, but a matrilineal system, involving male transfers, would seem unlikely to evolve from the male-based hominoid pattern. The only way in which the contradictions between the basic hominoid social structure and the requirements of the (more open) terrestrial environment could be resolved could have been through in-creased kin-based male cooperation – in other words, away from simple polygyny to kin-regulated polygyny, where groups of related males remain loosely associated in larger groups, within which are more specific polygynous family structures. Such a system would be consistent with both the (assumed) trends towards increased kin-ties in hominids, with the observations of hominid sexual dimorphism in early stages becoming reduced but not disappearing, and with the expectations of evolutionary ecology for a terrestrial primate living in open environments. A model for the evolution of hominoid mating strategies is shown in (Fig. 7.11).

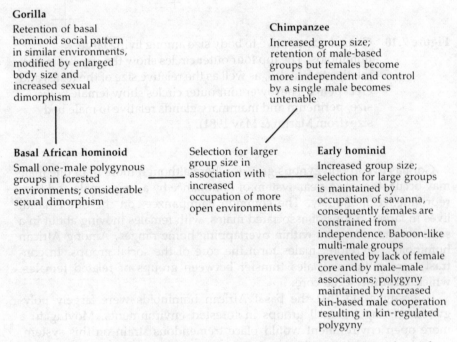

Gorilla
Retention of basal hominoid social pattern in similar environments, modified by enlarged body size and increased sexual dimorphism

Chimpanzee
Increased group size; retention of male-based groups but females become more independent and control by a single male becomes untenable

Basal African hominoid
Small one-male polygynous groups in forested environments; considerable sexual dimorphism

Selection for larger group size in association with increased occupation of more open environments

Early hominid
Increased group size; selection for large groups is maintained by occupation of savanna, consequently females are constrained from independence. Baboon-like multi-male groups prevented by lack of female core and by male–male associations; polygyny maintained by increased kin-based male cooperation resulting in kin-regulated polygyny

Figure 7.11 Tentative model of the evolution of African hominoid social systems. The suggestion is that in a basic harem-holding polygynous system, increased group size and male-based associations develop as a response to environmental constraints.

Population density

Some of the predictions relating to foraging behaviour – lower population density and more extensive ranging – have already been discussed in Chapter 6. Population density is difficult to establish in the fossil record: those calculations that have been made (Boaz 1979; R. A. Martin 1981) give only the broadest of estimates. One interesting observation, however, is that modern hunter–gatherers do live at very low population densities, and when correction has been made for body size and resource availability, they have a lower biomass than other terrestrial primates (Foley 1984b) (Fig. 7.12).

Both population density and sexual dimorphism are variables for which hominids can be scaled continuously with other terrestrial primates. There are others, though, where the hominid pattern may be seen as a direct result of terrestriality, and yet their adaptive strategy diverges markedly from that of the other terrestrial primates. These must now be considered.

Bipedalism

Given their arboreal ancestry it is obvious that a major problem facing

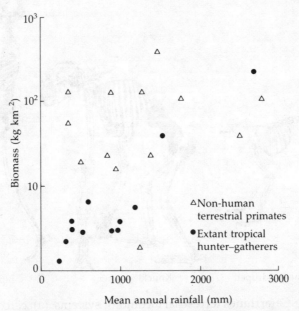

Figure 7.12   Relationship between mean annual rainfall and biomass of tropical hunter–gatherers compared with non-human terrestrial primates (from Foley 1984b).

terrestrial primates is movement on the ground. Novel forms of locomotion would be expected. The type of locomotor system to evolve would be a compromise between two factors: between the need to move efficiently and safely, and the need to use the forelimb in particular for feeding and other activities. Unlike most other mammals, primates do not feed directly with their mouths, and so require some level of manual dexterity.

Several systems of locomotion have evolved among the terrestrial primates. It is generally accepted that they fall into three basic categories: quadrupedalism, knuckle-walking and bipedalism (Fig. 7.13). Of these three locomotor types, bipedalism, the one adopted by the hominids, is the most specialized, requiring major anatomical modifications. The limb proportions (the ratio of arm to leg length) differ considerably from those of most ape and monkey species, where either arms and legs are of similar length, or the arms are longer than the legs (see Napier & Napier 1967). The foot has also been altered; with the alignment of the big toe with the other toes it has lost its grasping ability, but increased its supportive capacity. The pelvis of a biped has to support much greater weight than in a quadruped. Consequently, among hominids, it has become less elongated and more rounded and bowl-like, to support the spinal column. The spine itself has become more robust, particularly in

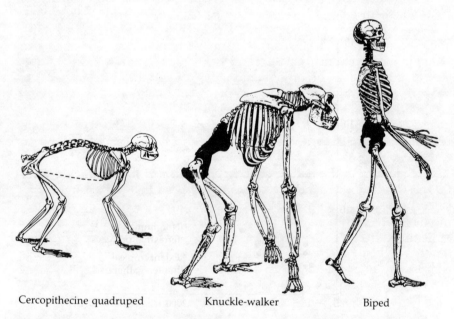

Cercopithecine quadruped   Knuckle-walker   Biped

Figure 7.13   Catarrhines terrestrial locomotor systems: (a) cercopithecine
quadrupedalism, (b) African ape knuckle-walking and
(c) hominid bipedalism (from Weiss & Mann 1975)

the lower region, and has taken on an S-shaped curve to facilitate weight transmission. The cranium is also modified, with the foramen magnum moved to a more basal position. Bipedalism is written throughout the anatomy of the hominids. The evolutionary inference that must be drawn is that becoming bipedal is a radical departure from modern primates (it should not necessarily be assumed that it is such a radical departure from ancestral ones), and therefore indicates severe selective pressure.

As was briefly shown in Chapter 1, the earliest evidence for bipedalism is associated with the earliest known hominid – *Australopithecus afarensis* – suggesting that locomotor changes occurred close to the base of the lineage. The evidence comes from two sources. First is the actual cranial and postcranial morphology of the specimens that Johanson recovered from the Hadar in Ethiopia, dated close to 3.0 Ma old (Johanson, Taieb & Coppens 1982). In particular, the partial skeleton AL 288, colloquially known as 'Lucy', indicates in its limb proportions and structure that it belonged to a hominid capable of upright, bipedal locomotion. The second line of evidence comes from the footprints found in the volcanic ash at Laetoli in Tanzania. These tracks, dated to over 3.6 Ma old (Leakey, Hay et al. 1976; White & Harris 1977), show an extended sequence of bipedal footprints, lain down by three hominids. They represent the closest to proof it is possible to get that the early hominids were bipedal, or were at least fully capable of bipedal locomotion over considerable distances.

These data raise two questions. First, when did bipedalism evolve, and, second, was the bipedalism of the early hominids similar to that found in modern humans? With regard to the first of these questions, it is clear that bipedalism occurred sufficiently early for it to be considered to be part of the original adaptive shifts of the hominids. If the recent reports (Hill 1985) of a jaw of *A. afarensis* nearly 5 Ma old from Tabarin near Lake Baringo in Kenya are confirmed and extended to include postcranial material, then it is well possible that bipedalism occurred even earlier.

The question of the nature of early bipedalism is more difficult. Over the past decade the general consensus has been that the australopithecines possessed a form of bipedalism that was energetically and biomechanically very similar to that of modern humans, and that the few structural differences that could be observed led to only minor functional differences. The analysis of the material from Hadar has disrupted this consensus. Jungers and his co-workers (Jungers 1982; Jungers & Stern 1983; Stern & Susman 1983) have suggested that *A. afarensis* was not a biped in the same sense as modern humans. Their principal line of argument is that the femur of AL 200 (Lucy), when adjusted for equivalence of size, is the same length as that of a chimpanzee. Furthermore, the forelimb is relatively long. They argue that the pattern of locomotion of this species involved considerable movement in an arboreal environment. The importance of movement in the trees is confirmed, they argue, by the fact that the phalanges of *A. afarensis* are curved, a trait normally found in arboreal primates. They would thus argue that at this early stage – that is, between about 5.0 and 2.5 Ma ago – hominids had not adopted a fully bipedal form of locomotion.

This view has been challenged by Wolpoff (1983), Lovejoy (1979, 1980) and Latimer (1984). Wolpoff argues that Jungers (1982) failed to take allometric factors fully into account, and suggests that the femur of AL 200 is as long as would be expected for an individual of that body weight, as leg length decreases disproportiontely fast with diminishing body size. He states that 'Lucy's limb proportions cannot be construed as evidence against a fully modern pattern of bipedalism' (1983: 449). Latimer (1984) also questions Jungers and Stern's results, arguing that joint morphology is a better indicator of locomotor pattern than limb proportions, and in this respect *A. afarensis* is most similar to modern humans.

This debate has still to be fully resolved, but certain limited conclusions can be drawn. Principal among these is that whether or not the earliest known hominids had exactly the same form of bipedalism as modern humans, their anatomy has been fundamentally reorganized for bipedal locomotion. *Australopithecus afarensis* was more bipedal than any living hominoid, and in all likelihood, was a habitual biped more than anything else. Furthermore, the primitive characteristics related to arboreality found in the forelimb do not necessarily indicate time spent in the trees. As McHenry (1982) has pointed out, selection on the forelimb is likely to be less intense than on the hindlimb during the transition to bipedalism, and so it would be expected that an early biped would have a more specialized hindlimb than forelimb. This is exactly the pattern to be found in *A. afarensis*.

With this evidence for the early presence of bipedalism, it is possible to turn now to the question of why bipedalism should have evolved rather than one of the other locomotor forms found among the other terrestrial primates. As McHenry (1978) has documented, bipedalism has been accounted for by a variety of hypotheses: savanna-dwelling (Darwin 1871), tool-making (Washburn 1950, 1960, 1967), feeding adaptations (DeBrul 1962; Jolly 1970), carrying (Hewes 1961, 1964; Kortlandt 1967; Lovejoy 1981), predation (Ravey 1978), display (Livingstone 1962), thermoregulation (Wheeler 1984, 1985); and bioenergetics (Taylor & Rowntree 1973). These explanations really fall into two separate categories – those that account for the origins of bipedalism in terms of its direct locomotor advantages, and then those that see it as a byproduct of other selective factors, usually to do with the advantages of having a specialized grasping forelimb.

Experiments and observations on the relative efficiencies of different locomotor systems have not been conclusive. At normal speeds, capuchins and chimpanzees use the same energy levels for both quadrupedalism and bipedalism (Taylor & Rowntree 1973). At maximum speeds, however, bipedalism turns out to be about twice as energetically expensive as true mammalian quadrupedalism (Taylor, Schmidt-Nielson & Raab 1970). However, no primate locomotor system is as efficient as the typical quadrupedalism of dogs and bovids, and, furthermore, Rodman & McHenry (1980) suggest, it is normal speeds, not maximum speeds that are critical. According to their data the human gait is more efficient at normal speeds than chimpanzee quadrupedalism or bipedalism, and, other things being equal, would therefore be expected to evolve.

Speed is not the only consideration in determining the bioenergetics of locomotor systems. The length of time over which activities have to be maintained is also critical. It has been argued (Campbell 1974; Nabakov & McClean 1980; Bortz 1985) that a characteristic of modern humans is their ability to run over very long distances and for prolonged periods of time. This *endurance* contrasts both with other hominoids and with other animals that are incapable of prolonged running (Gericho & Hoffmeyr 1976). Hoffmeyr, Louw & du Preeze (1973) report that zebra collapse after being chased over 800 yards (780 m), and ethnographers have reported on the ability of hunter–gatherers to run down prey until they are exhausted (Dorman 1925; Silberbauer 1981; Schell 1981, quoted in Bortz 1985). These data would suggest that the energetic advantages of bipedalism lie in long-distance endurance. It should be noted that this conforms to the expectations of longer distance foraging associated with increased body size discussed in Chapter 5, and also with the model of extreme thermal stress elaborated in Chapter 4. There it was argued that in their thermoregulatory characteristics hominids represented a form of extreme specialization. Intense diurnal activity, including prolonged running and walking to and between resource patches, is likely to have been a major selective pressure leading to the evolution of bipedalism among hominids. Furthermore, Bortz (1985) has argued that this level of physical exercise will stimulate brain growth, and consequently may have acted as selective pressure for hominid encephalization.

Prolonged and long-distance foraging might have been the selective pressure leading to bipedalism, but directional change in evolution is affected not just by current selective pressure, but also by evolutionary history (see page 59). Evolutionary history determines the presence or absence of appropriate biological raw material on which selection can operate, and so influences the level of preadaptation. Thus, the differences in locomotor behaviour of the terrestrial primates may be influenced not only by their immediate selective environment but also by their evolutionary heritage.

Various authors have considered the necessary preadaptations of bipedalism (Washburn 1960; Stern 1971, 1976; Tuttle 1975). Many of these ideas have been incorporated by Aiello (1981) in an elegant analysis, following work of Rose (1973), showing that there is some relationship between body size and locomotor pattern in living and fossil primates (Fig. 7.14). Of particular importance, though, is the distinction she makes between above-branch and below-branch feeding among arboreal species. Below-branch feeding seems to involve the necessary preadaptations of all the living hominoid species. Some relationship between feeding behaviour, locomotor pattern and body size seems to occur, with a tendency for below-branch feeding being confined to the larger end of the size spectrum. Among living species it occurs among the gibbons, the orang-utan and the New World semibrachiators. However, Aiello has shown that in terms of limb proportions and morphology, the medium-sized Miocene Hominoidea (*Proconsul* sp. and *Paidopithex rheanus*) are similar to the below-branch feeders. This fact, and the absence of below-branch feeders among the Cercopithecidae, is of considerable significance.

Some idea of the processes of differentiation of locomotor system among the terrestrial primates can be gained from this distinction (Fig. 7.15). The early catarrhines included both above- and below-branch feeders. The ancestral cercopithecoid forms, though, were entirely above-branch feeders. Thus, when a shift to a more terrestrial adaptation occurred among some of them, they lacked the necessary preadaptations for bipedalism. Their evolutionary history, perhaps reinforced by selection for rapid antipredator movement on account of their small body size, pushed them in the direction of quadrupedalism rather than bipedalism.

The history of the Hominoidea was rather different. Owing to their early and greater diversity in the early and middle Miocene, both their body size and their locomotor patterns were more highly differentiated. Both above-and below-branch feeders occurred, in a size-related pattern. 'Monkey-like' quadrupedalism (possibly including terrestrality) occurred among these early forms, as a consequence of above-branch feeding. For below-branch feeders, on the other hand, the quadrupedal option was closed off. For the potential terrestrial primate, bipedalism was the main possibility unless constrained by other factors. Among the hominids these other factors were apparently not significant. Among the African pongids, on the other hand, they were. In particular, given a more forested environment the maintenance of an arboreal capability was important. Semibrachiation associated with terrestrial knuckle-walking is the appropriate solution, allowing both terrestrial movement and arboreal feeding. Thus, the smaller African pongids, the common and pygmy chimpanzees (*Pan troglodytes* and *P. paniscus*), are more semi-terrestrial knuckle-walkers. This may in part account for the close similarity between the early australopithecines and the pygmy chimpanzee (Zihlman, Cronin et al. 1978).

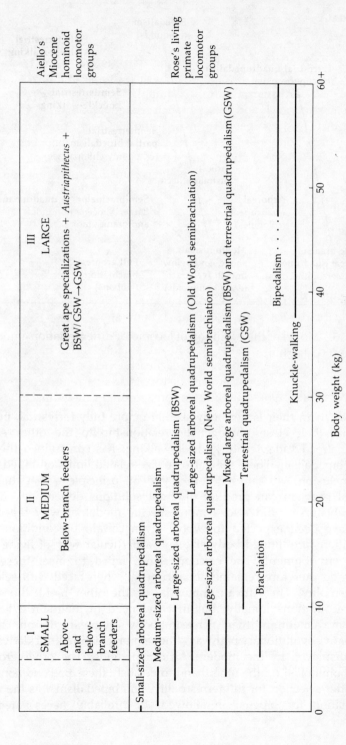

Figure 7.14 Body size and locomotor systems of primates (BSW = branch sitting and walking; GSW = ground standing and walking) (after Rose 1973; Aiello 1981).

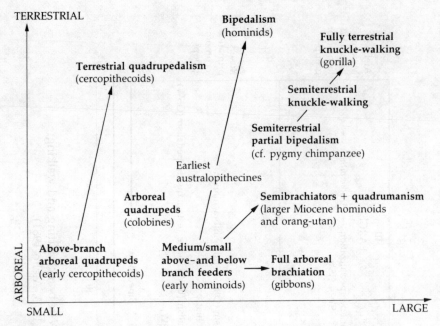

Figure 7.15   Model of the evolution of locomotor differentiation among
catarrhines.

Gorillas, with their larger body size, are more fully terrestrial, but it is
likely that their close phylogenetic relationship to the other African
pongids, already adapted to knuckle-walking, has constrained the evolution of bipedalism. There may also be size-related limits on bipedalism.

In conclusion, we can see both a general principle – that the same
ecological problem can produce different solutions depending on evolutionary history – and also a more specific model of why bipedalism
might have been expected to evolve given certain preconditions. The
preconditions are limited body size and a particular way of living in an
arboreal environment. The cercopithecines failed to meet these conditions, and therefore remained quadrupedal when faced with selection
for terrestriality. The African hominids, on the other hand, did satisfy
these preconditions initially, but first the need to maintain a level of
arboreal movement and then increasing body size meant the pursuing of
an alternative evolutionary pathway – the semibrachiating/knuckle-walking
system displayed by the modern African pongids. The other group of
African hominids, on the other hand, did satisfy these preconditions, and
came under selection for full terrestriality. Full bipedalism was the result.
Preadaptation for bipedalism allowed, or probably necessitated, the

modification of the forelimb for full dexterity, thus allowing, as a consequence of this particular adaptive solution, the development of the other
traits so often linked with bipedalism – tool-making, carrying, feeding,
etc. Given this model, perhaps the most fascinating question that remains
to be answered is that of the extent to which other hominoids came under
similar selective pressure and so started down the path towards bipedalism.

Shelter

Ground-dwelling brings with it problems other than that of locomotion.
Trees act not just as a source of food for arboreal animals, they are also
places of refuge and shelter. What, though, does a diurnal terrestrial
primate do at night and in times of danger?

The basic answer for the living terrestrial primates is that they, too, will
make use of trees wherever possible (Altmann & Altmann 1970). Both
species of chimpanzee will make nests for sleeping in trees at night, and
will often flee into the trees when threatened. Virtually all species of
baboon and macaque will, whenever possible, occupy sleeping trees. As
the Altmanns have pointed out (1970), these sleeping groves are important focal points in the activity patterns of the baboons of Amboseli
National Park in Kenya. The vervet monkey (*Cercopithecus aethiops*), the
most terrestrial of the *Cercopithecus* species, will also escape to trees from
ground predators and sleep in them (Struhsaker 1967). The patas monkey
(*Erythrocebus patas*), despite living in areas with very few trees, will
endeavour to find some at night (Hall 1966). This often necessitates the
breaking up of the social group, with individuals scattered widely
through the trees that are available. Only the gorilla, the largest of the
primates, consistently makes ground nests (Fossey & Harcourt 1977). This
species is constrained from climbing by its size, which also frees it from
the threat of predators with the exception of modern humans.

What happens, though, when trees are not available, as might occur in
the more open regions of the savanna? Baboons, when denied access to
trees, will seek other protected areas. Hamadryas baboons (*Papio
hamadryas*) in Ethiopia (Kummer 1968) frequently sleep on the cliff faces of
the fault scarps of the African Rift Valley, and similar habits can be
observed among olive baboons (*Papio anubis*) at Gilgil in Central Kenya;
and in South Africa caves are sometimes used. Essentially, it seems that
when trees are not available other locations are sought that might provide
the same level of protection from terrestrial predators.

A broad generalization from these observations might be that terrestrial
primates will seek trees at night and at times of danger. When these are
not available they will find alternatives that might offer similar levels of
safety – cliffs, caves, etc. Where either trees or other locations are in short

supply, as they might well be in some areas, then severe competition for refuge areas might lead to selection for alternative solutions.

The competition will be driven by several factors. First and most important will be the declining availablity of trees with the decline of woodland areas and the colonization of increasingly open habitats. As will be discussed in Chapter 9, the period of the Pliocene and early Pleistocene is one in which there were many species of terrestrial primate, and this diversity might have increased the levels of competition. Alternative behaviours, such as the use of ground nests, might well have been adaptive as a means of avoiding competition. A second factor is the increased ranging behaviour associated with increased body size and terrestriality (see above, page 168). With longer day ranges and more movement around a home range, a premium would be placed on cognitive skills; learning, spatial memory and problem-solving (see also Cant & Temerin 1984). Examples of such cognitive skills are the mental maps of hamadryas baboons that allow for efficient foraging in an environment where the availability of water and sleeping sites is extremely low (Sigg & Stolba 1981). Such cognitive skills can then be expanded to solve further problems – such as how best to locate and utilize ground nests and other terrestrial focal points. Pressure for these would be enhanced further by the hominids' increasing specialization in locomotor form and larger body size; thus, trees would become a less-ideal place of shelter for early hominids. Other factors may also be involved, such as an increasing risk of parasite infestation in preferred sleeping tree groves (Hausfater & Meade 1982), but, overall, scarcity of sleeping trees can be expected to lead to selection for increased ground-nesting among specialized terrestrial primates.

Among modern humans, 'ground-nesting' places (i.e. home bases and settlements) are universal and central to many aspects of social and economic behaviour. Although with hindsight, the development of a home base seems to be inevitable for hominids, it remains to be shown when and how this adaptive change occurred.

Most evolutionary developments are based on modifications of pre-existing adaptations or changes in function of existing ones. For example, the evolution of bird flight is usually thought to have resulted from the modification of feathers from their original insulating function to an aerodynamic one. Similarly, ground-sheltering and home bases are likely to have been a development of function of pre-exisiting foci of diurnal activity. Several such foci would already have existed. One example of this is the use made by primates of shade while resting during the day between feeding bouts (see Chapter 5 for a discussion of diurnal activity patterns). Another would be water sources, utilized each day, and a third would be areas rich in food resources, for example a particular vegetation area or, if meat-eating were practised, the carcass of an animal. However, with this last, and with water-holes, the presence of predators may have been a deterrent to increasing the amount of time spent there. These focal areas would be prime places for ground nests.

The development of focal points on the landscape for both diurnal and nocturnal activity, and the possibility of combining several activities at the same point, would provide the basis both for the solution of the problem of shelter in a treeless terrestrial environment and for the development of the home base. The suggestion being made here is that these home bases were a solution to the problem of diurnal and nocturnal shelter, and that developments made possible by the presence of a focal point for activities (food-sharing, increased social activity, etc.) would have been incidental byproducts of this development.

This suggestion contrasts with some recent explanations of the development of home bases. Isaac (1978a,b, 1981, 1983) has suggested that home bases are an essential component of hominid foraging patterns. Incorporation of meat into the diet, he has argued, depends on the development of a division of labour. The separation of foraging activities would have resulted in a premium on food-sharing, which in turn would depend on the presence of a central place to which food could be transported for sharing. A home base, therefore, would be central to the development of early hominid foraging behaviour.

This model has been discussed widely, and criticized extensively by Binford (1981, 1984). Criticisms have been directed partly at the assumption that meat-eating presupposes food-sharing or a division of labour, partly at the adequacy of the fossil and archaeological evidence. Potts (1984b) has argued that the early archaeological localities share little in common, other than the juxtaposition of animal bones and artefactual debris, with modern home bases. In fact, he argues, the areas where carcasses are located would be places where hominids would minimize rather than maximize their activities on account of the threat of interactions with large carnivores.

This critique would seem to undercut the possibility of areas of rich food resources being transformed into home bases. Potts (1984b) has suggested an alternative explanation. In a computer simulation he was able to show that an efficient way of exploiting carcasses, whether hunted or scavenged, would be to set up caches of stone tools (Fig. 7.16) – that is, areas where unmodified or modified stone tools would be left for future use. These caches would be distributed across the landscape, and carcasses transported to them when discovered. They would very soon resemble the Plio-Pleistocene archaeological sites, with accumulations of stone and bone. They would also be energetically efficient. Caching of stone tools and return to them, either with or without resources, has now been observed for chimpanzees in West Africa. Boesch & Boesch (1983) have reported such behaviour in relation to the explotation of palm oil nuts for which some populations use a stone hammer to gain access to the protein-rich kernel.

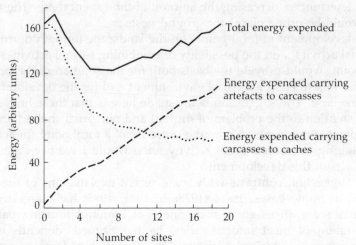

Figure 7.16   Computer simulation of early hominid foraging behaviour.
This simulation examines the relative costs of either carrying
artefacts to carcasses or transporting parts of the carcass to
caches of stone tools. Potts has suggested that the optimal
behaviour for a hominid would be to create such caches. See
text for discussion (from Potts 1984b).

Potts is keen to point out that these are not home bases. They are,
though, the antecedents of home bases, aggregations of stone artefacts
that would have acted as yet another spatial focus for early hominid
activity. But the extent to which these are 'real' caches, as opposed to the
byproducts of repeated utilization of certain areas of the landscape, is
uncertain. What Pott's model highlights, though, is that as foraging areas
increase, as has been argued consistently throughout this book, pressure
to discard and reuse material across the landscape is likely to increase. In
conjunction with the growing pressure to form ground nests, these points
on the landscape would become focal points for a variety of activities.

What we can see here is the convergence of several processes. On the
one hand is the need for shelter on the ground, on the other a change in
foraging behaviour brought about by the development of tool-making as
an aspect of meat-eating. The conjuction of these two were the antecedents of the home base – in other words, a central focus for several
activities and behaviours. The principal consequences of this would have
been a gradual shift away from multiple use of stone caches as part of an
orthodox pattern of primate foraging, towards one in which foraging
involves starting from and returning to a single central place, as is the
case with modern hunter–gatherers (see Fig. 7.17).

A pertinent question, though, is at what stage does this conjunction –
that is, the development of central-place foraging – occur? The structure

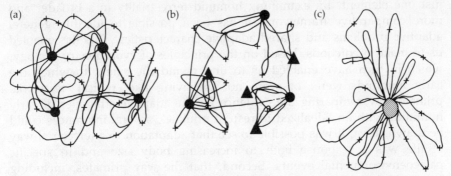

Figure 7.17 Spatial patterns of foraging behaviour resulting from different organizational systems and types of spatial foci. (a) Foraging with sleeping areas (●) as only focal point. (b) Foraging with separate caches of stone tools and/or areas for resource-processing (▲) and sleeping (●). (c) Central-place foraging by modern hunter–gatherers; all activities except actual food procurement occur at a central place.

of some of the early archaeological sites at Olduvai, Koobi Fora, etc. suggests the transport of either carcasses/bones and/or artefacts to a focal point. This might form the basis for central-place foraging, although not necessarily for all the related modern human behaviours associated with this. Whether australopithecines and/or *Homo habilis* were still sleeping in trees or other shelters, or that sleeping areas were distinct from these activity areas is uncertain.

With the appearance of *Homo erectus* the density of artefactual material increases markedly, and it is possible that fire makes its first anthropogenic appearance (Gowlett, Harris et at. 1981). The quantity of bone material is often very high. However, in a recent analysis Binford (1984) has argued that there is no indication of use of animal products (i.e. butchery practices) or the development of a home base until the appearance of anatomically modern humans. Although some of his analysis can be questioned (Scott 1986), it is not yet possible to place a certain date on the development of a home base in the modern sense. The structure of these localities undoubtedly differs from that of modern hunter–gatherers, but the gradual increase in the density of material, both artefactual and osteological, indicates a trend towards more spatially focused behaviour among early hominids during the Pleistocene. At present, it is only possible to conclude that early on in hominid evolution the path towards increasingly centralized activities had already begun.

We have seen in this chapter that terrestriality is an important trend in primate evolution in the Old World, a trend in which hominids represent just one element. By examining hominid terrestriality in a broader and more comparative framework, it has been possible to identify general adaptive problems and shared adaptive characteristics. This has enabled us to make predictions, based on the principles of evolutionary ecology, which in turn have enabled us to understand the extent to which the early hominids were, or were not, behaving like 'typical' terrestrial primates. By comparing the evidence for the adaptive strategies of early hominids with an 'idealized terrestrial primate', several inferences could be drawn. First, it was possible to see that adaptation to a terrestrial way of life was a response both to increasing body size and to specific palaeoenvironmental events. Second, that the way primates, including hominids, have adapted to a terrestrial way of life has depended not just on the immediate selective constraints of their new environment, but also on their evolutionary history. And, third, that in many ways hominids do conform to the physical, ecological and behavioural patterns found among the terrestrial primates as a whole, but that there are also ways in which they represent a novel adaptation. In particular, the ways in which the hominids have solved two major problems of terrestriality – locomotion and shelter, through bipedalism and the use of ground nests – have served as the principal basis for the evolution of many human and hominid characteristics.

Although these solutions are consistent with the expectations of evolutionary ecology, they nonetheless represent an extreme not found elsewhere. In explaining the radical nature of many hominid characteristics, emphasis has been placed on the changes in hominid foraging behaviour. In this, through various means discussed in the previous chapters, early hominids have departed from the adaptations of the other catarrhine primates. It is therefore necessary to look more closely at the nature of their foraging behaviour in the context of the environment in which they lived – in the seasonal, semi-arid African savanna. The early hominids came under particularly acute selective pressures.

8 Hominids in a seasonal environment

In discussing bipedalism it was suggested that both immediate selective pressures and evolutionary history contributed to hominid adaptations. Although the tropical origins of the primates, the constraints of body size and the pathways to bipedalism reflect to a large extent the structural constraints of the past, on their own they cannot determine the direction of evolutionary change, which must rest with the requirements of the environments in which any animal lives. It is now pertinent to examine more closely the specific environmental problems that hominids faced, and, in particular, the constraints that operated on the way in which they obtained the resources necessary for survival.

Although the broad tropical adaptations of hominids have already been discussed, the exact potential and problems of the specific tropical environment in which they lived have yet to be discussed. From the ecological character of this environment will derive the survival problems to which hominid adaptation should be a solution. The particular environment in which the fossil hominids seem to have lived, was the semi-arid, savanna of Africa. One of the principal ecological characteristics of this environment is its marked seasonal variability, and this has had a significant effect on hominid evolution.

This chapter will therefore look at the evidence for the environment of early hominids, the pattern of seasonal availability of resources, the ways in which hominids may have exploited these resources, and the evolutionary consequences of this. First, though, it is necessary to discuss how foraging strategies become established within and between populations. The classic mechanism through which this occurs is competition.

Competition

The nature of competition

'Competition occurs when two or more.... organismic units interfere with or inhibit one another' (Pianka 1978:114). Such inhibition or interference is usually in relation to some resource that both require and yet is in limited supply. The competition between the two may take place through the efficiency with which each organismic unit utilizes the resource, with little or no direct interaction between them. Alternatively, it may involve active interference, where one or both organismic units disrupt in some way the behaviour of the other (Pianka 1978).

The conditions necessary for competition to take place are relatively simple. Resources, of whatever sort, must be limited in some way such that demand exceeds availability. From this simple condition flows several important ecological consequences.

The principal consequence is that competition is nearly always disadvantageous to all the organismic units involved. As a result of either increased time/energy costs or reduced access to resources, either fitness and/or population levels will be reduced. Many observations and experiments have shown that organisms do better in the absence of their competitors (e.g. Crowell 1962; Grant 1972). This means that wherever possible it should pay an organism to avoid competition.

It follows, therefore, that resources should be used in such a way that competition is avoided or minimized. Competitor avoidance is a major tenet of modern ecology (Colinvaux 1973). The costs of competition are such that it is usually more beneficial to occupy a small area of 'ecological space' exclusively than to share a larger one with other populations. By so avoiding competitors an organismic unit will come to occupy a unique ecological niche. This is the basis for the partitioning of the ecological world into separate niches occupied by different species using different foraging strategies; ultimately, it is also the basis for evolutionary diversity. The separation of species into different niches as a result of the effects of competition is sometimes referred to as the 'Gause exclusion principle' (Colinvaux 1973), which states that no two species can occupy exactly the same ecological niche indefinitely; one will utilize the niche more efficiently than the other, and will thus come to expand at the expense of the other until extinction occurs.

At its most basic, the Gause exclusion principle is somewhat tautological and therefore of little analytical value, but it does direct attention to the question of how much overlap of adaptive behaviour can be tolerated under different conditions. It also points the way to another ecological consequence of competition, which is that death for the individual and extinction for the species are the products of competitive interactions for the loser in any situation, and monopolization of resources, rather than the sharing of them, are the products for the winner.

A final ecological, or perhaps more strictly behavioural outcome of a situation where resources are limited is the development of active interference on the part of one or more organismic units. By actively interfering, rather than just foraging more efficiently, an individual or population may gain disproportionate access to a resource. Examples of such interference are known among the large terrestrial carnivores (Kruuk 1972; Schaller 1972), and interference based on toxins is known to occur widely among plants.

However, although many structural and functional aspects of an ecosystem may derive from the effects of competition, important questions and qualifications remain. What has been presented above is the classic view of the role of competition, but it has not been accepted uncritically. Three questions in particular can be asked. First, at what level does competition occur? Second, how important is competition in ecology and evolution? And, third, how does competition determine foraging behaviour?

The first of these questions emphasizes the need to be aware of the different levels at which processes operate in ecology. Competition can occur between individuals within a population, between separate populations within a species, and between species. Competition between conspecifics is likely to be the most intense, as their requirements will overlap to the greatest degree. Furthermore, conspecifics also compete for reproduction, as well as food and space, thus adding another dimension. The intensity of competition at this level, however, is likely to be mitigated by the close degree of genetic relatedness and the high costs of interference for all individuals. Competition will also occur between species, as they must share the same space and limited energy and materials. In this case, though, the intensity of the competition is going to be eased by the differing requirements that different species have, and the low frequency of interaction.

The importance of competition

The character of competition will therefore vary with level, with the most intense occurring between individuals of the same species. The second question – the significance of competition in determining adaptation – is thus most problematic at the interspecific level, where there is considerable controversy about how frequently competitive interactions occur (Wiens 1977; Diamond 1978; Pianka 1978; Schoener 1983).

The view that interspecific competition is significant can be traced back to Darwin's formulation of the theory of natural selection (see Chapter 3). Critics, however, have suggested various ways in which competition between species either cannot be shown to occur or is unlikely to occur. For the former of these two, several authors have used simulation techniques to show that community structures thought to be the product of competition can be produced by random processes. Competition might therefore be a superfluous mechanism, and the partitioning of the biological world into discrete niches can occur without it. Although these studies do not preclude the existence of interspecific competition, other authors have argued that on biological grounds competition is seldom likely to occur in a significant form. The main basis for saying this lies in the variable nature of environments. According to Wiens (1977), environments fluctuate to such an extent (because of both biotic and abiotic factors) that populations are seldom at carrying capacity, and therefore competition for resources is unlikely to take place. Only occasionally in 'crunch periods' would food or space be in short supply, and although competition might then occur, the subsequent laxity of the variable environment is likely to allow the population to drift back to its original position. Another line of reasoning against the significance of competition is that predators act to keep the populations below carrying capacity, and therefore again competition for resources is prevented from occurring (Connell 1975).

The case against the importance of competition is therefore that either predators or environmental fluctuations keep populations below a level where resources become scarce. However, although there are circumstances where these conditions might hold, they cannot be said to be a general description of the whole biological world. The variability of the environment does not lead to no competition at all, but to variability in the level of competition through time. The degree of competitive interaction between species will vary according to the rate of fluctuations in the environment and the degree of overlap between their requirements. As long as 'crunch periods' occur sufficiently frequently in relation to the generation length of the organism, then competitive efficiency is likely to be an influential factor. As most environmental variability is seasonal, this condition would normally hold. And the degree of niche overlap will depend partly on the environment and partly on the degree of evolutionary and ecological divergence that has taken place between species. Thus species can be expected to undergo periods of both intense and lax competition.

A model of competition

Given, then, that interspecific competition is significant in ecological terms, but is by no means constant, how may it be expected to affect foraging behaviour? An answer to this question, based on variability in environment, has been provided by Schoener (1983). Although they are not discrete, it is possible to identify two phases or conditions between which an individual will oscillate during its lifetime. These are periods of scarcity and periods of plenty (Fig. 8.1). During the former, competition is high; during the latter, it is low. As the environment becomes more

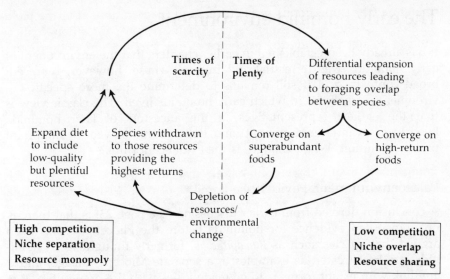

Figure 8.1   Model of competition in a temporally variable (i.e. seasonal) environment (based on Schoener 1983).

plentiful, different resources expand at different rates. Species will converge on these newly abundant resources, and there will be a high degree of overlap. In particular, species will concentrate either on resources that are superabundant, regardless of their overall value, or on resources that give a high return in relation to effort. Observations of a community at this time will show great overlap and the sharing of resources. However, as times get lean again, either because of resource depletion caused by an increasing population or because of a changing environment, these resources will no longer be available or accessible. During this phase, species will withdraw to those resources that offer the highest returns, and because of the high costs of competition these resources will often be those to which they have exclusive access. High competition will thus lead to competitive avoidance, interference, monopolization and extinction.

This model has some strong points. It accounts for the partitioning of the environment, yet within a framework of variable environments. Furthermore, it can operate on several timescales, from short-term seasonal and annual variations (ecological time) to long-term patterns of change (evolutionary time). More importantly, it links the principle of competition to that of optimization discussed in Chapter 3, and thus allows competitive characteristics to affect foraging behaviour. The ways in which this link may have been important in the evolution of hominids are the central concern of the rest of this chapter.

The early hominid environment

It has already been established in earlier chapters that the environment of early hominids was terrestrial and tropical. These, however, represent broad contexts, and it still remains to determine the more specific environment, or habitat, in which early hominids lived. The classic view is that the earliest representatives of the ancestors of later hominids lived in a savanna environment, and that this his played an important part in evolution. What, though, is the evidence for this?

Palaeoenvironmental evidence

A conclusion derived from earlier discussion (see page 23) is that there is no undisputed evidence for hominids before the Pliocene. It has been argued that species such as *Ramapithecus*, formerly thought to be hominids, are best treated as examples of a separate Miocene lineage, and if any link with extant forms is to be made it lies with the orang-utan. It is thus with the australopithecines of the Pliocene and early Pleistocene that a consideration of environmental context must begin. Furthermore, when the distribution of the earliest unambiguous hominids is examined (see Fig. 2.6), it can be seen that they are confined solely to sub-Saharan Africa and, more specifically, to the eastern and southern regions. These areas, which constitute 'high Africa' (Grove 1967), are today characterized by a climate that is dry by comparison with the central and western portions of the continent, and by an environment that varies from woodland through to open grassland except in a few localized parts. It does not necessarily follow, though, that the same environments occurred in the Plio-Pleistocene.

A battery of techniques are available for reconstructing palaeoenvironments (Butzer 1972; Raup & Stanley 1978) although these are seldom highly resolved or free from errors caused by taphonomical biases (Behrensmeyer & Hill 1980; Shipman 1983). For the South African and East African sites both sediments and fossils have been used. In parts of East Africa pollen has been recovered, but the principal environmental indicator has been the macrofauna. Detailed reconstructions of local environment have been made (see especially Hay 1976 on Olduvai Gorge), but Table 8.1 summarizes the main palaeoenvironmental evidence for the African Plio-Pleistocene.

These 'static' reconstructions may be placed within the pattern of ecological variability described briefly in Chapter 5 (see page 107). There it was shown that tropical environments vary in relation to rainfall, and that the critical parameters of rainfall – annual mean and distribution – are closely related (see Figs 5.4 and 5.5). From this it is possible to plot the Plio-Pleistocene sites against climatic parameters and in relation to the modern environmental mosaic (Fig. 8.2). The evidence would seem to

Table 8.1 Palaeoenvironmental reconstructions of early hominid localities in Africa

Locality	Palaeoenvironment
Tabarin	Lake margin, with locally variable savanna elements (Hill, Drake et al. 1985)
Middle Awash	Fluvial conditions with extensive tectonic activity associated with the formation of the East African Rift Valley (Kalb et al. 1982: Clark & Kurashina 1979; Clark et al. 1984)
Laetoli	Grassland savanna with well-defined wet and dry seasons (Hay 1981)
Hadar	Lake and associated floodplain, with braided streams and rivers (Aronson & Taieb 1981; Gray 1980)
Omo (Shungura)	After 2.1 Ma ago dry thorn savanna flanking river banks with gallery forest and swamps; before this date the environment was probably more forested (Bonnefille 1976, 1979: Brown 1981)
Koobi Fora	Before about 1.6 Ma ago, a fresh lake with floodplains, gallery forest and dry-thorn savanna; during later times the lake fluctuated from fresh to brackish (Isaac 1984)
Olduvai	Salt lake with surrounding floodplains with seasonal streams and rivers and dry grassland savanna; tectonic changes after 1.5 Ma ago resulted in the drying up of the lake (Hay 1976, 1981: Isaac 1984)
Peninj	Open grassland surrounding a salt lake, fed by fresh rivers (Isaac 1984)
Chesowanja	A small lake with surrounding floodplain and grassland (Bishop, Hill & Pickford 1978: Isaac 1984)
Transvaal	Makapansgat, Sterkfontein, Swartkrans, Kromdraai, and Taung: all these were mosaic savanna environments, with Makapansgat Member 3 and Sterkfontein Member 4 being less open (more bush/woodland) than Swartkrans Mb1 and Sterkfontein Member 5 – this suggests a trend from wetter to drier conditions through time (Vrba 1975, 1976, 1985)

suggest that hominids were living in what may be described as the drier or semi-arid range of African environments. The known fossil localities fall between mean annual rainfall levels of approximately 1500 and 300 mm per year, with 4–10 dry months per year. In environmental terms, this suggests a range of habitats from seasonal forest at one extreme, through wooded savanna to open savanna. Most of the sites fall within either wooded savanna or tree and bush open savanna. Only one

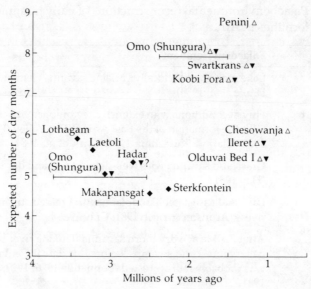

Figure 8.2   Seasonal context of African early hominid localities (see text for discussion). The vertical axis shows the estimated length of the dry season based on the palaeoenvironmental reconstructions: ♦ gracile australopithecines;/, ▵ robust australopithecines; ▾ *Homo*.

site – Peninj in Tanzania – exhibits the characteristics of full grass savanna. There is no noticeable chronological patterning to the environmental context of the fossil localities, and only slight geographical sorting. Most of the South African sites seem to be at the wetter end of the environmental spectrum.

Habitat preference

From this it would seem reasonable to conclude that the early hominids preferred a relatively dry open environment, with only limited tree and canopy cover and plant forms dominated by grasses. However, before accepting this conclusion, two alternative possibilities should perhaps be mentioned. The first is that the reconstructions of the environment pertain to 'macroenvironments', and that hominids occupied rather specific 'microhabitats' within them. In particular, they may have been confined to more enclosed gallery forest along permanant waterways. Certainly, such a possibility exists, but in areas of East Africa today the area of tree cover around lakes and rivers is usually extremely limited, and unlikely to offer a suitable habitat for a wide-ranging species, although it would undoubtedly form an important part of it.

The second possibility is that for taphonomical reasons only the drier extreme of the hominid environmental range is represented in the fossil record. The hominids we know of might therefore be the marginal populations excluded by competition from the more favoured wetter regions. Although it is true that the fossil record from the wetter regions of Africa is extremely poor, and therefore it is difficult to test this hypothesis directly, it is not very probable. It is clear from the archaeological record of the later periods of the Pleistocene that as hominids spread through the other parts of the Old World, it was open environments that they occupied preferentially, and certainly there is no evidence for hominids living in tropical rainforests until well into the late Pleistocene. Given the ubiquity of archaeological material (especially stone tools) from a range of drier tropical and subtropical environments throughout the early and middle Pleistocene, it is improbable that the preferred habitat of earlier hominids was tropical forest.

Thus the most likely interpretation of the palaeoenvironmental evidence is that the early hominid localities were in a wooded and more open savanna environment. Although the possibility that hominids were living elsewhere cannot definitively be excluded, we know for certain that they were living in these environments, and it is therefore not unreasonable to examine the type of ecological problems they would have had to solve.

Savanna ecology

The term savanna has been applied to those regions of the tropics where grass is the principal component of the flora and there may be an open canopy of trees or shrubs (Harris 1980). Considerable confusion and ambiguity have been associated with the word and the habitat, in terms of whether it is a vegetational or a climatic concept, whether it is an anthropogenic or natural climax habitat, and whether the term applies to communities outside the tropics. Most of these issues have now been more or less satisfactorily resolved. Most authorities recognize the savanna as a long-established tropical habitat, with distinctive vegetation, occurring in regions where there is a pronounced dry season (Harris 1980:7). Open savanna grasslands, which occupy 11 per cent of the global land surface, occur because of the limitations on plant productivity caused by prolonged periods without rain.

Savanna occurs in tropical regions receiving between 250 and 2000 mm of rain per annum, and with a dry season lasting between 2.5 and 10 months in any year. These areas are also characterized by considerable variability in the amount and distribution of rain from year to year. Further variation is produced by differences in soil and geological substructure, which can result in irregular runoff. In altitude, savanna vegetation may occur from sea level up to 2000 m, but the topography is normally flat or gently undulating. Owing to the aridity of the environment, fires are common, and play a significant part in maintaining the structure of the plant communities (Harris 1980).

Savanna environments vary considerably in their vegetation. Although they all share the characteristic of continuous grass cover, they differ in other components. Tree cover may be almost continuous, grading down to isolated widely scattered trees; alternatively, bushes and shrubs may make up the non-graminaceous vegetation. Continuous, uninterrupted grassland also occurs (Fig. 8.3). This variation in vegetation depends on the frequency of rain, grazing and fire. Most of the production is above ground; productivity is variable but annual net primary production averages 1197 g m^{-1} yr^{-1} (Harris 1980: 17), which compares with figures of 2400 g m^{-1} yr^{-1} for tropical rainforest and 200 g m^{-1} yr^{-1} for deserts (Murphy 1974).

Although primary production is low, many savanna environments are characterized by a highly abundant and diverse large mammal fauna. Ungulate herbivores, often present as vast concentrated herds, are a distinctive and dramatic sight on African savannas today, and were so in other regions previously. Their biomass is directly related to mean annual rainfall (Coe, Cummings & Phillipson 1976) (Fig. 8.4). Species diversity is also high, with 20 or more species existing sympatrically in many regions. The use of the plant resources is highly partitioned according to plant types and sequences of grazing. The wealth of large herbivores is complemented by a relatively large number of carnivores.

Overall, then, the savanna is determined by the level of rainfall. As a result of the scarcity of moisture it provides low-quality plant foods but a considerable quantity of animal resources. However, probably the most

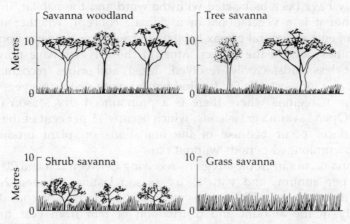

Figure 8.3   Types of savanna environment (after Harris 1980).

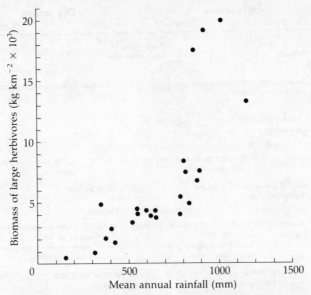

Figure 8.4 Relationship between biomass of large herbivores and mean annual rainfall in the semi-arid regions of sub-Saharan Africa (based on Coe, Cummings & Phillipson 1976).

significant character of this habitat is its marked seasonality. Both plant and animal resources vary dramatically in abundance, distribution and availability through the year, and this provides one of the most critical factors determining adaptation.

Seasonality and resource availability

The seasonal cycle

This pattern of high availability of animal and low availability of plant foods in the environments occupied by early hominids is enhanced when seasonal variation is taken into consideration. Figure 8.5 is a summary of the resource availability in a savanna environment in relation to a model wet/dry tropical cycle. This cycle may occur once or twice per year, and there will also be considerable variation in the lengths of each phase of the cycle. It does, though, usefully incorporate the main trends, and consequently the problems faced by early hominids.

Availability of plant foods in Africa has been studied recently by Peters, O'Brien & Box (1984). Plant production is highly seasonal. Grasses produce new shoots and stems after disturbance and at the onset of the

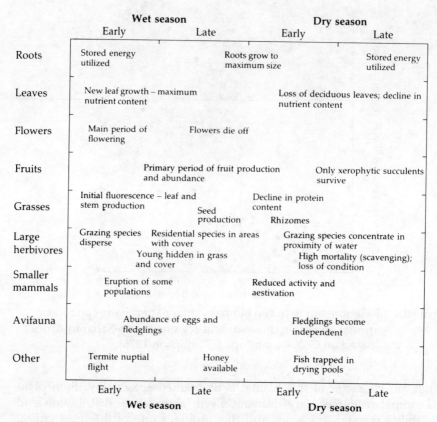

| | **Wet season** | | **Dry season** | |
	Early	Late	Early	Late
Roots	Stored energy utilized	Roots grow to maximum size		Stored energy utilized
Leaves	New leaf growth – maximum nutrient content		Loss of deciduous leaves; decline in nutrient content	
Flowers	Main period of flowering	Flowers die off		
Fruits		Primary period of fruit production and abundance	Only xerophytic succulents survive	
Grasses	Initial fluorescence – leaf and stem production	Seed production	Decline in protein content	
			Rhizomes	
Large herbivores	Grazing species disperse	Residential species in areas with cover	Grazing species concentrate in proximity of water	
		Young hidden in grass and cover	High mortality (scavenging); loss of condition	
Smaller mammals	Eruption of some populations		Reduced activity and aestivation	
Avifauna	Abundance of eggs and fledglings		Fledglings become independent	
Other	Termite nuptial flight	Honey available	Fish trapped in drying pools	
	Early	Late	Early	Late
	Wet season		**Dry season**	

Figure 8.5 Summary of availability of seasonal resources in tropical savanna Africa.

rains, when there is rapid growth. As the dry season progresses this slows down, the grass turns brown and protein content falls (Harper 1977). In perennials, new green production during the dry season may be stimulated by grazing and by burning. Among annual grasses seeds are set and leaf production comes to an abrupt end. For the plants with surface or subsurface storage organs (hemi-cryptophytes) production is concentrated in rhyzomes and corms (Harper 1977). Accordingly, during the wet season considerable green plant material is available, declining subsequently. In the early dry season, seeds, corms and rhyzomes may be available, although heavy consumption of these would place the vegetatively reproducing perennials at a selective advantage. During a prolonged dry season, green growth would disappear except in the proximity of permanant water. With regard to other plant types, these may best be considered in terms of leaves, roots, fruits and flowers. In most species of tropical plant, production of flowers and fruit occurs in the wet season (Hladik 1977), and these would be available for consump-

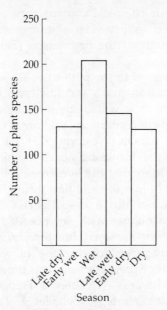

Figure 8.6 Number of edible plant species per season in 'dry' sub-Saharan Africa (data from Peters, O'Brien & Box 1984).

tion during this period and during the early part of the dry season (Fig. 8.6, Table 8.2). Some species react to prolonged drought by producing seeds and fruits (Harper 1977), resulting in local abundance of food in the extreme dry season (Lee 1968). Most tropical species are evergreen to maximize growth during the brief growing season, and thus leaves (which, in semi-arid environments are usually small) are perennially

Table 8.2 Number of plant food types eaten by baboons, chimpanzees and humans by seasons in Africa (from Peters, O'Brien & Box 1984); in parentheses are the numbers eaten when 'all year round' resources (which may include species for which there is no seasonal information) are excluded

	Season			
	Late dry/ Early wet	Wet	Late wet/ Early dry	Dry
Flowers	5 (5)	1 (1)	0 (0)	3 (3)
Fruits, etc.	48 (46)	118 (116)	73 (71)	51 (49)
Leaves	22 (7)	34 (19)	18 (3)	20 (5)
Underground parts	55 (0)	55 (0)	55 (0)	55 (0)
Total	130 (58)	208 (136)	146 (74)	129 (57)

available, although their chemical content may vary (Hladik 1977). The roots of some herbs act as dry-season storage systems, and so form a valuable resource throughout the dry season (Tanaka 1976; Peters et al. 1984; Vincent 1985).

Large herbivores respond to the pattern of seasonal variation in plants. These mammals depend on grass and low-level browse. Consequently, during the wet season they will disperse widely to exploit seasonally ephemeral growth, and concentrate around areas of permanant water and grazing during the dry season (Western 1975) (Fig. 8.7). The exception to this may be some of the browsing species which sometimes disperse during the dry season to exploit the evergreen foliage (Kingdon 1981).

The combined effect of loss of condition through a dwindling food base and consequently high mortality and spatial concentration of the second-ary biomass provides carnivores with rich possibilities for scavenging and predation during the dry season (Houston 1979). Although the large herbivores are more dispersed during the rainy season, many of the residential species produce their young at this time (Kingdon 1981). These are usually hidden in the grass (Delaney & Happold 1979), and may be exploited by a searching strategy (Schaller & Lowther 1969). Smaller animals may aestivate during the dry season and breed during the wet.

Other potential resources are insects' and birds' eggs/fledglings. Termites, which erupt in massive numbers in a nuptual flight at the onset

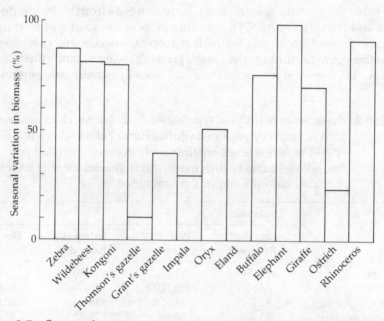

Figure 8.7   Seasonal variation in biomass of large animals in Amboseli National Park, Kenya (data from Western 1973).

of the rains (Thoillay 1970), are exploited during this brief period by both chimpanzees and contemporary human populations. Most birds lay their eggs either towards the end of the dry season or in the early wet season (Owen 1974). Although they place their nests to avoid predation, the eggs and young can be collected by primates (Teleki 1981). Once they are independent and flying, though, they would normally be immune from terrestrial predators.

It can be seen that resource availability varies markedly through the seasonal cycle. Survival in a savanna environment thus depends on strategies that ensure access to resources under conditions that differ markedly from one part of the year to another.

Responses to seasonality: a comparative approach

Given this pattern of seasonal food availability in a savanna environment, what adaptive strategies could feasibly be pursued by early hominids? This question can be approached in the context of the general model of competition presented at the beginning of this chapter, and in the light of the knowledge that primates, as a whole, are opportunistic omnivores in the sense that they can metabolize energy from a very broad range of resources (Harding 1981).

A model of adaptation to seasonal stress

A simple model of alternative 'coping strategies' for surviving a poor season can be formulated (Fig. 8.8). As a general rule, animals, when faced with a period of resource shortage, will cut down on non-essential activities. Energy expenditure will be concentrated on foraging behaviour, at the expense of other, particularly social activities. In this way, they may be able to 'hang on' until conditions improve. At one extreme, this

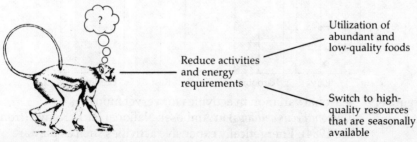

Figure 8.8   Alternative responses to a 'poor season'.

may involve complete hibernation or aestivation, but it is usually less marked.

Beyond this general adaptation are two alternative strategies. In the first, the poor season is coped with by incorporating into the diet resources of very low value (i.e. usually those with very high processing time and low nutritional quality, but which are plentiful). The costs of this strategy are increased foraging time. The other strategy is to incorporate into the diet high-quality resources that become abundant seasonally, but which would normally not be part of the repertoire because the costs of exploiting them might be high. This strategy involves a major switch in diet, and thus a major increase in the diversity of resources taken by an animal on an annual basis. This obviously depends on such resources being available, and, in the context of the savanna conditions in which early hominids were living, the complementary relationship between the availability of plant and animal foods is critical. Before looking at this in detail, though, it is appropriate to look at the existence of these coping strategies in non-human primates.

Primate seasonality

Reduction of activities in times of stress can be seen in various primate species. The most extreme is the dwarf lemur (*Cheriogaleus medius*), which has been reported to aestivate. They are able to survive inactive for long periods by building up fat reserves in their tails (Hladik, Charles-Dominique & Peters 1980). More common, though, is a reduction in

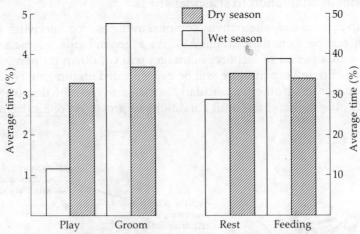

Figure 8.9 Seasonal variation in activities for vervet monkeys (*Cercopithecus aethiops*) in Amboseli National Park, Kenya (from Lee 1984). Energetically expensive activities such as play are reduced during the dry season.

energetically expensive social activity. For example, Lee (1984) has shown that vervet monkeys (*Cercopithecus aethiops*) will reduce the amount of time spent in play during the dry season (Fig. 8.9).

Both of the alternative strategies can also be observed among living non-human primates, on both short and long timescales. For example, the Kazakati chimpanzees studied by Suzuki (1969) incorporate into their diet during their poor season a greater diversity of plant foods than they do when times are good (Fig. 8.10). In this case they are exploiting lower quality resources into their diet, and becoming less-selective feeders. A similar pattern can be seen also among common chimpanzees (*Pan troglodytes*) of the Gombe in Tanzania and in Gabon (Hladik 1977), where the proportion of leaves in the diet increases during the dry season (Fig. 8.11). On a longer timescale, gelada baboons (*Theropithecus gelada*), now living only in the highland areas of Ethiopia, have specialized in the processing of grass. Grass is a good example of a low-quality resource that exists in abundance in savanna regions. By processing large quantities of this resource through a series of specialized dental and locomotor adaptations, geladas are able to survive through periods of considerable resource scarcity (Table 8.3) (Jolly 1972; Dunbar 1977, 1983).

All the above are examples of primate species that opt for lower quality resources in the dry season. The second strategy, which often requires a much more flexible behavioural repertoire, is perhaps less common. Savanna-dwelling chimpanzees show some sign of increasing their

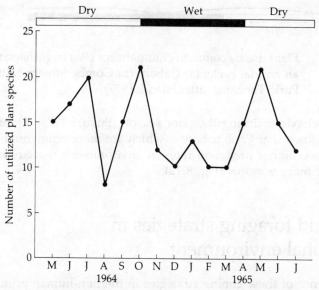

Figure 8.10   Number of plant food types exploited by common chimpanzees (*Pan troglodytes*) in a savanna woodland environment (Kasakati, Tanzania) (data from Suzuki 1969).

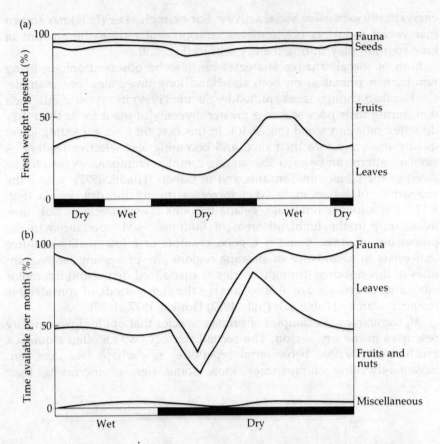

Figure 8.11 Plant use by common chimpanzees (*Pan troglodytes*) through an annual cycle: (a) Gabon; (b) Gombe Stream National Park, Tanzania (after Hladik 1977).

hunting behaviour during the poor season (Suzuki 1975). Dunbar (1983) has also shown that *Papio* baboons, which are more omnivorous than the gelada, have higher predation rates in environments that are more arid, and hence more seasonal (Fig. 8.12).

Hominid foraging strategies in a seasonal environment

The presence of these coping strategies in the non-human primates leads us on to examine the extent to which seasonality may have been important in the adaptations of early hominids, and whether the two alternative coping strategies may have been an element of hominid evolutionary

Table 8.3 Seasonal use of plant foods by gelada baboons (*Theropithecus gelada*) (from Dunbar 1977)

| Plant type | Part eaten | Percentage of records | | |
		Wet season	Early dry season	Late dry season
Grasses	Leaves	93.0	17.3	24.7
	Rhizomes	—	6.5	66.9
	Seeds	—	69.7	—
Herbs, plants	Leaves, stems	0.2	0.4	2.7
	Roots, tubers	3.3	0.9	—
	Flowers	0.2	3.0	0.1
	Seeds	—	1.3	5.2
Thistles	Leaves	0.1	0.8	0.1
Bushes	Leaves	0.2	—	0.2
	Flowers	—	—	0.1
	Fruits	2.9	—	—
Insects	—	0.1	—	0.1
No. of records		3051	231	3291

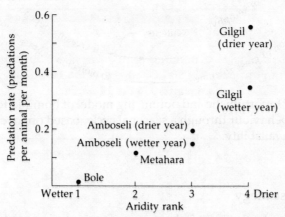

Figure 8.12 Predation rates for *Papio* baboons in East Africa (data from Dunbar 1983).

ecology. Such a consideration can start with a simple description of a generalized strategy of resource utilization by an omnivore tracking resources as they become available (Fig. 8.13).

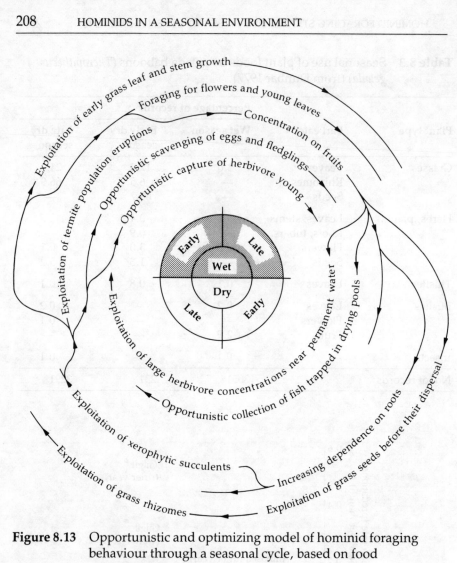

Figure 8.13 Opportunistic and optimizing model of hominid foraging behaviour through a seasonal cycle, based on food availability.

Wet-season strategy

As can be seen from Fig. 8.5 the wet season is the period in which the widest range of resources is available. In these circumstances it may be expected that hominids would select those resources that provide the highest rate of return (Pyke, Pulliam & Charnov 1977), that is, those resources with a low search and/or pursuit time relative to yields. This would be consistent with the behaviour of an organism in the 'time of plenty' described in the competitive model shown in Fig. 8.1. Which resources fulfil these criteria depends partly on the time lag between the onset of the rains and the appearance of the resources. Termites, for instance, react instantly to the coming of the rains (Thoillay 1970), and would provide, briefly, a superabundant resource at the end of a period of resource scarcity. Among the flora, the grasses would be the first to produce new shoots, and fresh grass may provide a suitable resource, as they do for the gelada baboon (Post, Hausfater & McCuskey 1980).

As the wet season continues, flowering and fruiting plants would become abundant, and would thus form the main resource base for hominids during the wet season, providing as they do, an easily obtained, high-quality resource that is the preferred food of most primates (Harding 1981). Available also, but requiring a much higher search time, would be the young of the bovid herbivores born in the wet season and hidden in the long grass (Delaney & Happold 1979), and the eggs and fledglings of a range of bird species (Owen 1974). Overall, the rains bring on the maximum amount of plant food, the optimal response to which would be intense exploitation before availability begins to fall off. Other resources would be incorporated on an opportunistic basis. In the wet season, then, hominids would be expected to pursue a broad-based, eclectic but largely herbivorous strategy, in which interspecific overlap would be considerable, but competition low.

Dry-season strategy

With the onset of the dry season, resource strategy would shift, Savanna-dwelling organisms would be entering the 'lean phase' of the competitive model (Fig. 8.1), in which competition would be expected to intensify. Avoidance of competitive interactions would therefore be advantageous. Flowering plants would become extremely rare, and as the dry season proceeds fruits would gradually become exhausted. Among the plant community, the main source of food during the early part of the dry season would be grass seeds and, later on, grass rhyzomes (Dunbar 1977). At the height of the dry season, the only major plant resource would be roots at various depths (Dunbar 1977). Access to these would partially depend on the use of digging sticks (Tanner 1981). It is in the context of this reduced availability of plant foods that the question of meat-eating becomes critical. As the dry season proceeds many of the large herbivores would concentrate around the waterholes where the grazing would last the longest (Western 1975). In these circumstances carnivory would offer a high-yield strategy to supplement the plant foods. Meat could be obtained either directly through predation or through scavenging animals killed by other predators, disease or malnutrition.

Increasing dependence on meat, then, as the dry season proceeds, would solve the problems of increasingly scarce plant resources, and thus intensified competition.

Seasonal variability and unpredictability

Would, though, such a strategy be robust enough to survive variations in seasonal patterning. It is well known that increased tropical seasonality is correlated with rainfall unreliability (Harris 1980): the rains may fail and the dry seasons may become extremely prolonged. A successful adapt-ation must at least be viable in the context of such uncertainty. The question is, would hominid dependence on meat be maladaptive under drought conditions? The answer to this depends to some extent on spatial patterning, but assuming that hominids were themselves confined to areas of permanant water, then in fact meat-dependence would become increasingly viable as resource-related animal mortality increases. Furthermore, it is under these stress conditions that the alternative plant-dependent strategies would break down.

The alternative problem of excessive and prolonged rains and reduced dry seasons would also have adaptive consequences. Paradoxically, some plants may respond to these conditions by prolific leaf and shoot pro-duction, rather than sexual reproduction (Harper 1977), resulting in fewer fruits but increased leaf and grass availability. Overall, this would enhance the resource base of parts of the herbivore community.

Hominoids for all seasons

Hominid diversity and seasonal strategies

The strategy described above is one based on the early hominids being entirely opportunistic and taking resources from their environment as they become available. Furthermore, it assumes that hominids were uniform both in their requirements and in their coping strategies. As we have seen, though, by the late Pliocene and the early Pleistocene it is not possible to treat the hominids as a uniform group. They display consider-able variability, much of it in their dental and masticatory system, and so this may be a factor to be taken into account in analysing their foraging behaviour and seasonal coping strategies.

There has long been a recognition that the megadonty (enlarged teeth) of the robust australopithecines (Fig. 8.14) is a reflection of a low-quality diet, with coarse, hard food particles that require considerable grinding force. Jolly (1970) suggested that this was due to specialized dependence on grass seeds. Walker (1981) argued, on the basis of patterns of tooth microwear, that coarse, hard, dry fruits found in savanna environments were a significant part of the robust australopithecines' diet. Grine's (1981) analysis also indicated that hard objects were an important element of the diet of these hominids. In a recent review Kay (1985) suggested

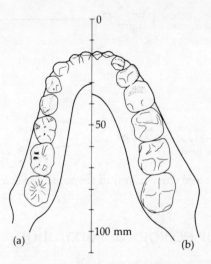

Figure 8.14 Relative tooth size of early African hominids: (a) *Homo habilis* (Olduvai); (b) *Australopithecus boisei* (Peninj). Both specimens are drawn so that the distance between canines is equal, showing the differences in size of the posterior tooth rows.

that the collective evidence – body size, thickness of tooth enamel, tooth size, height of molar crowns and tooth microwear – supported the idea of a diet containing very hard substances, involving little preparation by the incisor teeth, and with low fibre content; for example, fruits and seeds with hard pods and husks. It might equally by concluded that these very robust teeth would have been an advantage if long periods of time were spent feeding on this type of plant material.

The other evolutionary trend found among early hominids is that shown by the genus *Homo*. Although early specimens have larger teeth than modern humans, they do not possess the dental specializations of australopithecines. Theirs is a much more generalized masticatory system, perhaps indicating a more omnivorous diet.

These dental differences are interesting in the context of the seasonality of the environments in which the early hominids were living. Given that selection is more likely to operate on dental function and efficiency during times when resources are at their scarcest, it may be argued that the differences between hominids reflect their dry season strategies. The pattern found in the robust australopithecines is more consistent with the low-quality coping strategy, while that found in *Homo* might indicate an expansion of the resource base to include new foods that will enhance survival through a period of plant food scarcity – vertebrate meat (Fig. 8.15).

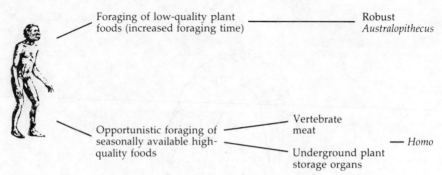

Figure 8.15   Alternative early hominid responses to seasonal stress.

Conditions for ecological separation

The suggestion that the divergence of the early hominids reflects different coping strategies during the poor season raises several important questions. Principal among these are whether the environmental conditions are likely to prompt these responses, and why two strategies should evolve. In other words, under what conditions would each be expected to evolve?

Local conditions would be the first and most significant factor that would determine which of the two coping strategies will be optimal in local conditions. Where large-mammal biomass does increase markedly in the dry season, the switch to meat resources would seem, for a hominid, to be a suitable option, particularly if plant diversity and productivity is particularly low. A suitable model for this might be an area such as Amboseli National Park (Fig. 8.16), where animals congregate onto the remaining water resources in the dry season, producing very high population densities and lax competition between carnivores, and where, because of the salinity, plant resources are extremely poor. Such an environment would promote selection for omnivory.

However, not all East African savanna environments are like this. Where local conditions allow it, many mammals do not congregate locally, but rather undertake long-distance seasonal migration. The Serengeti in Tanzania is the best-known such system (Fig. 8.17). Here in the plains, dry-season population densities are much lower, and in many parts of the woodland they remain much the same throughout the year. Under these conditions a switch to meat-eating would not be adaptive, and we would expect hominids to drop down the food-quality chain and to adopt a low-quality diet. These ecosystems would be more likely to favour an australopithecine solution to the problems of the poor season.

If this is correct then we would expect scattered throughout the semi-arid regions of Africa, in the early stages of hominid differentiation,

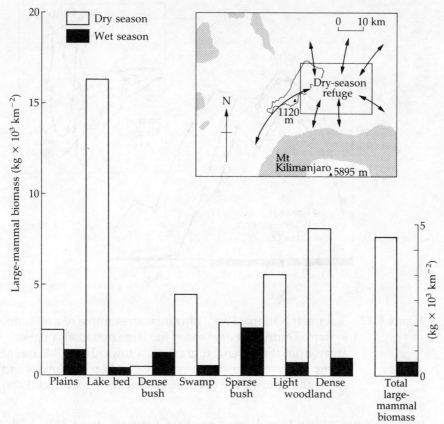

Figure 8.16 Amboseli National Park, Kenya: an example of a seasonally dispersing–concentrating large-mammal system. During the wet season, animals disperse widely, returning to the Amboseli as the dry season develops. Consequently, biomass, and therefore prey availability, is higher in the dry season (data from Western 1973).

populations pursuing alternative ways of getting through the dry season, dependent on the local conditions.

Other factors will also contribute to this pattern. If conditions remain stable we would then get the build up of two different hominid strategies in different parts of Africa. Overlap and sympatry could occur between the two. Once established, the strategies could well be sufficiently distinct to reduce competition at critical times of the year. Although it is unlikely that the 'Homo strategy' could occur in areas where the australopithecine one is selected for, on account of the paucity of animal resources, australopithecines may well have been able to survive in areas where Homo existed. Robust australopithecines would consequently be expected

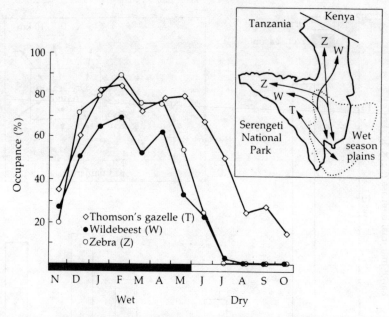

Figure 8.17   Serengeti National Park, Tanzania: an example of a migratory system. During the dry season the large mammals migrate away from the Serengeti grasslands towards the Maasai Mara Game Reserve. Consequently there is a drop in biomass and availability during the dry season (data from Maddock 1979).

to occur more widely than *Homo* (see also Chapter 9, page 242). Lack of direct competition and frequency-dependent selection would thus maintain the co-existence of more than one type of hominid. This, after all, is the basis for niche separation among many sympatric species.

Early hominid meat-eating

Incorporating meat into the diet is, according to the preceding discussion, likely to have developed in the context of seasonal stress among early African hominids. Such a strategy would minimize seasonal fluctuations in resource availability, and so competition with herbivorous animals. Equally, interspecific competition with the large carnivores is likely to be less intense as the dry season is a period of plenty for them, and, according to the model (Fig. 8.1), dietary overlap could be tolerated. In developing meat-eating, hominids would be transforming a highly seasonal, and hence problematic environment, into one where seasonal variation is smoothed out by switching resources. The price of this, as we have seen in preceding chapters, is increased foraging levels and activities, larger home ranges, increased body size, and considerable change in thermoregulatory behaviour.

The evidence for early hominid meat-eating is currently a matter of considerable debate and confusion. The critique mounted by Binford (1981, 1983) on the assumption of (1) early hominid meat-eating and (2) congruence between early hominid and modern hunter–gatherer behaviours has done much to stimulate critical testing of the palaeontological and archaeological evidence. In a recent review of the problem, Potts (1984a) has shown that hominids certainly *were* involved in processing animal products, including meat. Bunn & Kroll (1986) have also, on the basis of their analysis of the Olduvai Bed I faunal remains, argued strongly that Binford's case has been overstated. While the extent, and the means of acquisition (hunting versus scavenging) is at present unresolved, the large accumulations of bones associated with stone tools, and the distribution of cut marks on both meat-bearing and non-meat-bearing bones would seem to indicate that by shortly after 2.0 Ma ago some African hominids were exploiting a range of mammal species, including most body sizes, to an extent unknown in modern non-human primates. This does not mean that these early hominids were hunter–gatherers in the organizational sense, merely that they were omnivores in a significant manner.

Perhaps of greater interest here is the extent to which this meat-eating by early hominids was a response to dry-season stress, or at least was occurring preferentially in the dry season. At present, no method of directly determining the season of death of the animals associated with early hominids exists or has been implemented fully. One possible approach is to look at the species with which hominid artefacts are associated. Prey attributes can be used to infer predatory behaviour (Foley 1983). Perhaps the seasonal variation in behaviour and distribution of the various ungulate species can be used to determine the pattern of predation or scavenging. The modern East African fauna displays considerable variation in its seasonal behaviour (Fig. 8.17). It could be argued that, for a water-dependent predator such as early hominids probably were, highly mobile, seasonally congregrating animals will only be available in the dry season. Their presence among the fauna associated with early artefacts might indicate seasonality in predatory behaviour of early hominids. A preliminary examination of some of these faunas (Fig. 8.18) is not conclusive. The earliest sites show no significantly high proportion of seasonal species, but some of the early *Homo erectus* sites do. Further data and more detailed determination are needed, but this approach may help resolve not merely whether hominids were meat-eating, but also under what circumstances. In the context of the current debate about the bone assemblages of the early African Pleistocene it is important to remember that *why* hominids should be eating meat is an important part of whether they were.

	Seasonality		
	Highly seasonal	Slightly seasonal	Residential
Water-dependent	Elephant	Reedbuck Buffalo	Hippopotamus Bushpig Bushbuck Waterbuck
Partly water-dependent	Zebra Roan antelope Sabel antelope Wildebeest	Kob	Greater kudu
Mostly independent	Hartebeest Topi	Black rhino White rhino Giraffe Thomson's gazelle	Warthog Eland Lesser kudu Impala Duiker Klipspringer
Independent		Grant's gazelle Oryx Steinbuck	Gerenuk Dikdik

(left vertical label: Water relations)

Figure 8.18   Cross-tabulation of the modern African large-mammal community in relation to its seasonal variability and water dependence. For example, elephants are highly variable in their seasonal distribution and also require regular watering. This type of cross-tabulation can be used to identify potential prey species. See Foley 1983 for a discussion of the methods involved.

Evolutionary and behavioural consequences

The consequences of living in a seasonal environment are, at their most general, the need to be able to exploit a diverse set of resources patchily distributed through time, and, at a more specific but less secure level, to incorporate meat into the diet. However, whatever the direct causes of these changes in foraging behaviour, they are likely to have further consequences for the overall adaptation of hominids. Few changes in evolution are free of 'knock-on' effects, that may themselves come to act as selective pressures inducing yet further change.

Several evolutionary consequences of the foraging pattern described here may be briefly mentioned.

1. **Encephalization quotient.** As has been discussed extensively, brain size in mammals scales with body size (see Chapter 6). However, although the relationship is statistically significant, variation does occur.

As Eisenberg (1981) has shown, this variation is patterned in relation to certain categories of animal. Those species that have a complex foraging strategy – that is, depend either on a diverse set of resources or on unpredictable and variable resources – tend to have a larger brain size relative to body size than those that have a ubiquitous food source (Eisenberg 1981:283). Thus, in an extension of the predictions made in Chapter 6 relating to the diversity of the diet, the shifts in foraging strategy described here should result in an increase in brain size relative to body size. Such an increase is now known to have begun with the australopithecines at least (Martin 1983), and to have continued throughout the Pleistocene. Thus the selective pressures of the seasonal environment would have affected hominid brain size through the influence they had on foraging behaviour.

2. **Food-sharing.** Isaac (1978a,b) has produced a model of hominid behavioural evolution in which food-sharing plays a central part. This has been extensively criticized (Binford 1981, 1983, 1984; Gowlett 1984; and see Chapter 7). However, the incorporation of meat into the diet is liable to have social and behavioural consequences. Apart from nutritional differences, a significant way in which meat is different from plant foods is the 'package size'. The carcass, or even the partial carcass, of a typical savanna mammal represents a considerable quantity of food, and usually more than a single individual can eat. A carcass can thus become a rich resource on which several individuals can feed simultaneously, a situation that is seldom the case with plant foods. The opportunity thus arises for sharing, not in an active or social sense, but simply as a function of very rich patches of food. In these circumstances, selection will favour the development of reciprocal altruism in the form of what Isaac has referred to as tolerated scrounging. Although this was probably a long way from active food sharing as found among modern hunter–gatherers, carcasses are likely to have become the focus (as they do for some non-human primates) of intense social activity. The very large accumulations of bone, such as at the Olduvai site FLK NN, in which hominids have clearly participated in some form, again seem to suggest that the presence of focal points on the landscape can have major consequences for behaviour. In Chapter 7, the need for shelter led to one such focal point; meat-eating, in the form of scavenging or hunting, is likely to have led to another.

3. **Spatial organization.** We have already seen that both increasing body size and terrestriality are likely to lead to an increase in home range for a species. The same holds true for the utilization of animal resources; carnivores and omnivores have larger home ranges than herbivores. A further factor, though, is territoriality. Brown (1964) developed a model of territoriality, based on the costs and benefits of defending an area or resource, which is widely used (Fig. 8.20). According to this model,

(a)

Water relations		Seasonality		
		Highly seasonal	Slightly seasonal	Residential
	Water-dependent			*Strepsiceros* *Kobus* sp.
	Partly water-dependent	*Equus oldowayensis*		
	Mostly independent	*Parmelarius altidens* Alcelaphini indet.		*Phacochoerus* sp.
	Independent		*Oryx* sp. *Antidorcas bondi?*	

Stylohipparion sp.   *Kolpochoerus limnetes* *Notochoerus* sp.

(b)

Water relations		Seasonality		
		Highly seasonal	Slightly seasonal	Residential
	Water-dependent		Reduncini	*Kobus sigmoidalis* Hippopotamidae
	Partly water-dependent			
	Mostly independent	*Damaliscus* cf. *niro* *D. aegalaius*	*Giraffa juma*	*Aepyceros* Cephalophini
	Independent		*Antidorcas recki?*	

?

Mesochoerus limnetes *Metridiochoerus andrewsi*

Figure 8.19 Cross-tabulation of the estimated seasonality and water dependence of species of large mammal recovered from East African Plio-Pleistocene deposits: (a) Olduvai FLK *Zinj.* site; (b) Koobi Fora KBS site; (c) Olduvai TK Upper; (d) Olorgesailie.

territoriality – which is the defence of a resource, and thus usually involves the exclusive use of an area by an individual or group – should develop only when the benefits of exclusive resource utilization exceed the costs. This is likely to occur only where resources are both predictable and at a high density. A characteristic of the seasonal savanna environment that has been described here is that although some resources may

(c)

Water relations	Seasonality		
	Highly seasonal	Slightly seasonal	Residential
Water-dependent			*Hippopotamus gorgops*
Partly water-dependent	*Equus oldowayensis* *Hippotragus gigas*		
Mostly independent		*Ceratotherium simum*	
Independent			

Stylohipparion sp.   *Kolpochoerus*

(d)

Water relations	Seasonality		
	Highly seasonal	Slightly seasonal	Residential
Water-dependent	*Elephas recki*	*Redunca* *Homiocerus*	*Hippopotamus gorgops* *Tragelaphus* *Kobus*
Partly water-dependent	*Equus* aff. *grevyi* *E. oldowayensis*		*Strepsiceros*
Mostly independent		*Ceratotherium simum* *Giraffa camelopardis* *G. gracilis*	*Taurotragus* *Aepyceros*
Independent			

     ?   ?   ?
Stylohipparion albertensis   *Sivatherium olduvai*   *Metridiochoerus meadowsi*

exist in high density, they are seldom highly predictable. Thus, strict territoriality, contrary to what popular writers such as Ardrey (1961) have suggested, is unlikely to have evolved. Instead, conditions where resources cannot be predicted are likely to have promoted high mobility, with complex patterns of concentration and dispersion as are found among other species.

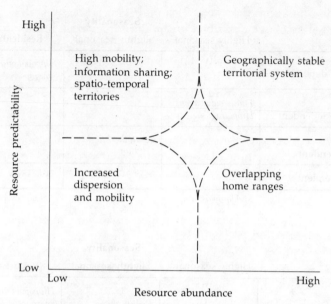

Figure 8.20   Optimality model of territoriality. Exclusive use of an area
will evolve where the benefits exceed the costs of defence.
This ratio will depend upon environmental conditions. For
example, full territoriality is to be expected where resources
are abundant and predictable (after Brown 1970; Dyson,
Hudson & Smith 1978).

4. Tool-making. The earliest evidence for stone tool-making is at about
2.3 Ma ago (Isaac 1984; Harris 1986), some 3 million years after the first
known hominids, and comes from the same areas and habitats as these
earliest fossils. It has long been thought that it was the butchering of
animals that stimulated the development of tool-making. However,
equally plausible arguments have been made in favour of tool-making as
a part of plant exploitation strategies, and, furthermore, non-human
primates can hunt and consume prey without the use of tools. One area
where tools would be of some use, and would give hominids an advantage, is the scavenging of very large, thick-skinned mammals. These
animals, which are usually immune from predation, often remain un-
touched for some time after death, as no animals can break the skin and
gain access to the meat. Tools might well have given the hominids the
ability to have early access to these carcasses, and thus a competitive
advantage over other scavengers at least in the initial phases of exploitation.

The early phases of meat-eating among hominids are likely to have been
opportunistic and infrequent. They are unlikely to be sufficiently high to

bring into operation the metabolism-blocking processes that Speth & Spielmann (1983) have described for modern temperate hunter–gatherers. Nonetheless, they would represent significant increases relative to other primates that do occasionally take meat, and thus substantially alter foraging behaviour. The advantages, especially during the dry season, that would have accrued from having a rich source of food in what would otherwise be a habitat with low-quality foods would be marked. Once established as a potential source of food, selection for further dependence on meat would occur, thus reinforcing the initial adaptation (autocatalysis). The documenting of the development of aspects of the meat-acquisition behaviour of early hominids would unravel the way in which this might have taken place. What is critical here is less the manner in which the development of meat-eating took place, than the fact that the initial advantage lay in the way in which it solved a particular environmental problem – that of resource ecology during the dry season.

The development of new adaptive strategies and behaviours has consequences as we have seen, that modify other aspects of the behaviour and adaptation of an organism. These new adaptations, though, can also have consequences for the other species of a biological community. Organisms must constantly adapt to the presence and activities of those species with which they are sympatric, with which they must compete, and on which they depend for resources. It is this that leads to co-evolution.

9 Hominids and community evolution

An intuitive assumption often made about human evolution is that it occurred 'at the end' – that is, after all the other animals 'finished' evolving. In books and courses on evolution, the emergence of the hominids is the final section, and hominids often appear to be the icing on the biological cake. Such an assumption, though, is erroneous. During the period in which the hominids have appeared and evolved many other species have undergone major evolutionary changes, only taking their present form either at the same time or after the appearance of the hominids. As we have seen, hominids have not adapted in isolation from the principles governing adapatation in the rest of the biological world, neither has their evolution occurred in isolation from that of other species. The adaptive strategies, such as those that were a response to the problems of seasonality discussed in the last chapter, would have altered the environment of other species, leading to evolutionary changes among them, which in turn would have affected early hominids.

The idea that populations impose reciprocal selective pressures on each other underlies the concepts of coevolution and community evolution. In this chapter we shall be examining the evolutionary interactions that occurred between hominids and other species with which they were sympatric. These interactions have two consequences. First, they provide the basis for the overall structure of the biological community, which in turn becomes an important selective constraint. And second, they lead to particular evolutionary events and pathways, such as divergence, speciation and extinction. Through this approach we will be able to see that adaptive shifts among hominids, and ultimately the evolution of modern humans, are not timeless evolutionary developments, but precise responses to the problems of survival in a specific evolutionary community.

As we have seen in the last chapter, however, there is a further complexity that must also be taken into account in considering co-evolution. Just as there was a variety of organisms coexisting and coevolving with hominids during the Plio-Pleistocene, so too it must be remembered that hominids were themselves a diverse and variable group of animals. It has been claimed that there is evidence for at least two species of hominid at Hadar (Olson 1981), for at least two species among the East African fossil assemblages between 3 and about 1.3 Ma ago, and for two species in South Africa between 2 and 1 Ma ago. So for a period of at least 2 million years there was more than one hominid species, probably living sympatrically. Coevolution will have occurred not just between hominids and other species, but between the different hominid populations. Consequently, this chapter, as well as looking at the re-lationships between hominids and the other African savanna mammals, will also discuss the ecological basis for the hominid adaptive radiation and the subsequent extinction of some hominids.

The hominid community

Definition

The first problem is to define the ecological and evolutionary community to which the early hominids belonged. To some extent this has already been done in the preceding chapter, where it was shown that early hominids were inhabiting the savanna regions (at least) of East and South Africa. However, a community is more than just a geographical unit – it refers more specifically to the organisms that interact ecologically (Pianka 1978:4). The idea of ecological interactions as the basis for defining a community is one that has been developed by Van Couvering (1980). She uses the term to mean an 'aggregation of plants and animals with distinct dynamic interactions' (p. 272). This definition introduces an element of selectivity to reduce the complexity and continuity of the biological world, as a result of which communities may be defined in various ways according to the particular focus of research interest. Accordingly, definition of the early hominid community requires identification of the important ecological links that hominids had with other sympatric organisms.

The species with which hominids had dynamic interactions are those that ate them, those that they ate, and those with which they competed. Such relationships are essentially with the other large mammals and with plants. Consequently, it is the large mammal community of the East African savanna that will form the basis for the analyses presented here. Although hominids must have had dynamic interactions with other organisms – say with parasites or with insects – these will leave no trace

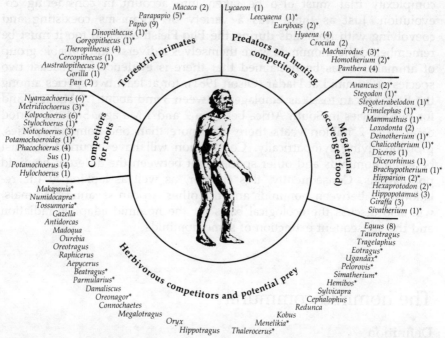

Figure 9.1   The early hominid ecological community: the principal genera of large mammal found in Africa during the Pliocene and early Pleistocene. Extinct genera are marked with an asterisk (source of data: Maglio 1978).

in the fossil record. Figure 9.1 shows the species that were contemporary with the early hominids, classified according to the type of ecological relationship they were likely to have had.

Species richness

The basic question that must then be asked about this community is what effect it may have had upon the evolution of the hominids and their adaptation. This means that we must investigate and describe its structure. Perhaps the most useful concept here is that of diversity or species richness – that is, the number of species in a community, either in total or according to various ecological criteria, such as trophic level and body size. The species is therefore the principal unit of analysis used here.

Communities vary in their species richness. Some, such as tropical rainforests, have large numbers of species per unit area. Others, such as the arctic or the tundra, have relatively few. There is, though, a pattern to this variability, recently synthesized for mammals by Eisenberg (1981:219).

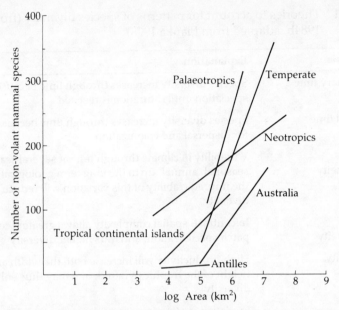

Figure 9.2   Regression lines for number of non-volant mammal species
against total geographical area (from Eisenberg 1981: fig. 38).

Tropical communities are more diverse than temperate ones, and
continents have more species than islands do. Continental islands have
more species than oceanic islands (Fig. 9.2). Furthermore, areas with high
productivity and stable climates are more diverse than those lacking these
attributes. For each type of community there seems to be an optimal or
equilibrium number of species, determined by various ecological parameters. This was the primary conclusion derived from the work of
MacArthur and his colleagues, and one among several theories of diversity (Table 9.1). Deviation from the predicted equilibrium – for example,
impoverished areas of the tropics such as southern India – can be
explained in terms of historical factors, including recent extinctions due to
human activity or environmental change or specific environmental
characteristics. In the case of southern India, the highly monsoonal
climate is an important factor.

The stage of species equilibrium is that at which any ecosystem is
saturated with species. Essentially this means that all potential niches are
occupied, and that a new species can be added only at the expense of
another. Resources set the limits on the biomass of an ecosystem.
Populations will move towards those limits by increasing in size. Ecosystems will then (rapidly?) become saturated with individuals, although
they may not be saturated with species at this stage. However, as time
proceeds, individuals of species that can exploit the resources most

Table 9.1 Theories to account for patterns of species diversity (from Foley 1984b, adapted from Pianka 1978)

Hypothesis	Explanation
Evolutionary time	Species diversity increases through time because of speciation until saturation is reached
Ecological time	Species diversity increases through time because of time for dispersal and colonization
Temporal heterogeneity	Variability in climate through time at several scales – seasonal, annual, up to the long term geological – and the unpredictability of this variation will reduce species diversity
Spatial heterogeneity	In contrast, spatial complexity allows greater scope for patch specialization, and thus higher diversity
Productivity	High productivity will increase both the width and the height of the trophic pyramid, and may thus enhance diversity
Predation	Predation is often frequency-dependent, and so will maintain diversity by preventing any one species from becoming dominant
Rarefaction	Reduced abundance per species will allow greater species diversity within a community
Competition	As diversity increases there is a greater premium on competitive ability, resulting in the success of a large number of species with highly specialized competitive ability

efficiently, and so require less ecological space, will replace more generalized individuals. Through time, therefore, the ecological niches will become narrower, and species richness will increase until saturation or equilibrium is reached. Perturbations of the environment will slow down this process. The patterns of species richness can accordingly be related to saturation, and a general model produced (Fig. 9.3) that incorporates both immediate, neo-ecological factors and the impact of historical events, such as changes in sea level or climate.

What do these patterns mean for the component species that go to make up any community? Both saturation and high diversity mean that there are likely to be high levels of competition, and a high premium for organisms able to exploit a narrow ecological niche efficiently. Where saturation has not occurred, opportunistic species would have higher chances of survival, and mean niche breadth would have been higher.

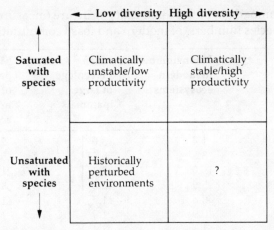

Figure 9.3   Factors leading to variation in the species richness of
communities.

Modern and fossil African communities

This discussion of the patterns of species richness would suggest that the
African communities of which the early hominids were a part should be
relatively rich in mammalian species. Certainly, modern African savanna
ecosystems are. According to Eisenberg (1981:219), East Africa has a
mammal species density of 1.98×10^{-4} per km^2. This high species
richness occurs also at a family and generic level (Maglio 1978), and
compares with a tropical mean of 0.76×10^{-4} per km^2.

This exceptionally high species richness can be accounted for by
Eisenberg's general principles. East Africa is part of a continental land-
mass; it is a tropical region; it has a high primary productivity relative to
biomass; and it has suffered relatively few extinctions in the Pleistocene
compared with other areas. The question that follows, though, is whether
the Plio-Pleistocene fauna had the same ecological structure and species
richness?

An answer to this question is gained by comparing the species richness
of the fossil assemblages with those of the modern ecosystems. Obviously
such comparisons involve problems relating to the representativeness of
fossil assemblages. These include sample size, palimpsest formation, and
differential preservation, and so these points will be considered alongside
the interpretation of the ecological similarities and differences. Overall,
modern ecosystems are richer than fossil ones (Table 9.2). A mean value
for all the East African nature reserves is 70.2 species, higher than that of
most fossil assemblages. However, this can be partly accounted for by
size. It is known that small animals stand less chance of fossilization than
large ones (Behrensmeyer & Dechant Boaz 1980), and so will be poorly

Table 9.2   Comparison of the community structure (measured in terms of species numbers) of modern and fossil communities in Africa

Taxon	Mean number in modern ecosystems	Mean percentage of large mammals	Mean percentage of all mammals in modern ecosystems
Small primates	1.4	3.0 ⎫ 11.1	2.0
Large primates	3.8	8.1 ⎭	5.4
Small carnivores	15.0	32.1 ⎫ 44.7	21.0
Large carnivores	5.9	12.6 ⎭	8.4
Proboscidea	0.8	1.7	1.1
Rhinoceros	0.9	1.9	1.3
Equidae	1.1	2.4	1.6
Hippopotomidae	0.8	1.7	1.1
Suidae	1.5	3.2	2.1
Giraffidae	0.9	1.9	1.3
Small bovids	6.4 ⎫	13.7 ⎫	9.1 ⎫
Medium bovids	4.1 ⎬ 14.4	8.8 ⎬ 30.8	5.8 ⎬ 20.5
Large bovids	3.9 ⎭	8.3 ⎭	5.6 ⎭
Total of large mammals	46.8 (46.5)	99.4	66.7
Total Mammals	70.2	—	—

represented in fossil assemblages. When small mammals are discounted from both assemblages, much of the difference between the modern and ancient communities disappears – a mean value of 46.8 species for modern (Table 9.2) and 35.9 for Plio-Pleistocene localities in East Africa. Furthermore, when the small fossil assemblages are removed on the grounds that they may be unrepresentative, then the mean diversity of the Plio-Pleistocene rises to 43.1 species. Given the probability of incomplete sampling of the fossil fauna, this suggests that the two systems have approximately similar levels of species richness.

What, though, of the actual structures of these communities? Are the species richness data made up of the same type of animal? Andrews, Lord & Evans (1979) and Van Couvering (1980) have developed methods for determining the environment of a fossil assemblage by building up profiles of their ecological structure. Communities are characterized by varying proportions of different types of animals – for example, grassland communities have higher proportions of grazers, and forest communities have higher proportions of frugivores. By describing modern communities in terms of these frequencies it is possible to compare them with fossil assemblages. An ecological profile that is similar to a modern one will indicate a similar community structure.

In the analyses presented here five basic categories have been selected

Mean number of species in fossil assemblages (N=24)	Mean percentage of large mammals in fossil assemblages	Mean number of species in fossil assemblages with ≥30 species (N=17)	Mean percentage of large mammals in fossil assemblages
0.21	0.6	0.3	0.7
4.5	12.6	5.9	13.7
3.2	8.9	4.4	10.2
3.7	10.3	4.9	11.4
2.2	6.1	2.3	5.3
1.5	4.2	1.7	3.9
1.7	4.7	1.6	3.7
1.7	4.7	1.9	4.4
4.0	11.2	4.5	10.4
2.8	7.8	3.2	7.4
}10.3	}28.8	}12.4	}28.7
35.9	99.9	43.1	99.8

to form the ecological profile: primates, large carnivores, megafauna (rhinos, proboscids, hippos and giraffes), pigs, and large cursorial herbivores (equids and bovids). These represent both taxonomic and feeding categories. Small mammals have been excluded to maximize comparability between modern and fossil communities. Data on the composition of the modern East African community were derived from the lists given by Williams (1971). Fossil data were obtained from faunal lists of the major Plio-Pleistocene localities in East Africa. All the communities, both modern and fossil, are drawn from broadly similar habitats – that is, woodland–grassland environments. No tropical forests are represented.

When these two sets are compared, some interesting patterns emerge (Tables 9.3 and 9.4, Figs 9.4 to 9.6). The modern fauna are dominated by the cursorial herbivores – the grazing and browsing bovids and equids. These, of course, constitute the great herds that are such a splendid sight on the savanna today. They can make up as much as 59.5 per cent of the large-mammal species, and on average represent 49.3 per cent. In contrast, among the fossil assemblages they have an average relative frequency of 35.8 per cent. Another way of looking at this is to say that the modern fauna is clearly dominated by a single ecological/taxonomic category, which is not the case with most of the fossil assemblages.

Table 9.3 Faunal composition of modern communities in East Africa (data: Williams 1971)

Community	Primates		Large carnivores		Megafauna		Pigs		Large cursorial herbivores	
	N	%	N	%	N	%	N	%	N	%
Aberdares	4	18.2	3	13.6	2	9.1	2	9.1	11	50.0
Amboseli	4	11.8	5	14.7	4	11.8	2	5.9	19	55.9
Marsabit	5	20.8	6	25.0	3	12.5	1	4.2	9	37.5
Maasai Mara	7	17.1	6	14.6	4	9.8	3	7.3	21	51.2
Meru	6	14.3	6	14.3	5	11.9	3	7.1	22	52.4
Nairobi	6	18.2	6	18.2	3	9.1	1	3.0	17	51.5
Nakuru	4	16.0	5	20.0	2	8.0	0	0.0	14	56.0
Samburu/Isiolo	5	15.2	6	18.2	4	12.1	1	3.0	17	51.5
Tsavo	5	13.5	6	16.2	3	8.1	1	2.7	22	59.5
Lake Manyara	5	20.8	3	12.5	4	16.7	1	4.2	11	45.8
Mikumi	3	12.5	5	20.8	4	16.7	1	4.2	11	45.8
Ngorongoro	2	7.7	5	19.2	4	15.4	2	7.7	13	50.0
Ruaha	5	16.1	5	16.1	4	12.9	1	3.2	16	51.6
Serengeti	7	16.7	6	14.3	4	9.5	2	4.8	23	54.8
Kidepo	6	13.3	5	16.7	4	13.3	1	3.3	16	53.3
Murchison	6	22.2	4	14.8	4	14.8	2	7.4	11	40.7
Queen Elizabeth Park	10	34.4	14	13.8	3	10.3	3	10.3	9	31.0
X̄	5.2	17.0	5.4	16.6	3.6	11.9	1.6	5.1	15.4	49.3

Table 9.4 Faunal composition of fossil communities in East Africa (data: M. D. Leakey 1972; Coppens & Howell 1978; Johanson, Taieb & Coppens 1982; Harris 1983)

Community	Primates		Large carnivores		Megafauna		Pigs		Large cursorial herbivores	
	N	%	N	%	N	%	N	%	N	%
East Turkana CU 2	3	9.4	3	9.4	11	34.4	3	9.4	12	37.5
East Turkana CU 3	8	16.3	7	14.3	11	22.4	3	6.1	20	40.8
East Turkana CU 4	9	16.4	7	12.7	12	21.8	4	7.3	23	41.8
East Turkana CU 5	7	17.1	4	9.8	9	22.0	4	9.8	17	41.5
Omo Usno	8	22.2	9	25.0	10	27.8	5	13.9	4	11.1
Omo Member B	12	28.5	3	7.1	10	23.8	6	14.3	11	26.2
Omo Member C	10	18.5	9	16.7	11	20.4	7	1.0	17	36.5
Omo Member D	6	21.4	3	10.7	10	35.7	3	10.7	6	21.4
Omo Member E	7	23.3	3	10.0	7	23.3	3	10.0	10	33.3
Omo Member F	8	19.5	7	17.1	10	24.3	4	9.8	12	29.3
Omo Member G	9	16.1	8	14.3	13	23.2	6	10.7	20	35.7
Omo Kalam	6	16.7	2	5.6	7	19.4	6	16.7	15	41.6
Hadar	5	10.6	9	19.1	12	25.5	3	6.4	18	38.3
Olduvai Bed I (L)	3	11.1	3	11.1	8	29.6	3	11.1	10	37.0
Olduvai Bed I (M)	3	10.0	3	10.0	6	20.0	5	16.7	13	43.5
Olduvai Bed I (U)	0	0.0	2	8.7	7	30.4	3	13.0	11	47.8
Olduvai Bed II (M)	1	3.1	1	3.1	7	21.9	7	21.9	16	50.0
X̄	6.2	15.3	4.9	12.0	9.5	25.0	4.4	11.8	13.8	35.2

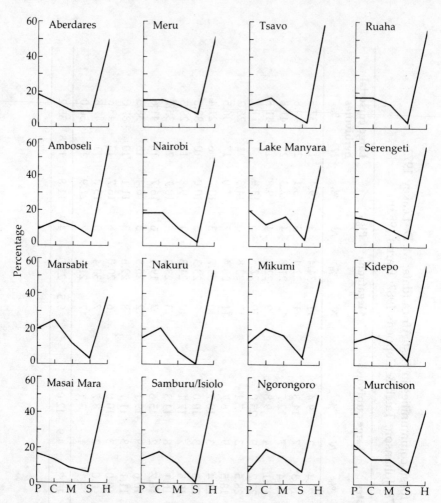

Figure 9.4   Community structure of modern East African ecosystems
(national parks and game reserves). Each graph shows the
relative diversity profile for different categories of larger
mammal. Key: P, primates; C, carnivores; M, megafauna; S,
pigs; H, large herbivores (bovids and equids).

Differences also occur among the other ecological categories. The fossil
assemblages have both absolutely and relatively more pigs and megafauna, and in absolute terms more primates, especially large primates. On
the other hand, the present-day communities have on average more large
carnivores.

A further point to note is that although the modern communities
display relatively little variation in their structure, the fossil communities
differ quite considerably from one another (Figs 9.4 and 9.5). In parti-

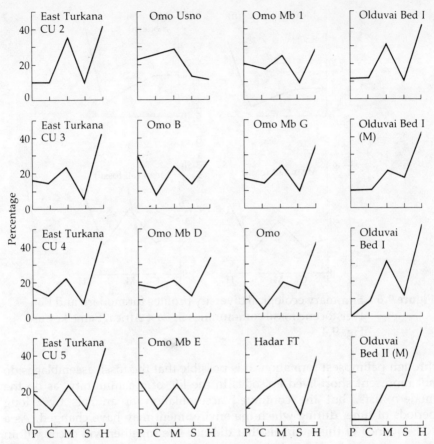

Figure 9.5 Community structure of Plio-Pleistocene ecosystems based on fossil assemblages. Same key as Fig. 9.4.

cular, the Omo assemblages, with their high proportion of primates and low proportion of bovids and equids, stand out as a rather different type of community. This raises the question of whether at least some of the variability that can be observed within the fossil assemblages and between them and the modern communities is the product of the processes of fossilization rather than the processes of ecology. Certainly, it is reasonable to say that the smaller mammals are underrepresented, and that the lack of small bovids might be accounted for in this way. However, it is also true to say that certain groups of animals – especially the pigs and the megafauna – are far more diverse during the Plio-Pleistocene than at the present time, for they are more abundant in absolute as well as relative terms.

While underrepresentation of fossils may be a problem owing to differential survival during burial, overrepresentation may also occur

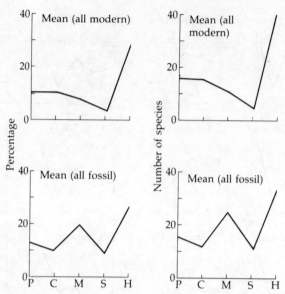

Figure 9.6 Summary ecological diversity profiles for modern and Plio-
Pleistocene fossil communities in East Africa. Same key as
Fig. 9.4.

through palimpsest formation. It is possible that the fossil assemblages do
not represent short-lived episodes in the life of a community, as do the
modern lists, but the continued accumulation of animals over long
periods of time, during which the environment may have changed. As a
consequence of this, animals that did not live together will occur within
the same palaeontological assemblages. Some idea of this effect can be
gained by 'collapsing' several faunal lists from modern communities onto
each other and observing the effect on overall species diversity. Using a
random set of runs whereby the faunal lists from 10 communities are
aggregated and the changing species diversity plotted, it is possible to
see (Fig. 9.7) that it does increase in overall terms, but that the component groups do not change significantly enough to mimic the patterns of
Plio-Pleistocene diversity. Although this cannot be said to be conclusive
on the grounds that we do not have any means of determining whether
the spatial variability over East Africa today is comparable with that in the
Pliocene and Pleistocene, it does to some extent support the notion that
there are structural differences between the Plio-Pleistocene and the
large mammal communities of the modern savanna.

These data are relatively crude measures of community structure, and
are likely to be skewed by various taphonomic factors, and by collation of
data across long periods of time; for example, Omo covers a period of
more than 2 million years, during which environmental change is known
to have occurred (Bonnefille 1976, 1985).

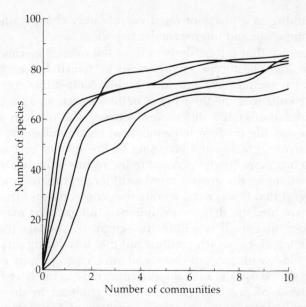

Figure 9.7   Simulation of the effect of palimpsest formation on ecological diversity. The method consists of simulating the effect on total diversity of adding together species lists from East African ecosystems. Each line represents a run of 10 such additions. This process of collapsing ecosystems onto each other should mimic the effect of long-term environmental change on fossilization processes. The simulation was constructed from modern East African faunal lists from national parks and reserves. For each run the communities were selected at random. Data from Williams (1971).

Evolutionary context of the early hominids

The high diversity of the early hominid community and its structural character enables us to make some statements about the ecological, competitive and evolutionary environment in which hominid adaptations first evolved. According to the principles discussed earlier in this chapter, and in the preceding one, high diversity suggests high levels of competition – that is, either direct competitive interactions, or a niche structure maintained by competitor avoidance that has itself evolved through competition. In either case, it suggests an environment where selection would have been intense, owing to the saturation of the ecological space with individuals and species. For the most part, it might be expected that this selection would have a stabilizing effect on the overall structure of the community. Each species is held in check by its interactions with species occupying adjacent niches. However, any species able to break out of these constraints would have a major effect on the community as a whole, resulting in a phase of rapid evolutionary change among a wide range of competing and interdependent species.

The inference that can be derived from the overall species richness of the African Plio-Pleistocene environment in which the early hominids lived is that it would have provided highly competitive conditions that would have enhanced the intensity of natural selection. This is reinforced by a consideration of the differences between the modern and ancient fauna. Whereas the modern large-mammal communities are particularly rich in herbivores grazing and browsing on low-quality herbage, the Plio-Pleistocene has more species occupying the niches of higher quality plant food – for example, the greater number of large primates and pigs. This would suggest that it was here, among the omnivores and frugivores, the more selective feeders, that the evolutionary interactions may have been at their most intense. It is within this group of animals that the early hominids fall, and it is worth pointing out that it is during this period that early hominids were most diverse and undergoing rapid evolutionary change – from the earliest australopithecine grade to the later *Homo erectus* grade. Patterns of hominid evolution thus conform to the patterns of evolutionary change and ecological structure of the community as a whole.

However, to document this interaction between hominids and their sympatric competitors it is necessary to look at the specific interactions that would have occurred. To do this requires further consideration of the variable nature of the hominids themselves during this period.

Evidence for hominid diversity

Although the broad outline of hominid evolution presented in Chapter 2 indicated several sympatric species of early hominid in Africa, for much of the rest of the book there has been an implicit assumption that the hominids represent a homogenous group, with much the same ecological problems and adaptive solutions. This, however, is an oversimplification. Although it has been useful to look at the early hominids at a broad and general level, and thus make comparisons with other groups of animals, it is also necessary to take into account the fact that during the Plio-Pleistocene at least the hominids were a diverse African taxon, displaying considerable variability. Hominid diversity is an important evolutionary and ecological consideration.

For more than one species to coexist requires that there is more than one adaptive strategy, and consequently more than one ecological niche. This in turn suggests that not all hominids faced the same ecological and environmental problems, or, that if they did, then more than one adaptive solution was appropriate. In order to take this into account, and to incorporate competition between hominids into evolutionary models, it is necessary to examine the fossil evidence for hominid diversity and coexistence.

Levels of variability

Hominid variation can occur at several levels, resulting in different levels of diversity. Variation may be principally at a subspecific level, resulting in a heterogenous population, but still unbroken gene flow. Alternatively, the variation may be sufficiently great for gene flow to be interrupted, and hence for separate species to form. If this is maintained over prolonged periods of time, then the differences will become sufficient for taxonomists to recognize different higher taxa, such as genera. For the African fossils all these different levels can be identified.

As suggested in Chapter 2 (see page 25), two genera of early hominid are usually recognized from the Pliocene and Pleistocene in Africa – *Australopithecus* and *Homo*. Early members of the genus *Australopithecus* are thought to represent the earliest forms of hominid, and on anatomical grounds these two genera represent two divergent evolutionary trends. The former are characterized by small rounded crania, with thin skull bones but often marked ridges and crests, and very heavy masticatory apparatus and dentition; the latter, *Homo* has a larger and longer cranium and reduced dentition.

Within each of these genera there are also significant patterns of variation that suggest several species (see Figs. 2.8 and 2.10). The variability is both chronological and spatial. From the earliest localities of East Africa – Tabarin, Laetoli and Hadar – comes the primitive species *Australopithecus afarensis*. There is, however, some suggestion that the large number of specimens from Hadar do not all belong to the same taxon. Olson (1981) has argued that even at 3 Ma ago there were already at least two species of hominid in East Africa. Slightly later, and from South Africa, is the gracile *Australopithecus africanus*. Rather more distinctive are the robust australopithecines. While possessing the basic characteristics of the genus, they are larger, more heavily built, and exhibit very pronounced cranial musculature. The most extreme specimens of this type are known from East Africa (*Australopithecus boisei*), and Howell (1978) has identified two species from South Africa (*Australopithecus robustus* and *Australopithecus crassidens*).

The genus *Homo* appears to be less diverse. Only two species have been described for the Pliocene and the early Pleistocene, *Homo habilis* and *Homo erectus*, although there have been suggestions of a third (*Homo ergaster*?) among the Koobi Fora specimens (Howell 1978; Walker & Leakey 1978). *Homo habilis* is larger than the gracile australopithecines, with a larger and longer brain case. *Homo erectus* is larger still, with pronounced brain enlargement as well as increased body size and robusticity.

It should not be ignored, however, that variation also occurs within these species and at this stage there is no consensus about whether this variability is indicative of sexual dimorphism – as has been claimed for Hadar and Laetoli (Johanson & White 1979; White, Johanson & Kimbel 1983) – or geographical and chronological variation within a single poly-typic species (Tobias 1980).

Coexistence

For the period 4 to 1 Ma ago, then, at least seven species of hominid are represented: four or five occur in East Africa, and five in South Africa. Furthermore, they overlap quite markedly in time (Fig. 9.8), although some time trends can be discerned (e.g. a trend from more lightly built to more robust austalopithecines, and another with *Homo erectus* replacing *H. habilis*). It is possible to say, though, that during the Plio-Pleistocene more than one species of hominid may be said to have coexisted within the African savanna community. What remains to be determined is the

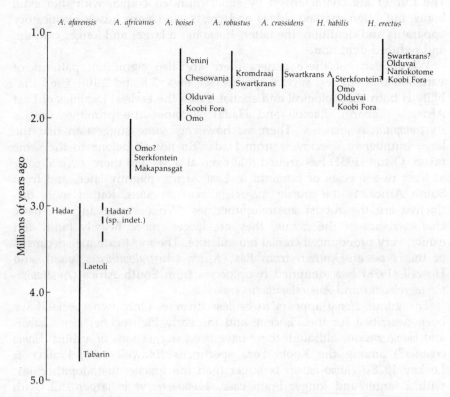

Figure 9.8 Estimated temporal duration of Plio-Pleistocene hominid taxa (*Australopithecus* and *Homo*) in Africa.

degree of coexistence and ecological overlap. For example, the early hominids may have been fully sympatric or they may have coexisted only at a regional or continental scale.

Howell (1978:222–3) has examined the evidence for hominid sympatry in some detail. He has stated that at Swartkrans, Olduvai Beds I and II, Koobi Fora (above and below the KBS Tuff), and at Omo G to H, *Homo* sp. (presumably *habilis*) occurs in the same geological deposits as a robust australopithecine. Furthermore, at Omo, *Australopithecus boisei* appears in the same strata as *Australopithecus africanus*, and at Koobi Fora and Olduvai *Homo erectus* and *Australopithecus boisei* are sympatric. It is possible to conclude, therefore, that the early hominids not only coexisted in the same biogeographical regions for a considerable period of time, but also that they were sympatric in a way understood by ecologists studying the direct interactions of living organisms.

The fossil evidence shows that the hominids underwent an adaptive radiation in Africa during the Plio-Pleistocene. Furthermore, over a large geographical and temporal range they were sympatric, and so must have interacted ecologically. The diversity of hominid forms may be used as a basis for considering specific coevolutionary relationships and the part they have played in hominid evolution – relationships between different hominids and relationships between hominids and other species.

Community ecology and coevolution

Three main points about the early hominid ecological community have been established so far. The first was the overall high species diversity among the larger mammals, the second that among the ecological group to which the early hominids belonged there was much higher diversity than at present. And the third point was that the hominids were themselves undergoing an adaptive radiation. These observations can be the starting point for an analysis of the part that interspecific relationships may have played in hominid evolution. Such an analysis would consist both of a consideration of whether hominid evolution conforms to a general pattern of community evolution, and also of specific competitive and coevolutionary relationships.

A fit between the development of hominid adaptive patterns and the evolution of the tropical African savanna community has been suggested eleswhere (Foley 1984b). Many authors have noted that there is a recurrent pattern to the development of communities, from the first establishment of a new environment to the achievement of some level of stability. In suggesting this it is important to note that, as Hoffman (1979) has argued, it is not the communities as a whole that are evolving – that is, the community as a whole does not represent the unit of selection –

Stage 1	Stage 2	Stage 3
New environment established	Increasing specialization and adaptive radiation	Niche stabilization
		Increasing competitive exclusion and extinction
Colonization by opportunistic species	Niche partitioning	
		Re-establishment of new generalists
Low species diversity	Maximum species diversity	Reduced species diversity

———————————— Time ————————————→

Figure 9.9 Model of community evolution based on changing patterns of competition on the establishment of new environmental conditions (after Foley 1984b).

but that there are general properties of individual and interspecific interaction that are common to all ecosystems, and so give rise to a repeated pattern of community development.

One such pattern is shown in Fig. 9.9. When a new environment is established it will be colonized by opportunistic species that have high rates of reproduction and dispersal. They will seldom be highly efficient in their utilization of the new environment, but gain their temporary advantage from their rapid reproductive rates, their broad habitat tolerance, and the lack of competitors. At the early stages of the establishment of a new environment these species would be dominant, and, because of this and the lack of time available for species to move in, species diversity or richness will be low. However, as the new environment becomes saturated with individuals and with new species, the advantage begins to shift from opportunistic generalists to specialist species that can exploit the resources more efficiently. Depending on the geographical context and the timescale involved, new species will either colonize these habitats from outside, or selection will favour the evolution of those species that are best able to survive in increasingly competitive conditions. During this stage, species diversity should increase, particularly among those species exploiting the higher quality resources. As this trend continues, there will be further partitioning of the niches, resulting in a twofold process. First, survival within a narrower niche will require increasing dependence on lower quality resources as well as the rich ones, and, second, broad-based species will become increasingly rare and ultimately extinct. A fall in species diversity may occur with an increase in the rate of extinction. Furthermore, during the later phases of this development the potential available for scavengers and predators would increase as the secondary biomass rose.

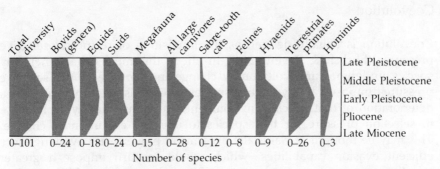

Figure 9.10   Patterns of species diversity among large mammals during
the African later Cenozoic (after Foley 1984b; data from
Maglio 1978).

How does the changing pattern of diversity and community structure
of the African savanna community compare to this? An examination of
Fig. 9.10, which shows graphically the pattern of species richness change
during the later Cenozoic, indicates that species richness increases from
the Pliocene into the early Pleistocene, after which there is a decline. This
is true of the overall diversity, but can also be seen in detail in the
changing diversity of the component ecological and taxonomic groups. Of
particular interest is the way in which the high-quality feeders reach an
early peak, and then decline dramatically, whereas the low-quality
herbivores have only slightly reduced diversity during the later periods of
Pleistocene. Carnivores also increase rapidly in diversity, although in-
terestingly enough (see below, page 260), they then decline markedly.

It can be argued, then, that the fossil record for Africa over the past
million years shows a pattern of increasing and then declining diversity
that conforms to the expectations of a model constructed to describe the
evolution of communities in general. Furthermore, the adaptive radiation
of the hominids, reaching peak diversity between 2 and 1 Ma ago,
indicates that their evolution, as low-density, high-quality feeders and
omnivores, fits in with the expected pattern. This is not to say that the
evolution of the hominids could have been predicted – that is obviously
far more complex and relates to the other factors described in the earlier
chapters of this book. It does, however, suggest that hominids filled
niches that could have been expected to occur in the development of a
new community, and as such they are an integral part of the African
savanna community.

Their exact position, though, within that community, depends on more
specific factors, and in particular the type of resources available and the
presence or absence of competitors. This can be seen when we look at the
ecological and evolutionary character of the hominids and their close
competitors.

Coevolution

Coevolution is usually defined as the imposition of reciprocal selective pressures (Ehrlich & Raven 1964). In effect, this means that when any species undergoes an evolutionary change in response to the selective pressures imposed by sympatric species, then this in turn results in a deterioration of that species environment, and consequently an increase in selection pressure for that species to undergo evolutionary change. This may be thought of classically in terms of prey species evolving more efficient evasion capabilities, which would in turn impose a greater selective pressure on a predator to increase their capture ability, and so on. It would also apply more widely, for example to parasites and their hosts, and between competitors. Janzen (1980) has suggested a narrower definition of coevolution to restrict the concept to evolutionary changes involving direct and unavoidable interspecific dependence, but from an evolutionary ecological perspective there is no doubt that evolutionary patterns can be usefully thought of in terms of reciprocal evolutionary pressures. This conforms to the idea of evolution as a game, with the goal being reproductive success, in which the players (individuals and populations) pursue different strategies. As in all good complex games, a major determinant of strategy is what the other players are doing. This is the context in which coevolution is used here.

A starting point for considering the evolution of the early hominids in relation to other species with which they were sympatric is an analysis of the patterns of abundance of the terrestrial primates. As we have seen, the early hominids were just one among several groups of primate that have adopted a terrestrial mode of life, and, because of their similar ecological requirements, they are likely to have interacted considerably when they occurred sympatrically. Within the African savanna there are two major groups of terrestrial primates – the baboons (the Papionini) and the hominids (Hominidae). Other groups, such as the *Cercopithecus* monkeys may have been more terrestrial in their ancestral forms.

Baboons and hominids display some interesting patterns of abundance and distribution. Abundance is here defined as the number of individuals per species. Among the terrestrial primates the most common species in the early Pleistocene is *Theropithecus oswaldi* – the giant gelada. In East Africa these outnumber members of the other main group of baboons, the *Papio* complex (Jolly 1972). This contrasts markedly with present-day patterns. *Papio* is now ubiquitous throughout eastern and southern Africa, whereas *Theropithecus* is now confined to a single species (*T. gelada*) that occurs only in limited parts of the Ethiopian highlands.

With the fossil hominids, too, there is also a strikingly unequal pattern of abundance (Howell 1978). Assuming that the fossil assemblages are reasonably representative, australopithecines seem to have been almost twice as common as members of the genus *Homo*. At Koobi Fora, above the KBS Tuff, *Australopithecus boisei* outnumbers *Homo* by 2 to 1, and the same pattern is found in the Shungura Formation at Omo (Howell 1978). Under rather different taphonomical conditions, *Australopithecus* outnumbers *Homo* in the South African Transvaal cave sites (Brain 1981). The most extreme example is Swartkrans Member 1, where there are a minimum of 3 *Homo* individuals, but 87 *Australopithecus robustus* individuals.

These relative and absolute abundances may at least partially be a function of the greater robusticity of the australopithecines and hence their greater resistance to postmortem damage, but they also caution us against assuming that *Homo* – our own ancestors – were inevitably competitively superior to the australopithecines. Rather, it is necessary to consider the adaptations of the hominids in specific contexts to explain their changing adaptive success. Dietary and dental evidence is particularly important here. Both *Australopithecus* and *Theropithecus* appear to be more specialized than their sister taxa, *Homo* and *Papio*. *Theropithecus gelada*, the extant form, subsists principally on grass and rhyzomes (Dunbar 1977). This adaptation has affected the gelada's dental morphology. As discussed in Chapter 4 (see Fig. 4.3), Jolly (1972) has shown how its anterior dentition is greatly reduced, and its cheek teeth expanded and flattened. Furthermore, the locomotor and postural adaptations of geladas have also been modified for this specialized ground feeding (Jolly 1972; Dunbar 1977). This contrasts with the dentition of the other baboons, which have a more generalized and frugivorous diet. A similar contrast occurs between *Homo* and *Australopithecus*, especially the robust australopithecines. The latter have remarkably enlarged posterior teeth and reduced anterior teeth (see Fig. 8.14).

This evidence suggests that *Theropithecus* and *Australopithecus* represent the more specialized taxa, and, in particular, are specialized towards hard, small and low-quality food that occurs in savanna environments. This, as already suggested in Chapter 8, occurred as a response to the pressures of seasonality in a savanna environment. *Homo* and *Papio*, on the other hand, seem more generalized. During the Pliocene and the first part of the early Pleistocene the specialized taxa were more abundant than their generalized sister taxa, and so seem to have had the most successful adaptations. This can be placed into the context of the general model of community evolution discussed above (see Fig. 9.9).

The dominance of *Australopithecus* and *Theropithecus* occurs during the period of maximum species richness. Their specializations, and presumably narrower dietary niches, evolved as part of a general trend among the savanna community towards greater niche partitioning. These species were under similar selective pressures to the other herbivorous species, and evolving in response to the greater competitive ability and greater efficiency of the ever-expanding large-mammal fauna. Because of their specializations towards a food type that was abundant and widely dispersed, they became a common element of the fauna. *Papio* and *Homo*, on the other hand, did not become specialized in this way, but occupied a broader and more generalized ecological niche. Such an adaptation would greatly constrain the abundance of these species, which would exist at low population densities and with large home ranges.

The two evolutionary trends that have been identified among the early hominids – the australopithecines and the genus *Homo* – have already been related to alternative coping strategies, thus placing great emphasis in their evolutionary patterns on their foraging strategies. Equally import-ant, though, is the degree of specialization, regardless of the specific resources involved. The critical point here, in terms of the community-based approach that is central to this chapter, is that the trend towards specialization and narrower niches is consistent with a trend found among a whole range of large mammals at the same time. Again, the early hominids conform to the expectations of general evolutionary and ecological principles. Although their adaptive strategy is specific to their ancestral requirements and to the particular environment they were occupying, the pattern may be usefully compared with patterns found within the community as a whole. Hominid evolution is a coevolutionary phenomenon. The early hominids were changing in response to the changes going on around them, and no doubt this in turn influenced the evolution of the other species with which they were sympatric. It has been possible to show this with one particular group, the terrestrial primates, but the same pattern could probably be found with other groups. The principal point, though, is that the evolution of the early hominids can be fully understood only in the context of the evolution of the ecological community as a whole.

Speciation and extinction

The conclusions to be drawn from this and the preceding chapter are that the differences within the early African hominids may be related to their foraging behaviour and their degree of specialization. This pattern, it has been seen, makes sense both in terms of the local environmental con-ditions the hominids found themselves in and also in the context of the evolution of the savanna community as a whole. This conclusion leads us to a further area of evolutionary ecology – that is, speciation, or how it is that populations can diverge one from another and form new, isolated, species. Among these hominids we probably have contrasting solutions to the same ecological problem, as Dunbar (1983) has suggested, and also, as shown in the previous chapter, different populations facing different ecological problems. The questions we now need to answer, in the light of these results, are: How does the process of speciation occur? How often has it occurred in hominid evolution? And what affect does this fundamental evolutionary process have on the interactions occurring between populations – that is, coexistence or extinction?

Modes of speciation

The wide diversity of life-forms we can see today is a result of the divergence of populations. This is known as speciation when it results in the separation of gene pools and an end to interbreeding between populations. In referring to the different species of hominid, the conclusion is being drawn that they are genetically isolated, and that they are pursuing different adaptive strategies. To understand the basis for the divergence of the hominids it is necessary to know more about how speciation is thought to occur.

A great deal of discussion has occurred recently about the way new species form (see Eldredge & Gould 1972; Stanley 1975; White 1978; S. J. Gould 1980; Maynard Smith 1982; Mayr 1982). In considerations of speciation a distinction is usually drawn between *anagenesis* and *cladogenesis*. Anagenesis is the formation of new species by the transformation of an existing one through time. It usually refers to ancestor-descendent relationships. For example, *Homo sapiens* is usually thought to have evolved from *Homo erectus* by anagenesis. Anagenetically evolved species are in some senses pseudospecies, in that there is no clear line between the two species, merely a continuous transformation. Cladogenesis, on the other hand, is the formation of new species by splitting to form additional lineages, usually two. An example of this would be for an ancestral pongid to give rise to both chimpanzees and gorillas. The separation of *Australopithecus* and *Homo* is believed to have occurred in this way and so discussion will concentrate on it. Indeed, some authors have argued that all speciation is cladogenetic in nature, in the sense that even where there is no increase in the number of lineages, the new (descendant) species is derived from only part of the original ancestral population (Eldredge & Cracraft 1980).

Speciation is the development of reproductive isolation and the evolution of new ways of life. Perhaps the simplest and most likely way for reproductive isolation to occur is through geographical separation (allopatric speciation). If physical barriers form between populations for long periods of time, then they are likely to diverge either as a result of genetic drift, or through adaptation to different local conditions. When the barriers are removed and the populations overlap again (become sympatric) they are too different for successful interbreeding to occur. New species would then exist, the final outcome of which might either be coexistence or competitive exclusion (Fig. 9.11).

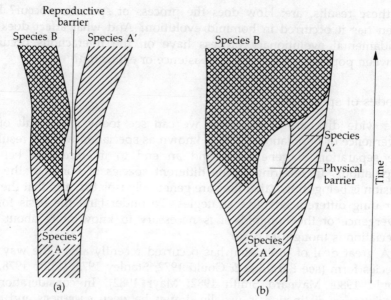

Figure 9.11   Allopatric speciation: the formation of new species is a result
of geographical isolation. In example (a) continued
coexistence of the daughter species occurs after the removal
of the geographical barrier. In (b) one species replaces the
other.

Speciation may also occur within sympatric populations. Several
mechanisms for this have been postulated (Table 9.5). These are all
biological mechanisms that prevent the successful production of fertile
offspring by certain individuals within the population. However,
although these mechanisms are theoretically sound, they are difficult to
test or observe in the natural world.

Whether sympatric or allopatric, perhaps the most important problem
in speciation is the relationship between the two essential components – a
new adaptation and reproductive isolation. The classic Darwinian view is
that reproductive isolation develops as a result of the emergence of new
adaptations. Populations begin to adapt to new conditions and change in
various ways as a result. This leads to the formation of reproductive
barriers. In other words, adaptation precedes reproductive isolation. New
species, therefore, form because there are new ecological niches. Recently, though, various authors have suggested that in the process of
speciation the sequence is reversed. Populations become either geographically or genetically isolated, and as a result start to evolve in different
directions, and towards new adaptive strategies. Reproductive isolation
precedes adaptation. The argument in favour of this is that in large
populations where gene flow is continuous, natural selection is unlikely

Table 9.5   Mechanisms of speciation (i.e. factors leading to reproductive isolation) (adapted from Ayala & Valentine 1979)

Allopatric speciation

Speciation can occur when populations are biographically isolated from each other (e.g. by mountains, rivers, etc.)

Sympatric speciation

Even when occurring within the same area reproductive isolation between populations can occur

1.   Prezygotic (preventing the formation of hybrid zygotes):
     - *Ecological isolation*: animals differ in preferred habitat, preventing mating
     - *Temporal isolation*: mating occurs at different times (of day or year)
     - *Ethological isolation*: behavioural differences between individuals prevent mating
     - *Mechanical isolation*: mating is prevented by anatomical differences
     - *Gametic isolation*: zygote formation is prevented despite mating

2.   Post-zygotic (hybrids are less viable at various stages than other offspring)

to be powerful enough to drive species towards new adaptations. By insisting on the reproductive isolation of small subpopulations it is possible to model for strong selection, sufficient to produce new adaptations relatively quickly before their being swamped by the inertia of a large gene pool.

The formation of new species, then, seems to involve both selection for new adaptive strategies, and the occurrence of the right demographic conditions. Perhaps the most important inference that we can draw and take to the problem of hominid speciation is that it is not merely a case of changing populations through time, gradually acquiring the right anatomical and behavioural characteristics, nor does it just depend on the right selective forces, but also on the spatial patterning of the populations. Speciation has a spatial dimension.

Hominid speciation

Speciation depends on isolation of some sort and divergent local selective pressures. In Chapter 8 it was suggested that the divergent local conditions were provided by the different types of ecosystems – those with dispersal/concentrating large-mammal systems, and those with migratory ones. Other factors may also have been important, such as local soil conditions, which can greatly affect the type of flora and hence the plant resources available. For these local differences to have an evolutionary significance it is essential that they should relate also to some level of isolation. Geographical isolation, as discussed above, would seem the most likely way in which this could be achieved.

In this context it is interesting to note that during the critical phases of early hominid evolution, the East African environment was likely to have produced exactly these conditions. First, as we have seen, the declining stability of the world's climate as it entered a glacial phase would have led to a fluctuation of the environments, and an oscillation between more forested and more open conditions. As discussed in Chapter 5, pockets of isolated savanna environment might well have been left that provided suitable conditions both for the emergence of the hominids as a whole and also for their fragmentation into a series of related taxa. Second, within East Africa itself, the Rift Valley system was forming, and the valley floor spreading. This was associated with high levels of tectonism and volcanic activity. These geological processes – blocking drainage systems, forming great fault scarps, spewing out sheets of lava and ash – would have led to more isolated conditions than would be found in more ancient and stable geological and environmental circumstances.

On the basis of these considerations it may be suggested that early hominid populations were frequently isolated, and, as a result of the ecological mechanisms discussed here, responded in various ways to local conditions. Hominid speciation is best seen in this light.

The divergence of hominid forms is usually treated in terms of the 'Homo-Australopithecus separation'. A major event leading to the separation of these two principal lineages occurred at some point in the past, resulting in a relatively simple evolutionary pattern (Fig. 9.12). More likely, though, is that throughout the hominid range in Africa, and over a prolonged period, a combination of geographical isolation and divergent selective pressures was producing populations that were adapting in rather different ways. Because the differences between the environments were likely to parallel themselves in different parts of the continent, the

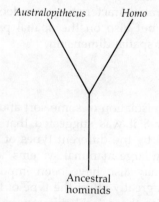

Australopithecus   Homo

Ancestral
hominids

Figure 9.12 'Classic' model of hominid speciation – a simple divergence into australopithecines and members of the genus *Homo*, the ancestors of later hominids.

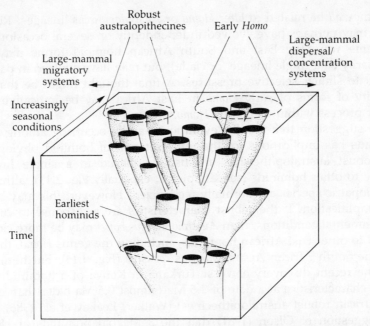

Figure 9.13 Model of early hominid radiation in relation to environmental conditions. The separation of the hominids is a response to increasing seasonality, and local environmental conditions, producing local populations adapting in parallel.

same basic adaptive trends would be expected to occur in parallel. In many cases, subsequent environmental change might result either in local extinction or in the merging together of populations and so the loss of extreme varieties. The net result of this would not, though, be a simple evolutionary bifurcation but a radiation of many forms, very often in parallel because ecological conditions would have been similar (Fig. 9.13). As suggested above, early hominid evolution should be a network of different solutions to different problems, contrasting solutions to the same problems, as well as the same solution to the same basic conditions. In the rather meagre fossil record we are likely to pick up only fragments of this radiation.

Such an approach solves certain problems of the early hominid fossil record. New finds seem to increase rather than decrease the complexity of interpretations, as characteristics appear independently in a variety of specimens and groups of fossils. This would be expected in the light of these evolutionary and ecological circumstances. Furthermore, it may well be that the ruthless application of Occam's razor to the fossil record – the simplest phylogeny is the best – is not always appropriate. For example, the specimens at Hadar may not be a single species, and neither need they *all* be related to later *Homo* or *Australopithecus* lineages. Robust forms may perhaps have evolved independently on several occasions. In the same way, the East and South African hominid forms may not necessarily be a single lineage (or clade), but may have evolved in parallel subject to similar selective pressures. A final thought might be that the diversity of forms of early *Homo* in East Africa may be indicative of a similar process within the genus *Homo*.

The suggestion that parallel evolution may be occurring among early hominids has implications for the interpretation of hominid phylogeny. The robust australopithecines are usually placed in a single lineage relative to other hominids (see Chapter 2, especially Fig. 2.11), although two allopatric species are normally recognized. However, this may be an oversimplification. If the robust characteristics are a response to certain environmental conditions, then *Australopithecus boisei* may be more closely related to other East African hominids, including the genus *Homo*, than it is to the South African *Australopithecus robustus* (Fig. 9.14). Furthermore, with the recent discovery at West Turkana in Kenya of a hominid with robust characteristics at a date of 2.5 Ma (almost 0.5 Ma older than other East African robust australopithecines) (Walker, Leakey et al. 1986), and the suggestion of Olson (1981) that the 3 Ma old hominids at Hadar include robust specimens, the possibility of an earlier and independent evolution of the robust adaptations should be considered. This would produce a far more complex pattern of early hominid phylogeny than is usually entertained (Fig. 9.14). Such a phylogeny, incorporating the recognition that the genus *Homo* may have been diverse as well, would require a revision of hominid taxonomy and nomenclature, including possibly the restoration of the genus *Zinjanthropus*.

This would explain the origins of hominid diversity. How, though, would it be maintained, and not just maintained but also reinforced, leading to the establishment of greater and greater differences between the hominines and the australopithecines? One of the principal means by which population and ultimately species differences may be maintained is through competitor avoidance, as discussed in Chapter 8. As generalized and specialized populations came into contact with each other, as they would through expansion following adaptive success, then advantages would accrue to them both if they avoided competition and niche over-lap. This would lead to further character displacement, whereby within each population selection would favour those individuals most different from the other population, resulting in increasing morphological and adaptive divergence. Although the early differentiation of populations into new species might be facilitated by geographical separation, further divergence may be enhanced by sympatry.

Another mechanism that would reinforce the differences between populations is frequency-dependent selection. This occurs when the advantage of any adaptive strategy depends on the frequency with which

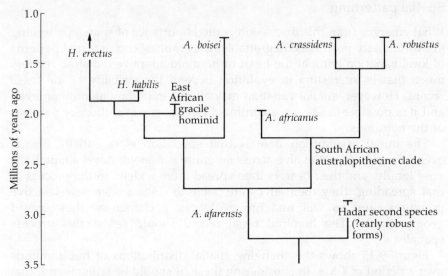

Figure 9.14 Tentative model of early hominid adaptive radiation in Africa involving high levels of speciation. The main points of contention here would be the presence of a second species before 3 Ma, and the separation of the eastern African and southern African specimens into different clades.

the adaptation occurs. The rarer it is, the greater the advantage. As a result of this selective advantage, the adaptation increases in frequency, but as this happens the advantages become less and less, until eventually the advantage switches back to the original, and now increasingly rare adaptation. Sometimes an equilibrium may be established, at other times frequencies may oscillate. In this way alternative adaptations may be maintained within a single ecosystem. In more concrete terms, as austra-lopithecines become more dominant within an ecosystem, then the greater their competitive interference with each other becomes. In this context, populations of *Homo* can be expected to do better, and thus increase in frequency. At some point, though, as their resources begin to be depleted, the balance should switch back to the australopithecines. As a result, species diversity can be maintained.

In summary, then, the formation of new species of hominid is a result of there being two alternative pathways based on different foraging behaviour. Which evolutionary pathway is followed depends on local conditions, but, once established, competition, character displacement, frequency-dependent selection and phylogenetic inertia will ensure that both are maintained and elaborated. In this way, it may be argued that far from being the straightforward unilineal process originally envisaged, early hominid evolution at least was a true adaptive radiation.

Spatial patterning

What emerges from this discussion is the importance of spatial patterning in evolutionary processes. Regrettably, the emphasis on repeated patterns of local variation lying at the heart of hominid adaptive radiation renders much that is interesting in evolution beyond the visibility of the fossil record. However, spatial variation may also be important at another level, and it is possible to see, on a continental scale, the evolutionary patterns of the hominids.

The initial assumption here is that speciation is essentially a local event. Species do not evolve across an entire continent; novel adaptations arise locally, and their bearers then spread more widely. In the process of that spreading, they themselves are liable to come under new selective pressures, and so will undergo evolutionary change as they spread geographically. The hominid fossil record should reflect this process spatially.

Figure 9.15 shows the changing spatial distributions of the hominids over a period of 4 Ma. In considering these, it should be remembered that in fact the fossil record is derived from only two main areas within Africa, the Transvaal and the East African Rift Valley, and so the reconstruction depends on extrapolation.

It is assumed that the origins of the hominids lie at a date greater than 6 Ma, somewhere in East Africa. However, given the overall distribution of the African hominoids, the centre of distribution might lie further to

Figure 9.15 (opposite)   Large-scale geographical patterns and early hominid evolutionary patterns in Africa. This figure shows that there is a spatial element to the evolutionary process that cannot be reduced to simple phylogenetic trees.

(a) Differentiation of African hominoids and origin of hominids.
(b) Establishment of hominid populations (*Australopithecus afarensis*) in eastern Africa.
(c) Earliest hominid differentiation – appearance of first populations with robust specializations.
(d) Expansion of hominids into southern Africa and evolution of *Australopithecus africanus*.
(e) Appearance of *Homo* in eastern Africa and partial expansion of *Homo* to southern Africa. Appearance in eastern and southern Africa of robust australopithecine populations.
(f) Evolution and expansion of *Homo erectus* plus late survivorship of robust australopithecine populations.

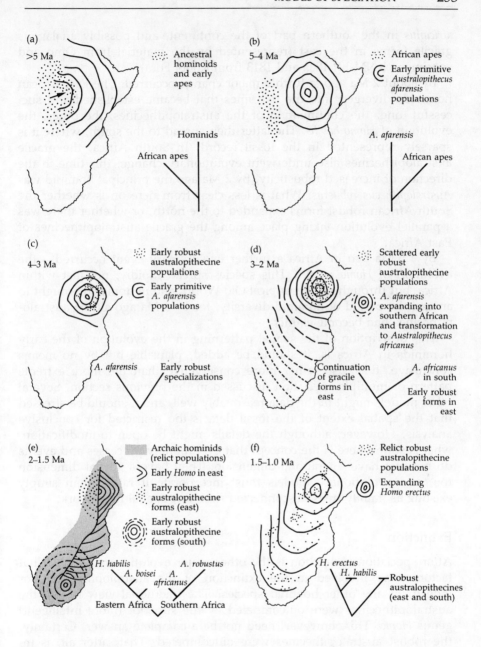

(a)
>5 Ma

- Ancestral hominoids and early apes

Hominids

African apes

(b)
5–4 Ma

- African apes
- Early primitive *Australopithecus afarensis* populations

A. afarensis

African apes

(c)
4–3 Ma

- Early robust australopithecine populations
- Early primitive *A. afarensis* populations

A. afarensis   Early robust specializations

(d)
3–2 Ma

- Scattered early robust australopithecine populations
- *A. afarensis* expanding into southern African and transformation to *Australopithecus africanus*

Continuation of gracile forms in east

A. africanus in south

Early robust forms in east

(e)
2–1.5 Ma

- Archaic hominids (relict populations)
- Early *Homo* in east
- Early robust australopithecine forms (east)
- Early robust australopithecine forms (south)

H. habilis   *A. robustus*
A. boisei   *A. africanus*

Eastern Africa   Southern Africa

(f)
1.5–1.0 Ma

- Relict robust australopithecine populations
- Expanding *Homo erectus*

H. erectus
H. habilis   Robust australopithecines (east and south)

the west. Between 5 and 3 Ma ago, the hominids seem to be confined to the eastern portion of the continent, and be relatively homogenous. The period from 3 to 2 Ma ago was one of major change. The hominids expanded to the south. It might be suggested that during this expansion the gracile *Australopithecus afarensis*, the basal hominid form, underwent evolutionary changes that resulted in the appearance of *Australopithecus africanus* in the southern part of the continent, and possibly analagous gracile forms in the east (represented by the material from Omo and specimens KNM-ER 1805 and 1813 from Koobi Fora).

By about 2 Ma ago, a further major change occurred. The East African hominids diverged into the two lines that became established and successful: one, the continuation of the australopithecines; the other, the evolution of *Homo habilis*. The latter then spread to the south, where it is sparsely represented in the fossil record. In South Africa, the gracile australopithecines also underwent evolutionary change, this time in the direction of increased robusticity. By 2 Ma ago the principal hominid was *Australopithecus robustus*. What is less clear from here on is whether the South African robust forms expanded to the north, or whether there was a parallel evolution taking place among the gracile australopithecines of East Africa.

By 1.5 Ma ago in Africa a further evolutionary event occurred – the evolution of *Homo erectus*. This species spread rapidly, not just within Africa, but throughout the tropical Old World, and in doing so brought to an end the period of hominid diversity, for by 1 Ma ago all the australopithecines had become extinct.

This description of the spatial patterning in the evolution of the early hominids in Africa is, it should be added, plausible but by no means conclusive. It is also rather more conservative than the more extreme pattern of multiple speciation discussed in the previous section. Several other models might fit the data reasonably well, and it should be stressed that the spatial extent of the fossil data is too restricted for conclusive analysis. However, although the details might be open to modification, what is sound here is the concept that evolutionary processes and events do not just have a temporal dimension. They have a spatial dimension too, and evolutionary models must incorporate it rather than simply existing as 'family trees' disconnected from any spatial framework.

Extinction

After speciation, extinction is the other major evolutionary event. What factors were involved in the extinction of the australopithecines, or indeed, of any other hominid species? The traditional view is that the australopithecines were outcompeted by the superior (more intelligent) genus *Homo*. This, however, need not be a complete answer. Certainly, the robust australopithecines were outcompeted. That, after all, is inherent to extinction. They were not, though, necessarily outcompeted by the other hominids, but by other species. In view of the model of divergence just presented, it seems likely that the two types of hominid overlapped ecologically relatively little by the later stages. Indeed, it was competitor avoidance that drove them apart. The effect of this character displacement, though, would have been to force each hominid increasingly into competition with other non-hominid and non-primate species. In the case of *Homo erectus*, this would have been the frugivores, the omnivores and the large carnivores. It has been suggested by Walker (1984) that *H. erectus* had by this time joined the large predator guild, resulting in considerable evolutionary changes within that guild. Certainly, the large carnivorous species do evolve at this time.

Australopithecus robustus/boisei, on the other hand, would be competing with the herbivores. During this time, these species were themselves undergoing rapid evolutionary change, including diversification. It is probably due to their increasing efficiency, abundance and diversity that both the australopithecines and the theropithecines came under considerable ecological pressure, and ultimately became extinct. The problems that the australopithecines faced, and never solved, were those of becoming sandwiched between more efficient herbivorous specialists on one side, and more efficient omnivores on the other. Their evolutionary options were extremely limited.

To return to the general model of community evolution presented in Fig. 9.9, by 1 Ma ago the third phase, that of an increased rate of extinction, had been reached. In the development of community structure through niche-partitioning, the niches had become so finely divided that within the savanna environment herbivorous specialization was not a viable option for a primate. Consequently, we can see in Fig. 9.10 the demise of the specialized terrestrial primates, with only the more omnivorous ones surviving.

If *Homo erectus* did play a part in the extinction of the other terrestrial primates, it might well have been as a predator rather than as a direct competitor. For example, at Olorgesaillie, a middle Pleistocene site in Kenya, the carcasses of 50 *Theropithecus* baboons are associated with Acheulean handaxes, and Shipman (1982), among others, has claimed that the hominids were directly responsible for their deaths. Binford & Todd (1982), though, have argued that there is no direct evidence that the hominids did other than to scavenge the carcasses.

Both in their origins as new species, and in their extinction, the australopithecines and their evolutionary history must be seen in the context of the ecological community as a whole. Concentration on the hominids in isolation, to the exclusion of their other sympatric species, is likely to overemphasize their ecological interactions, resulting in a narrow and anthropocentric view of hominid evolution.

The tempo of evolution

The analyses in this book have attempted to show the relationship between hominid characteristics and the evolutionary and ecological environment in which hominids had to survive. Such a relationship can be documented. So far, though, the pattern has been only loosely calibrated against time. Emphasis has been placed on the conformity between general principles and specific events and characteristics, rather than on evolutionary sequences through time. What has not been considered is whether the pattern of change described here has come about through gradual and continuous change, or through a more uneven and punctuated process. Attempts to calibrate the events of human evolution more closely highlight whether there are time lags between adaptive problem and response, and whether the adaptive solution is ultimately optimal. In this lies the importance of considering the tempo of hominid evolution.

The problem of evolutionary rates

The past few years have seen considerable debate about the rate of evolution (Eldredge & Gould 1972; Stanley 1979; S. J. Gould 1980). Early hominid fossils have been used both to support (Gould 1977) and refute (Cronin, Boaz et al. 1981) the punctuated equilibrium view of evolutionary patterns. Stimulated principally by palaeontologists, this debate has centred on whether evolution takes place at a gradual (and perhaps constant) rate, or whether it is marked by periods of rapid change followed by prolonged stasis. Evidence for a punctuated equilibrium model of evolutionary change has been used to argue that mechanisms other than natural selection are responsible for the pattern of evolution (Eldredge & Gould 1972; Stanley 1979; S. J. Gould 1980; Vrba 1980).

Maynard Smith (1982) has suggested that the debate has minor and major issues. The minor issue is the rate of evolution, and the major one the mode of evolution. For classical Darwinians the mode of evolution operates at the level of the individual. This mode is sufficient to explain all levels of evolutionary change, including the formation of new species. Accordingly, because adaptation and selection are so closely related, species formation is part of the adaptive trends of a lineage.

This, however, is no longer a consensus view. Several workers (Stanley, 1975, 1979; Eldredge & Cracraft 1980; S. J. Gould 1980; Vrba 1980) regard the mechanisms of speciation as distinct from those operating on individuals. New species arise (usually rapidly) among small isolated populations *as a result of isolation*, and the new adaptations that occur are not directionally related to the adaptive trends of the parent population. Consequently, the appearance of new species is not related to any directionality of evolutionary change within the ancestral populations. This is often referred to as the 'decoupling' of the mechanisms of evolution, for it proposes different modes for intraspecific change (natural selection) and interspecific change (species selection).

It has already been suggested that small isolated populations do play an important part in speciation (see page 245), but this need not necessarily be independent of general adaptive trends. Genetic drift is not the only process operating on small populations. Selection can still be significant, and selective agencies can be the same as those operating on large populations, but the small size of the gene pool allows populations to be modified relatively quickly. A rapid rate of evolution confined to small populations in which new species form does not necessarily mean that natural selection is not the principal mechanism of evolutionary change.

The main support for the decoupling of the formation of species from microevolutionary change derives from the argument about the rate of evolution. Williamson (1981) has suggested on the basis of his analysis of the molluscs in the fossil beds of Lake Turkana, that natural selection is unable to account for the prolonged periods of stasis observed, and therefore that some mechanism other than natural selection must be operating. This is part of the general argument about the factors affecting the rates or tempo of evolution.

Three factors seem to contribute to the rate of evolution, and it is the emphasis given to these that is at issue. One factor is the intensity and direction of selection; if selection is lax, or if it is strongly stabilizing, then the rate of evolutionary change will be low. If novel features are beneficial, or occur during periods of environmental change, then the rate of evolution will be rapid. Classical Darwinism places emphasis on the intensity of selection as determining the rate of evolution, but this does not predict a constant or slow rate. The other factors are the rate and character of mutation and the size and breeding pattern of the population. If rapid evolutionary change occurs when these conditions are right, then selection would play, as Gould and his co-workers have argued, a less-important part.

Hominid evolutionary rates

What, though, is the tempo of evolution, among the hominids? Various authors have addressed this problem. Gould (1977) asserted that no evolutionary change could be observed within any of the recognized species of early hominid, and therefore that the pattern of human evolution conforms to that of the punctuated equilibrium model. This has been elaborated by Eldredge & Tattersall (1982), who recognize a pattern of change and stasis in the hominid fossil record: *Australopithecus afarensis*, *A. boisei/robustus* and *Homo erectus* all remain virtually unchanged for a period of about 1 Ma, with abrupt morphological breaks between them. The pattern of stasis for *H. erectus* has been quantified by Rightmire (1981), although this has been challenged (Wolpoff 1984).

A detailed critique of the punctuated equilibrium model of hominid evolution has been presented by Cronin, Boaz et al. (1981). In contrast to Gould, they argue that the fossil record is far from complete, and that breaks in morphology can be accounted for by a lack of suitable geological deposits. Furthermore, they claim to recognize some continuous trends in hominid evolution. One of these is the continuity in certain anatomical features between *Australopithecus afarensis* and *A. africanus*; another is the intermediate position of KNM-ER 1470, between the genus *Homo* and *Australopithecus* (Walker 1976); a further example is KNM-ER 1813, another Koobi Fora specimen that might be considered a transitional form. Perhaps the best-documented case, though, of considerable and continuous evolutionary change is the transition from *Homo erectus* to *H. sapiens*. Although there has been some argument about terminology (itself perhaps evidence for continuity!), the middle Pleistocene record of Europe and Africa shows the continuous variability between these two chronospecies. Cronin, Boaz et al. (1981) do accept some punctuational events, principally the appearance of the robust australopithecines, although Alan Bilsborough (personal communication) has shown there to be some continuity between the gracile and robust australopithecines in South Africa.

Lack of clear-cut morphological criteria and stratigraphic confusion are bound to make it difficult to come to an unambiguous conclusion about the tempo of change within the hominid lineage. However, it does seem possible to conclude that the rate of evolution of the hominids is not constant. It has varied through time, with different aspects evolving at different rates over the period. This variation in rate is not in itself a denial of the Darwinian process, but, rather, raises the question of whether the varying tempo of hominid evolution can be related to the pattern of selection, and to the particular ecological conditions in which the early hominids lived.

Three periods of relatively rapid change can be identified: the appearance of the robust australopithecines, the appearance of *Homo erectus*, and the appearance of anatomically modern man. This is not to say that these were 'instantaneous' events, but that they were rapid relative to preceding phases of evolution. Before these events might be another phase, marked by the appearance of the first bipedal hominid, but there is insufficient fossil evidence to test this assertion.

The first of these events occurred at 2 Ma; the second at about 1.6 Ma, and the third between 0.1 and 0.05 Ma ago. According to the models presented in this chapter we would expect these to relate to periods of intense competition and evolutionary activity among other animals. Regrettably, it is difficult to gain sufficiently tight chronological control to test this adequately. From Fig. 9.16, it can be seen that the Pliocene, the period in which the robust australopithecines appeared, was a period with a very high rate of faunal turnover (approximately 75 per cent at the generic level), while the level of endemism remained constant and the rate of extinction declined. This suggests a period of evolutionary change as a whole. This is substantiated by a consideration of the patterns of

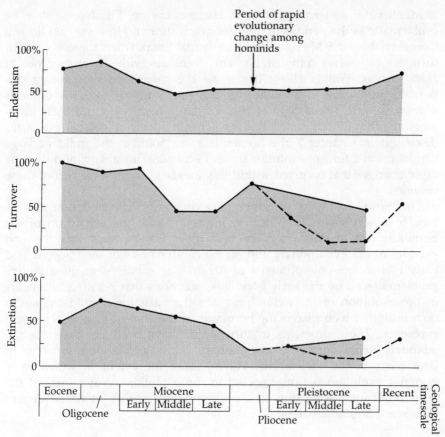

Figure 9.16   Patterns of later Cenozoic mammalian change in Africa (from Maglio 1978).

evolution of the best-known fossil groups. The pigs and the elephants, which have been intensively studied (White & Harris 1977; Harris 1983), undergo major evolutionary changes during this period. The appearance of the robust australopithecines, then, coincides with the appearance of many other species. Furthermore, Vrba (1985), who has argued that in South Africa the pattern of evolutionary change among hominids and bovids is related, has made a case that this period of rapid evolutionary change is related to major changes in climate and African environment at this time. Deep-sea cores indicate that the period 2.5 to 2.0 Ma ago is one of reduced global temperatures (Thunell & Williams 1983). Apparently, punctuational change may in fact be a response to novel and intensive selective pressures as a result of environmental change, mediated for the hominids through evolutionary change within the African savanna community.

Identifying patterns of faunal change in the Pleistocene can be problematic as the periods of time are much shorter. However, at Olduvai Gorge at about 1.6 Ma ago there is a faunal break when there is a major turnover of species composition. This coincides with the appearance of *Homo erectus*. Walker (1984) has made the suggestion that during this period there were major shifts in the predator/prey systems of large mammals, with the decline of the old, large herbivores and their predators. It may be suggested that as a result of the ecological pressures discussed in Chapter 7 the hominids were 'joining' the guild of large carnivores at a time of evolutionary and ecological instability, and that the rapid changes that occurred within the lineage of *Homo* were part of these changes.

The period following the emergence of *Homo erectus* is one of relative morphological stasis. It coincides, however, with the expansion of the hominids out of Africa for the first time. *Homo erectus* was the end product of the evolutionary and ecological dynamics of the Pliocene and early Pleistocene environments of Africa. The solutions to the adaptive problems faced by the early hominids, solutions that resulted ultimately in the evolution of *H. erectus*, provided the basis for a rapid change in distribution, which placed the hominids in the context of new ecological problems. These problems in turn would have been the basis for the adaptive, behavioural and evolutionary changes that were to occur in later parts of the Pleistocene. Having seen the extent to which early hominid evolution is firmly rooted in the evolutionary dynamics of the African savanna, it remains to examine briefly some of the consequences of moving into new habitats.

10 Hominids as colonizing animals

The principal focus of this book has been the early hominids of Africa Hominid evolution, at least in its earliest and perhaps most formative period, is, on present evidence, an African affair. As has been seen in previous chapters, the taxonomic group to which the hominids belong are the African apes, and furthermore, many hominid characteristics may be related to the ecological dynamics of the African environment. However, it should be remembered that this phase of evolution provided the basis for what was an equally important aspect of hominid evolutionary ecology – the colonization by hominids of all the major habitats of the world, and their spread to all of the continents. This chapter examines briefly aspects of that expansion in terms of some general principles of evolutionary ecology.

The critical theoretical context for this is that all animals are to a greater or lesser extent confined to certain habitats. These habitats provide them with food and shelter, while others cannot be exploited successfully, either because of physical barriers or because of competitive pressure. There are, though, certain general principles governing the extent to which species may be *stenotopic* (that is, confined to a specific habitat) or *eurytopic* (able to tolerate a wide range of conditions). In their earlier phases hominids seem to be restricted to certain African habitats. Through the Pleistocene these restrictions lapsed. The critical questions are what made this expansion possible, and what were the ecological and evolutionary consequences?

Out of Africa

It has to be admitted that the pattern of human expansion from Africa is far from understood, owing to the patchiness of research, taphonomical factors, and the absence of suitable dating techniques for critical periods of the middle and late Pleistocene. Some broad observations, though, can be made.

Sequence of colonization

1.   Before 1.5 Ma ago there is no reliable evidence for hominids outside the eastern and southern regions of sub-Saharan Africa.

2.   Between 1.5 and 1.0 Ma ago there is evidence for hominids in regions of sub-Saharan Africa and in Southeast Asia. By inference, it is necessary to suppose that they had also colonized intervening regions of the Old World tropics, including parts of the Middle East and the Indian sub-continent. However, firm evidence for this has yet to be established, despite claims for a very early date (c. 2.0 Ma) for the site of 'Ubeideya in Israel (Repenning & Fejfar 1982). Equally, the earlier suggestions that the fossil hominids associated with the Djetis Beds and faunas of Java date from 1.9 Ma ago (Curtis 1981) have been questioned (Matsu'ura 1982; Pope 1983; Sartono 1982). It now seems likely that the earliest evidence for hominids outside Africa is younger than 1.5 Ma old.

3.   Between 1.0 and 0.7 Ma ago is the date suggested for the earliest occupation of the warm temperate zones, including Mediterranean Europe. Although many claims for a much earlier occupation of Europe have been made (see Turner 1984: 196), the earliest established date comes from Isernia La Pireta in Italy (Coltorti, Cremacshi et al. 1982). Overall, a date on the early/middle Pleistocene boundary seems appropriate for the colonization of the warm temperate zones of the Old World.

4.   Between 700 000 and 300 000 years ago the more northerly temperate environments were colonized by *Homo erectus*.

5.   Between 300 000 and 40 000 years ago northerly latitudes, although probably not extreme arctic conditions, came within the compass of hominid occupation, this phase coinciding with the evolution from *Homo erectus* to *H. sapiens*.

6.   Between 40 000 and 10 000 years ago virtually the entire remaining areas of the globe were colonized. The extreme arctic environments were occupied, albeit at a time of extreme glaciation. This gave access to the New World, through which hominids spread very rapidly, and at this time, or possibly a bit earlier, the Australasian region was reached.

7.   After 10 000 years ago the areas of the world remaining unoccupied were the polar regions and some of the remoter islands. These have gradually been reached in later prehistory and on into historic times.

The ecology of hominid colonization

Several factors have undoubtedly affected this pattern of expansion. First and foremost has been the presence of geographical barriers and ecological barriers (in relation to species requirements). Geographical barriers, principally sea, mountains and glaciers, certainly played a major part in delaying the colonization of Australia. However, despite these specific factors, it is possible to see an ecological patterning in the hominids' colonization.

Figure 10.1 shows the sequence of habitat colonization by early hominids. From this it can be seen that it does not seem to be temperature alone that is significant, for, on present evidence, it seems that hominids moved into temperate latitudes before they were able to survive in tropical rainforests. Habitat structure and resource types were more important. It follows that a sequence of habitats was initially colonized in order of similarity to the original savanna environment. The temperate grasslands, despite their divergent patterns of seasonality and temperature, offered a preferable habitat compared with the closed and highly vegetated tropics. The second point is that preferred habitats display certain ecological characteristics. As can be seen from Fig. 10.2, environments that have a high turnover of energy (P/B ratio), rather than simply high availability of energy, are preferred. This suggests that the resources to which *Homo erectus* had access were those that underwent rapid growth and reproduction, or to the animals that exploited these species. These organisms tend to be highly nutritious, but also available for only short periods of time, illustrating the close relationship between hominid evolution and patterns of seasonality (Foley 1984b) (see also Chapter 8).

Turning to other factors, the pattern of human radiation is not one that has occurred in isolation. The early hominids spread out of Africa alongside, and in competition with, a range of other species. Recently Turner (1984) has usefully compared the colonization of high latitudes by hominids with that of other species. It is interesting to note that *Homo erectus* and a range of other species (lion, leopard, hyena and wolf) all reached temperate Eurasia at about the same time (Turner 1984: table 8.2). The suggestion may be made that hominids were part of a general biographic event, prompted and constrained by similar factors across a range of species. Hominid uniqueness may yet again be seen to be illusory. Rather, environmental factors clearly favoured organisms with certain characteristics; those characteristics are large body size, carnivorous behaviour, and sociality. Species with these attributes, despite their tropical origins, had the adaptive capacity to exploit new environments.

What was the basis of this capacity? Several broad ecological principles may be used to answer this question. First, it is well known that carnivores are more eurytopic than herbivores. Meat, as a resource,

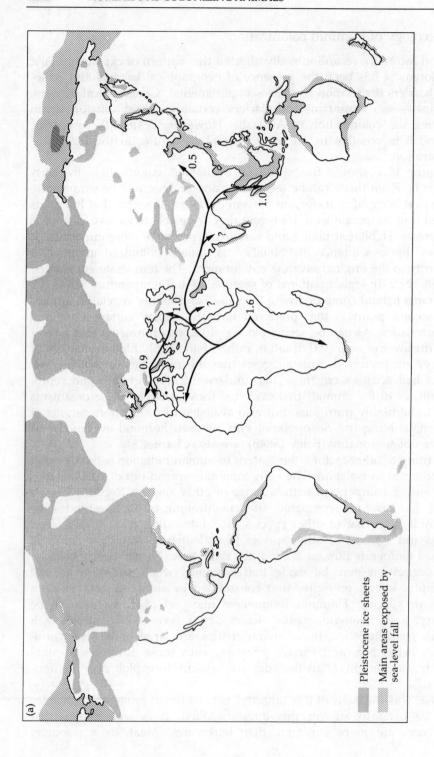

Pleistocene ice sheets

Main areas exposed by sea-level fall

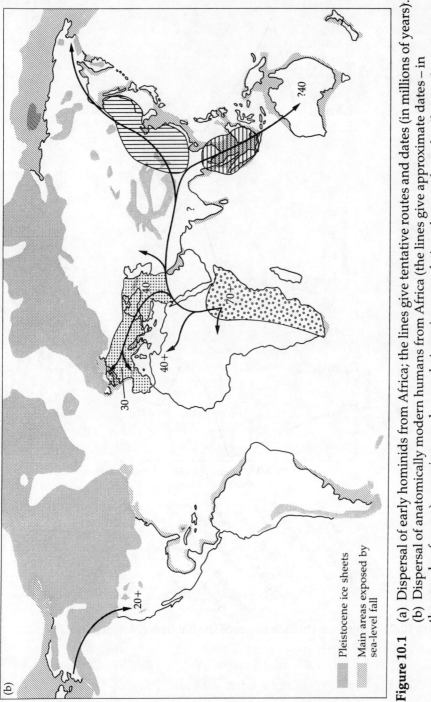

Figure 10.1 (a) Dispersal of early hominids from Africa; the lines give tentative routes and dates (in millions of years). (b) Dispersal of anatomically modern humans from Africa (the lines give approximate dates – in thousands of years) superimposed on archaic *sapiens* populations known from fossil records: (○), ancestors of anatomically modern humans in sub-Saharan Africa; (●), European and Western Asian neanderthal populations; horizontal and vertical lines, Eastern Asian populations.

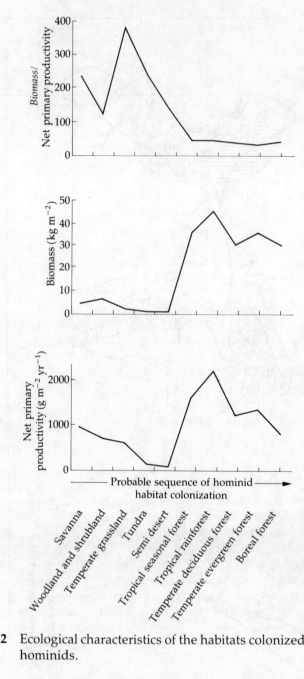

Figure 10.2 Ecological characteristics of the habitats colonized by early hominids.

requires less specialized and local adaptations than plants. A deer is very much like an antelope, and a front leg is very similar to a back leg, as far as a predator is concerned. In contrast, plants vary structurally and locally far more, requiring more specialized and finely divided niches. Thus, it would be expected that carnivores would be more likely to radiate geographically, without speciation or morphological alteration, than herbivores. This is best illustrated by the low diversity of large mammalian carnivores throughout the world, with each one occupying a very large geographical area, and the very high, regionally localized diversity of large herbivores. This, and the congruence in radiation between hominids and large carnivores, suggests that they were dependent to a considerable degree on meat, and that, regardless of its importance within the tropical savanna environments, meat-eating was a major contributing factor to hominid success.

A second general principle is that exogeny often provides a considerable advantage to an organism. It is frequently assumed that the key to ecological success is a close and highly resolved adaptation to local conditions. Although that is true, it is success bought at a price. The price is the breadth of the niche exploited. Local adaptation is usually obtained through specialization and through competition avoidance and intolerance. Under stable conditions with indigenous communities this is a clear trend, and a successful strategy. However, introduced, exogenous species may often be at an advantage, as a result of this ability to forage across a range of niches. Although they may be less efficient within a single niche than any single indigenous species, this may be offset by their ability to exploit resources from a variety of niches. Examples of this from the natural and human world are well known. The spread of red deer in New Zealand, of cattle in sub-Saharan Africa, of rabbits in Australia illustrate this point. It may be argued, therefore, that as fairly generalized foragers, hominids were at an advantage in temperate Eurasia (and ultimately in Australia and the New World) as an exogenous species. Indigenous temperate species may have been unable to compete with the presence of these newcomers, a possible factor in the extinction of many larger mammals during the Pleistocene.

The third general principle that may be used in the analysis of hominid expansion is that of environmental physiology, and in particular Allen's law. It has long been known that, as a result of the relationship between heat loss, body volume and surface area, cold environments favour large body size, and reduced limb proportions. In this context, it is perhaps interesting to note that, as Trinkaus (1981) and Stringer (1984) have documented, the distal limb segments of the neanderthals are among the shortest, relative to body size, known for human populations. In this physical characteristic neanderthals are closest to living populations from high latitudes. (Fig. 10.3). Postcranial evidence for other early *Homo sapiens* and for *Homo erectus* populations is regrettably absent, but it is

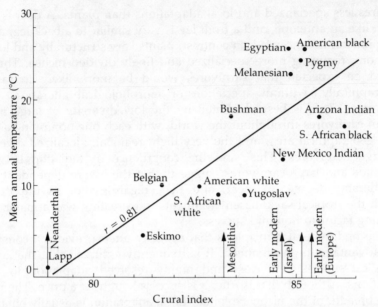

Figure 10.3   Relationship between mean annual temperature and mean
crural index (tibial length/femur length × 100) from some
modern human populations. This plot shows that distal limb
length tends to be longer for humans living in warmer
environments. When fossil hominids are considered, it can
be seen that neanderthals have limb proportions similar to
those of cold-adapted populations, whereas the earliest
representatives of anatomically modern humans are close to
tropical populations. This may indicate a tropical origin for
anatomically modern humans (data: Trinkaus 1981) (from
Stringer 1984).

clear that some hominid populations at least adapted to new and colder
environments through classical physiological techniques. There is indeed
some possibility that the increase in body size associated with *Homo
erectus* (see Chapter 6) may have at least contributed to the success of
human geographical spread.

Although general biological principles can to a larger extent be
employed to account for the expansion of hominids as part of a general
biogeographic event, certain problems remain. Survival in high latitudes
does pose certain specific problems, the solutions to some of which may
be used to account for some special hominid characteristics.

In a remarkably elegant paper Torrence (1983) has shown that hunter–
gatherers living in high latitudes are subject to time stress; that is, that a
particular problem faced in their environment is the limited time or
'window' through which they have access to resources. Two concepts are

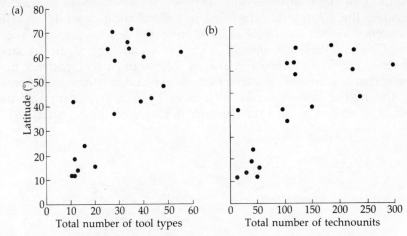

Figure 10.4   Relationship between latitude and (a) tool diversity and (b) tool complexity among modern hunter–gatherer populations (after Torrence 1983).

critical. One is that resource availability is highly seasonal, such that at certain times of the year resources are superabundant, but at others very scarce. And two, that because of the marked annual variation in day length, there is only a limited amount of daylight available for foraging and other activities during the winter. General principles can provide us with some expectations about how this time stress may be coped with.

When resources are available, but the time to gather them is limited, selection will clearly favour strategies involving either (1) the extraction only of resources giving high returns; and/or (2) an increase in the efficiency with which resources are extracted. The former often involves increasing carnivory, and this will almost certainly be the primary subsistence base for hominids in high latitudes. The second will therefore involve ways of increasing predatory efficiency. Hominid hunting success on the whole depends on technological efficiency, and therefore selection for efficiency should take the form of technological development. Two points are worth noting here. The first is that Torrence has shown quite clearly that among modern hunter–gatherers there is a close relationship between technological complexity and latitude (Fig. 10.4). High-latitude populations have more tool types, and these tools are themselves more complex, made up of more components. And the second is that although there is a general and global technological development during the Pleistocene, it is in the high latitudes that it is most marked; in parts of the tropics the artefacts remained simple. For example, in Southeast Asia, a basic pebble-tool technology is maintained throughout the Pleistocene, to be replaced only in the Holocene by a microlithic technocomplex.

Expansion to high latitudes thus exposed hominids to new selective pressures, the solution to which lay in technological dependence. This dependence in turn was likely to have promoted general cognitive skills, for as Gowlett (1984) has shown, stone tool technology requires a large number of conceptual steps and images. Although current evidence may suggest that anatomically modern humans evolved in Africa, their spread into the higher latitudes may well have been a significant selective pressure as well as being a consequence of that evolutionary shift.

Conclusions

Summing up the disparate threads of over 5 million years of evolution among several lineages is no easy task. Perhaps the real character of the early hominids must always remain the murky shadow behind the models we build. These models, though, and the tests of them that we can establish, are the only path to understanding the underlying reasons for the evolution of our own, unique, species. If the ecology, behaviour and evolution of the early hominids has not been illuminated by the preceding pages, it is to be hoped that the role of biological theory and model building in palaeoanthropology has.

The principal conclusion to be drawn from the evidence and arguments presented here is that the evolution of species bearing the attributes we think of as 'human' is not inevitable in the sense of being the pre-ordained outcome of a teleological evolutionary process, but that it is the expected product of the 'right' ecological and evolutionary conditions. Hominids and humans have evolved because, given the basic processes and mechanisms of biology and evolution, their adaptive characteristics 'solve' the problems posed by certain phylogenetic and ecological cir-cumstances. The purpose of this book has been to try and show the fit between the pattern of hominid evolution and those circumstances in the context of the principles of evolutionary ecology.

Under this scrutiny early hominids emerged as rather different beasts from the abnormally ambitious but dim-witted semi-ape of popular fiction. No aspect of evolution is intermediate, transitional, or incipient, making sense only in the context of later human history. Rather, each evolutionary change should be explicable in terms of its immediate short-term effectiveness, or the extent to which it solved the current problems of survival and reproduction. The past of our, or any, species must be analysed in the context of the events and processes contemporary with that past, not in the light of subsequent evolutionary happenings. In the arguments and models put forward here those contexts have been to the fore, and have been the driving force of human evolution. Among the most significant were characteristics that the hominids and their ancestors inherited as a result of their evolutionary history – their body size and their mammalian and primate heritage. This phylogenetic heritage, it was seen, played a large part in determining the evolutionary pathways taken. It represents a major constraint within which natural selection must operate. The responses of the early hominids to the problems they faced were conditioned by their ancestry. The evolutionary lesson for other animals is perhaps that if you want to be a hominid, where you start is as important as where you are going!

If phylogenetic heritage represents the internal motor driving evolution, then the environment represents the external one, and so the other context in which human evolution must be seen. A range of environmental conditions was seen to influence human evolution and indeed to form the necessary precondition for its occurrence. The tropical environments of the Old World, the seasonal African savannas, the temperate, increasingly cold environments of the Pleistocene, and the pattern of environmental change and instability all left their mark on hominid evolution. However, what became clear was that the environment is not just a passive backdrop for evolution, nor an independent force shaping species, but is itself made up of evolving species, competing organisms, and ever-shifting ecological relationships. It is the complex web of relationships between organisms that patterns evolutionary change, not simple, unidirectional 'environmental determinism'.

What, though, of the adaptive strategies of early hominids? They now appear as very much an African affair – part of the African hominoid radiation and part of a community of coevolving African mammals. Many lines of evidence now point to this more localized interpretation of the early hominids, and should stimulate a greater focus of research on the nature of the African environment in shaping the first stages of hominid evolution. What this interpretation might also do is to promote a recognition of the tremendous evolutionary significance that expanding *out of Africa* is likely to have had. Exogeny can be a major factor both in terms of the balance of ecological systems, and in determining the character of adaptive strategies. Above and beyond this, though, emerges the interesting point that throughout the bulk of human prehistory *dispersal*, not intensification, has been the principal means by which hominid populations have been maintained and increased. Dispersal is probably the norm as a survival strategy among most animal species, and, in this, early hominids seem to be no exception. Intensification of existing adaptations is perhaps a component of recent human prehistory and history.

Apart from their 'Africanness', another feature that appears fundamental to their evolution is their bipedalism. Not only is this stamped throughout their anatomy, it also appears early and is in some form characteristics of all hominids. Where intelligence and enlargement of the brain were once thought to have provided the initial kick in human evolution, it now seems that it was the form of locomotion that was critical. Recognition of this in the fossil record has focused the attention of palaeoanthropologists on what the early hominids were *doing* on two legs.

In trying to find out what they were doing it is important to bear in mind that there is no single lineage of hominid. Although there may be some dispute about exactly how many species of hominid there have been, there is now no doubt that there were, between 3 and 1 Ma ago, more than one contemporary hominid species. This is probably the far-reaching conclusion of palaeoanthropology of the past two decades, for it finally brings home the point that human evolution is like that of other species, and that there is no single way of being a hominid. Hominid adaptations are expected products of the processes of evolution and ecology, and variations of this theme and evolutionary experiments in hominid adaptations should exist. What might be particularly exciting is the possibility of earlier such experiments, producing hominid-like forms that bear no direct relationship to later species. These may be among the fossils still to be discovered.

As to *how many* such species there should be, we have perhaps not yet discovered the full range. As variety is the spice of palaeoanthropological life, the more species the better! However, what is perhaps likely, on the basis of what has been presented here, is that any new species that are found will repeat in some way the adaptive themes of those already known. It has been shown that *Australopithecus* and *Homo* represent trends of specialization and generalization. These are the alternative pathways of evolution for hominids, the outcomes of interspecific inter-actions, and the outcome of local competitive conditions. These are liable to have recurred across the African continent, and the fossil record should reflect these two trends.

Accordingly, *Australopithecus* and *Homo* display different adaptive characteristics. *Australopithecus* showed a tendency towards increasing size and robusticity, whereas *Homo* is more gracile. However, even within the lineage leading towards modern humans, these two divergent themes can also be seen. This repeated pattern indicates the way in which the ecological problems and adaptive changes are funnelled through the same basic evolutionary processes. It is the general patterns, variations in size and distribution and diversity, that will perhaps tell us most about the pattern of human evolution.

What we have seen in this book is that the story of human evolution is not just a question of searching for and finding spectacular fossils and building family trees, but is a task primarily concerned with what an animal in the past was doing – what it was eating, what sort of social behaviour it had, what physiological characteristics it possessed. It is these questions that lie at the heart of the evolutionary process, as much for human beings as any other species. This means that the discovery, and indeed the taxonomic description of the fossils, is only the starting point in the pursuit for our origins. Equally important is the reconstruction of a way of life, for that is what natural selection works on and produces. The study of human evolution must therefore be placed firmly within the orbit of all the fields of evolutionary biology. Neither the special characteristics of humans, nor the limiting nature of the fossil record, must be allowed to limit the questions we seek to ask about the evolution of our own species.

When Charles Darwin published the *Origin of Species* and the *Descent of Man* he struck the first blow against the uniqueness of our species among all the others on this planet. The discovery of fossils has provided other species that can fill may of the gaps, and so erode further that uniqueness. Studies of other animals, their behaviour in the wild, their anatomy in the dissecting room, and their biochemistry in the test-tube, have chipped yet more away from the pedestal on which we have wanted to place ourselves. This line of research has been among the most significant in anthropology and biology, but to some extent the real message on the Darwinian revolution is somewhat different. The essence of evolutionary theory is not that all species are the same, but that they are all produced by the same biological processes and by the mechanism of natural selection. Now that the biological and evolutionary character of the hominids has been established, the main task facing palaeoanthropologists is perhaps less to show that humans are not unique, for all species are unique, but to show how that uniqueness can be the product of processes that are themselves general to all living matter. We should recognize that we are a unique species, but also that we are just another unique species.

References

Aronson, J. L. & Taieb, M. 1981. Geology and paleogeography of the Hadar hominid site, Ethiopia. In: Rapp. G & Vondra, C. F. (eds) *Hominid Sites: their Geologic Settings*. AAAS Selected Symposium No. 63. Boulder, Co.: Westview Press, pp. 165–96.

Aiello, L. C. 1981. Locomotion in the Miocene Hominoidea. In: Stringer, C. B. (ed.) *Aspects of Human Evolution*. Symposia for the Study of Human Biology No. 12. London: Taylor & Francis, pp. 63–98.

Allen, E. et al. 1976. Against sociobiology. *New York Review of Books* (13 November):182.

Altmann, S. 1974. Baboons, space, time and energy. *American Zoologist* 14:221–48.

Altmann, S. & Altmann, J. 1970. *Baboon Ecology*. Chicago: University of Chicago Press.

American Journal of Physical Anthropology 1982. Vol. 57(4).

Andrews, P. J. 1981. Species diversity and diet in apes and monkeys during the Miocene. In: Stringer, C. B. (ed.) *Aspects of Human Evolution*. Symposia for the Study of Human Biology No. 12. London: Taylor & Francis, pp. 63–98.

Andrews, P. J. 1983. The natural history of *Sivapithecus*. In: Ciochon, R. & Corruccini, R. (eds) *New Interpretations of Ape and Human Ancestry*. New York: Plenum Press, pp. 441–64.

Andrews, P. J. 1984a. The descent of man. *New Scientist* (3 May): 24–5.

Andrews, P. J. 1984b. An alternative interpretation of the characters used to define *Homo erectus*. *Courier Forschungsinstitut Seckenberg* 69:167–75.

Andrews, P. J. & Tobien, H. 1977. New Miocene locality in Turkey with evidence on the origins of *Ramapithecus* and *Sivapithecus*. *Nature* 268:699–701.

Andrews, P. J., Lord, J. M. & Evans E. N. M. 1979. Patterns of ecological diversity in fossil and mammalian faunas. *Biological Journal of the Linnean Society* 11:177–205.

Anon. 1983. Oncogenes, reductionism and all that. *Nature* 301:369.

Ardrey, R. 1961. *African Genesis*. London: Atheneum.

Ayala, F. J. & Valentine, J. W. 1979. *Evolving: the Theory and Processes of Organic Evolution*. Menlo Park, Ca.: Benjamin Cummings.

Badgeley, C. & Behrensmeyer, A. K. 1980. Palaeoecology of middle Siwalik sediments and faunas, North Pakistan. *Palaeogeography, Palaeoclimatology & Palaeoecology* 30:133–55.

Beadle, L. C. 1974. *The Inland Waters of Tropical Africa: an Introduction to Tropical Limnology*. London: Longman.

Behrensmeyer, A. K. 1978. Taphonomic and ecologic information from bone weathering. *Paleobiology* 4:150–62.

Behrensmeyer, A. K. 1983. Patterns of natural bone distribution on recent land surfaces: implications for archaeological site formation. In: Clutton-Brock, J. & Grigson, C. (eds) *Animals and Archaeology: 1. Hunters and their Prey*. B. A. R. International Series No. 163. Oxford: B. A. R., pp. 93–106.

Behrensmeyer, A. K. & Dechant Boaz, D. E. 1980. The recent bones of Amboseli Park, Kenya, in relation to East African paleoecology. In: Behrensmeyer, A. K. & Hill, A. P. (eds) *Fossils in the Making*. Chicago: University of Chicago Press, pp. 72–93.

Behrensmeyer, A. K. & Hill, A. P. (eds) 1980. *Fossils in the Making*. Chicago: University of Chicago Press.

Behrensmeyer, A. K., Gordon, K. D. & Yanagi, G. T. 1986. Trampling as a cause of bone surface damage and pseudo-cutmarks. *Nature* 319:768–71.

Bernor, R. L. 1983. Geochronology and zoogeographic relationships of Miocene Hominoidea. In: Ciochon, R. L. & Corruccini, R. S. (eds) *New Interpretations of Ape and Human Ancestry*. New York: Plenum Press, pp. 149–64.

Binford, L. R. 1967. Smudge pits and hide smoking: the use of analogy in archaeological reasoning. *American Antiquity* 32:1–12.

Binford, L. R. 1977. *For Theory Building in Archaeology*. London & New York: Academic Press.

Binford, L. R. 1978a. Dimensional analysis of behavior and site structure: learning from an eskimo hunting stand. *American Antiquity* 43:330–61.

Binford, L. R. 1978b. *Nunamuit Ethnoarchaeology*. New York & London: Academic Press.

Binford, L. R. 1979. Organization and formation processes: looking at curated technologies. *Journal of Anthropological Research* 35:255–73.

Binford, L. R. 1980. Willow smoke and dogs' tails: hunter–gatherer settlement systems and archaeological formation systems. *American Antiquity* 45:4–20.

Binford, L. R. 1981. *Bones: Ancient Men and Modern Myths*. New York &

London: Academic Press.

Binford, L. R. 1983. *In Pursuit of the Past*. London: Thames and Hudson.

Binford, L. R. 1984. *Faunal Remains from Klasies River Mouth*. New York & London: Academic Press.

Binford, L. R. & Binford, S. R. 1966. A preliminary analysis of functional variability in the Mousterian of Levallois facies. *American Anthropologist* 68:238–95.

Binford, L. R. & Sabloff, J. 1982. Paradigms, systematics and archaeology. *Journal of Anthropological Research* 38:137–53.

Binford, L. R. & Todd, L. C. 1982. On arguments for the 'butchering' of giant geladas. *Current Anthropology* 23:108–10.

Birch, F. 1951. Recent work on the radioactivity of potassium and some related geophysical problems. *Journal of Geophysical Research* 56:107–26.

Bishop, W. W. & Miller, J. (eds) 1972. *Calibration of Hominoid Evolution*. Edinburgh: Scottish Academic Press.

Bishop, W. W., Hill, A. & Pickford, M. 1978. Chesowanja: a revised geological interpretation. In: Bishop, W. W. (ed.) *Geological Background to Fossil Man*. Edinburgh: Scottish Academic Press, pp. 309–27.

Boaz, N. 1979. Early hominid population densities: new estimates. *Science* 206:592–5.

Boesch, C. & Boesch, H. 1983. Optimization of nut-cracking with natural hammers by wild chimpanzees. *Behaviour* 83:265–85.

Bonnefille, R. 1972. *Associations polliniques actuelles et quaternaires en Ethiopie (vallées de l'Awash et de l'Omo)*. Thesis, University of Paris VI.

Bonnefille, R. 1976. Palynological evidence for an important change in the vegetation of the Omo Basin between 2.5 and 2 million years ago. In: Coppens, Y. et al. (eds) *Earliest Man and Environments in the Lake Rudolf Basin: Stratigraphy, Paleoecology, and Evolution*. Chicago: University of Chicago Press, pp. 421–31.

Bonnefille, R. 1979. Méthode palynologique et reconstitutions paleoclimatiques au Cénozoique dans le Rift Est Africain. *Bullétin de la Societé Géologique, France* 21:331–42.

Bonnefille, R. 1984. *The Evolution of East Asian Environment*, ed. R. Dr White. Centre of Asian Studies, University of Hong Kong.

Bonnefille, R. 1985. Evolution of the continental vegetation: the palaeobotanical record from East Africa. *South African Journal of Science* 81:267–70.

Bonner, J. B. 1968. Size change in development and evolution. *Journal of Palaeontology* 42:1–15.

Bordes, F. 1961. *Typologie du paléolithique ancien et modern*. Publications de l'Institut de Préhistoire de l'Université de Bordeaux Mémoir No. 1. Bordeaux: Imprimeries Delmas.

Bortz, W. M. 1985. Physical exercise as an evolutionary force. *Journal of Human Evolution* 14:145–55.

Bourlière, F. 1963. Specific feeding habits of African carnivores. *African Wildlife* 17:21–7.

Bown, T. M., Kraus, M. J., Wing, S. L., Fleagle, J. G., Tiffney, B. H., Simons, E. L. & Vondra, C. F. 1982. The Fayum primate forest revisited. *Journal of Human Evolution* 11:603–32.

Boyde, A. & Martin, L. 1984. The microstructure of primate dental enamel. In: Chivers, D., Wood, B. A. & Bilsborough, A. (eds) *Food Acquisition and Processing in Primates*. New York: Plenum Press, pp. 341–67.

Brace, C. L. 1964. The fate of the classic Neanderthals: a consideration of hominid catastrophism. *Current Anthropology* 5:3–43.

Brain, C. K. 1981. *The Hunters or the Hunted: an Introduction to African Cave Taphonomy*. Chicago: University of Chicago Press.

Bräuer, G. 1984. A craniological approach to the origin of anatomically modern *Homo sapiens* in Africa and implications for the appearance of modern Europeans. In: Smith, F. & Spencer, F. (eds) *The Origins of Modern Humans: a World Survey of the Fossil Hominids*. New York: Alan Liss, pp. 327–410.

Brody, S. 1945. *Bioenergetics and Growth*. Baltimore: Reinhold.

Broeker, W. S. & van Donk, J. 1970. Insolation changes, ice volumes and 18_0 record in deep-sea cores. *Reviews of Geophysics and Space Physics* 8:168–98.

Brose, D. S. & Wolpoff, M. H. 1971. Early Upper Palaeolithic man and late Middle Palaeolithic tools. *American Anthropologist* 73:1156–94.

Brown, F. H. 1981. Environments in the Lower Omo Basin from one to four million years ago. In: Rapp. G & Vondra, C. F. (eds) *Hominid Sites: their Geologic Settings*. AAAS Selected Symposium No. 63. Boulder, Co.: Westview Press, PP. 149–64.

Brown, J. L. 1964. The evolution of diversity in avian territorial systems. *Wilson Bulletin* 76:160–9.

Buchardt, B. 1978. Oxygen isotope palaeotemperatures from the Tertiary period in the North Sea area. *Nature* 275:121–3.

Bunn, H. T. 1981. Archaeological evidence for meat-eating by Plio-Pleistocene hominids from Koobi Fora and Olduvai Gorge. *Nature* 291:575–7.

Bunn, H. T. & Kroll, E. M. 1986 Systematic butchery by Plio/Pleistocene hominids at Olduvai Gorge, Tanzania. *Current Anthropology* 27(5) (in press).

Butzer, K. W. 1972. *Environment and Archaeology* (2nd edition). London: Methuen.

Butzer, K. W. 1982. *Archaeology as Human Ecology*. Cambridge: Cambridge University Press.

Butzer, K. W., Isaac, G. L., Richardson, J. L. & Washbourn-Kamau, C. 1972. Radiocarbon dating of East African lakes. *Science* 175:1069–76.

Cain, A. J. 1964. *Animal Species and Evolution*. London: Hutchinson.

Campbell, B. 1974. *Human Evolution: an Introduction to Man's Adaptations*. Chicago: Aldine.

Cant, J. G. H. & Temerin, L. A. 1984. A conceptual approach to foraging adaptations in primates. In Rodman, P. S. & Cant, J. G. H. (eds) *Adaptations for Foraging in Nonhuman Primates.* New York: Columbia University Press, pp. 304–42.

Cavalli-Sforza, L. & Feldman, M. 1981. *Cultural Transmission and Evolution.* Princeton, N. J.: Princeton University Press.

Chivers, D. 1977. The feeding behaviour of siamang (*Symphalangus syndactylus*). In: Clutton-Brock, T. (ed.) *Primate Ecology.* New York & London: Academic Press, pp. 355–83.

Ciochon, R. L. 1983. Hominid cladistics and the ancestry of modern apes and humans. In: Ciochon, R. & Corruccini, R. (eds) *New Interpretations of Ape and Human Ancestry.* New York: Plenum Press, pp. 781–843.

Ciochon, R. L. & Chiarelli, A. B. (eds) 1980. *Evolutionary Biology of the New World Monkeys and Continental Drift.* Plenum Press: New York.

Ciochon, R. L. & Corruccini, R. S. (eds) 1983. *New Interpretations of Ape and Human Ancestry.* New York: Plenum Press.

Clark, J. D. & Kurashina, H. 1979. Hominid occupation of the east-central highlands in the Plio-Pleistocene. *Nature* 282:33–9.

Clark, J. D., Asfaw, B., Assefa, G., Harris, J. W. K., Kurashina, H., Walter, R. C., White, T. D. & Williams, M. A. J. 1984. Palaeoanthropological discoveries in the Middle Awash Valley, Ethiopia. *Nature* 307:421–8.

Clark, J. G. D. 1968. *World Prehistory: a New Outline* (2nd edition). Cambridge: Cambridge University Press.

Clarke, D. L. 1968. *Analytical Archaeology.* London: Methuen.

Cloudsley-Thomson, J. L. 1975. *Terrestrial Environments.* London: Croom-Helm.

Clutton-Brock, T. H. & Harvey, P. 1977a. Primate ecology and social organization. *Journal of the Zoological Society of London* 183:1–39.

Clutton-Brock, T. H. & Harvey, P. 1977b. Species differences in feeding and ranging behaviour in primates. In: Clutton-Brock, T. H. (ed.) *Primate Ecology.* New York & London: Academic Press, pp. 557–84.

Clutton-Brock, T. H. & Harvey, P. 1979. Comparison and adaptation. *Proceedings of the Royal Society Series* B205:547–65.

Clutton-Brock, T. H. & Harvey, P. 1981. Primate home range size and metabolic needs. *Behavioural Ecology and Sociobiology* 8:151–5.

Coe, M. D., Cummings, D. H. & Phillipson, J. 1976. Biomass and production of large herbivores in relation to rainfall and primary production. *Oecologia* 22:341–54.

Colinvaux, P. 1973. *Introduction to Ecology.* New York: Wiley.

Coltorti, M., Cremaschi, M., Delitala, M. C., Esu, D., Fornaseri, M., McPherron, A. et al. 1982. Reversed magnetic polarity at an early Lower Palaeolithic site in Central Italy. *Nature* 300:173–6.

Connell, J. H. 1975. Producing structure in natural communities. In: Cody, M. L. & Diamond, J. M. *Ecology and Evolution of Communities.* Cambridge, Mass.: Harvard University Press, pp. 460–90.

Conroy, G. C. & Pilbeam, D. 1975. *Ramapithecus*: a review of its hominid status: In: Tuttle, R. (ed.) *Palaeoanthropology: Morphology and Palaeoecology*. The Hague: Mouton, pp. 59–86.

Coppens, Y. & Howell, F. C. 1976. Mamalian faunas of the Omo group: distributional and biostratigraphical aspects. In: Coppens, Y., Howell, F. C., Isaac, G. & Leakey, R. E. F. (eds) *Earliest man and environments in the Lake Rudolf Basin*. Chicago: University of Chicago Press, pp. 177–92.

Cronin, J. E. 1983. Apes, humans and molecular clocks: a reappraisal. In: Ciochon, R. & Corruccini, R. S. (eds) *New Interpretations of Ape and Human Ancestry*. New York: Plenum Press, pp. 115–38.

Cronin, J. E., Boaz, N. T., Stringer, C. B. & Rak, Y. 1981. Tempo and mode in hominid evolution. *Nature* 292:113–22.

Crook, J. H. & Gartlan, J. S. 1966. Evolution of primate societies. *Nature* munication in weaver birds (Ploceinae). *Behaviour Supplement* 10:1–178.

Crook, J. H. & Gartlan, J. S. 1966. Evolution of primate societies, *Nature* 210:1200–3.

Crowell, K. L. 1962. Reduced inter-specific competition among the birds of Bermuda. *Ecology* 43:75–88.

Curio, E. 1973. Towards a methodology of teleonomy. *Experientia* 29:1045–58.

Curtis, G. H. 1981. Establishing a relevant time-scale in anthropological and archaeological research. *Philosophical Transactions of the Royal Society*. B292:7–20.

Darwin, C. 1859. *Origin of Species*. Reprinted Penguin Books, 1968.

Darwin, C. 1871. *Descent of Man and Selection in Relation to Sex*. London: Murray.

Dawkins, R. 1976. *The Selfish Gene*. London: Oxford University Press.

Dawkins, R. 1982a. *The Extended Phenotype*. San Francisco: Freeman.

Dawkins, R. 1982b. Replicators and vehicles. In: King's College Sociobiology Group (eds) *Current Problems in Sociobiology*. Cambridge: Cambridge University Press, pp. 45–64.

Day, M. H. 1971. Postcranial remains of *Homo erectus* from Bed IV, Olduvai Gorge, Tanzania. *Nature* 232:383–7.

Day, M. H. & Molleson, T. 1973. The Trinil femora. In: Day, M. H. (ed.) *Human Evolution*. Symposium for the Study of Human Biology No. 11. London: Taylor & Francis, pp. 127–54.

DeBrul, E. L. 1962. The general phenomenon of bipedalism. *American Zoologist* 2:205–8.

Delaney, M. J. & Happold, D. C. D. 1979. *Ecology of African Mammals*. London: Longman.

DeVore, I. & Washburn, S. L. 1963. Baboon ecology and human evolution. In: Howell, F. C. & Bourlière, F. (eds) *African Ecology and Human Evolution*. Chicago: Aldine.

Diamond, J. M. 1977. Distributional strategies. In: Allen, H., Jones, R. & Golson, J. (eds) *Sunda and Sahul*. New York and London: Academic

Press, pp. 295–315.

Diamond, J. M. 1978. Niche shifts and the rediscovery of inter-specific competition. *American Scientist* 66:322–31.

Dobzhansky, T. 1974. Chance and creativity in evolution. In: Ayala, F. J. & Dobzhansky, T. (eds) *The Philosophy of Biology*. Berkeley: University of California Press, pp. 309–39.

Dorman, S. 1925. *Pygmies and Bushmen of the Kalahari*. London: Seeley Service & Co.

Dunbar, R. I. M. 1976. Australopithecine diet based on a baboon analogy. *Journal of Human Evolution* 5:161–7.

Dunbar, R. I. M. 1977. Feeding ecology of gelada baboons: a preliminary report. In: Clutton-Brock, T. (ed.) *Primate Ecology*. New York & London: Academic Press, pp. 251–73.

Dunbar, R. I. M. 1982. Adaptation, fitness and the evolutionary tautology. In: King's College Sociobiology Group (eds) *Current Problems in Sociobiology*. Cambridge: Cambridge University Press, pp. 9–28.

Dunbar, R. I. M. 1983. Theropithecines and hominids: contrasting solutions to the same ecological problem. *Journal of Human Evolution* 12:647–58.

Dyson-Hudson, R. & Smith, E. 1978. Human territoriality: an ecological reassessment. *American Anthropologist* 80:21–41.

Efremov, I. A. 1940. Taphonomy: a new branch of paleontology. *Pan-American Geologist* 74:81–93.

Ehrlich, P. R. & Raven, P. H. 1964. Butterflies and plants: a study in co-evolution. *Evolution* 18:586–608.

Eichna, L. W., Bean, W. F., W. B. Bean & Shelley, W. B. 1945. The upper limits of heat and humidity tolerated by acclimatized men working in hot environments. *Journal of Industrial Hygiene and Toxicology* 27:59–84.

Eisenberg, J. 1981. *The Mammalian Radiations: an Analysis of Trends in Evolution, Adaptation and Behaviour*. London: Athlone Press.

Eldredge, N. & Cracraft, J. 1980. *Phylogenetic Patterns and the Evolutionary Process*. New York: Columbia University Press.

Eldredge, N. & Gould, S. J. 1972. Punctuated equilibrium: an alternative to phyletic gradualism. In: Schopf, T. J. M. (ed.) *Models in Paleobiology*. San Francisco: Freeman, pp. 82–115.

Eldredge, N. & Tattersall, R. 1982. *The Myths of Human Evolution*. New York: Columbia University Press.

Ellen, R. 1982. *Environment, Subsistence and System: the Ecology of Small-scale Social Formation*. Cambridge: Cambridge University Press.

Eyre, S. R. 1968. *Vegetation and Soils: a World Picture*. London: Arnold.

Fagan, B. 1978. *People of the Earth* (2nd edition). Boston: Little, Brown & Co.

Fleagle, J. G. 1983. New interpretations of the phyletic position of Oligocene hominoids. In: Ciochon, R. & Corruccini, R. S. (eds) *New*

Interpretations of Ape and Human Ancestry. New York: Plenum Press, pp. 181–210.

Fleagle, J. G. 1984. Primate locomotion and diet. In: Chivers, D., Wood, B. & Bilsborough, A. (eds) *Food Acquisition and Processing in Primates*. New York: Plenum Press, pp. 105–18.

Fleagle, J. G. & Kay, R. F. 1983. Locomotor adaptations of Oligocene and Miocene hominoids and their phyletic implications. In: Ciochon, R. & Corruccini, R. S. (eds) *New Interpretations of Ape and Human Ancestry*. New York: Plenum Press, pp. 301–24.

Fleischer, R. L. & Hart, H. R., Jr 1972. Fision-track dating: techniques and problems. In: Bishop, W. W. & Miller, J. (eds) *Calibration of Hominoid Evolution*. Edinburgh: Scottish Academic Press, pp. 135–70.

Flenley, J. R. 1979. *The Equatorial Rainforest: a Geological History*. London: Butterworth.

Foley, R. 1978. Incorporating sampling into initial research design: some aspects of spatial archaeology. In: Cherry, J., Gamble, C. & Shennan, S. (eds) *Sampling in Contemporary British Archaeology*. B. A. R. British Series No. 50. Oxford: B. A. R., pp. 49–66.

Foley, R. 1981. Aspects of variability in palaeoecological studies. In: Sheridan, A. & Bailey, G. (eds) *Economic Archaeology*. B. A. R. International Series No. 96. Oxford: B. A. R., pp. 67–76.

Foley, R. 1982. A reconsideration of the role of predation on large mammals in tropical hunter–gatherer adaptation. *Man* (N. S.) 17:383–402.

Foley, R. 1983. Modelling hunting strategies and inferring predator behaviour from prey attributes. In: Clutton-Brock, J. & Grigson, C. (eds) *Animals and Archaeology: 1. Hunters and their Prey*. B. A. R. International Series No. 163. Oxford: B. A. R., pp. 63–76.

Foley, R. 1984a. Putting people into perspective. In: Foley, R. (ed.) *Hominid Evolution and Community Ecology: Prehistoric Human Adaptation in Biological Perspective*. New York & London: Academic Press, pp. 1–24.

Foley, R. 1984b. Early man and the Red Queen: tropical African community evolution and hominid adaptation. In: Foley, R. (ed.) *Hominid Evolution and Community Ecology: Prehistoric Human Adaptation in Biological Perspective*. New York & London: Academic Press, pp. 85–110.

Foley, R. 1985. Optimality theory in anthropology. *Man* (N. S.) 20:222–42.

Ford, C. S. & Beach, F. A. 1952. *Patterns of Sexual Behaviour*. London: Eyre & Spottiswood.

Forde, C. D. 1934. *Habitat, Economy and Society*. London: Methuen.

Fossey, D. & Harcourt, A. 1977. Feeding ecology of free-ranging mountain gorillas (*Gorilla gorilla beringei*). In Clutton-Brock, T. (ed.) *Primate Ecology*. London: Academic Press, pp. 415–49.

Frayer, D. W. & Wolpoff, M. H. 1985. Sexual dimorphism. *Annual Review of Anthropology* 14:429–73.

Friday, A. E. 1981. Hominoid evolution: the nature of the biochemical evidence. In: Stringer, C. (ed.) *Aspects of Human Evolution*. London: Taylor & Francis, pp. 1–24.

Futuyma, D. J. 1979. *Evolutionary Biology*. Sunderland, Mass.: Sinauer Associates.

Gamble, C. 1981. Scratches on the palaeolithic record. *Nature* 291:533–4.

Gannt, D. G. 1983. The enamel of Neogene hominoids: structural and phyletic implications. In: Ciochon, R. & Corruccini, R. S. (eds) *New Interpretations of Ape and Human Ancestry*. New York: Plenum Press, pp. 249–98.

Genet-Vargin, E. 1966. Conjures sur l'allure générale des Australopitheques. *Bulletin de la Societé Préhistorique Française* 63:cvi–cvii.

Gericho, M. & Hoffmeyr, J. 1976. Aetiology and treatment of capture stress and myopathy in springbok (*A. marsupialis*). *South African Journal of Science* 72:28.

Gibson, J. R. & McKeown, T. 1952. Observations in all births (23970) in Birmingham, 1974:6. Birthweight, duration of gestation and survival related to sex. *British Journal of Social Medicine* 6:152–8.

Gifford-Gonzalez, D. P., Damrosch, D. B., Damrosch, D. R., Pryor, J. & Thunen, R. L. 1985. The third dimension in site structure: an experiment in trampling and vertical dispersal. *American Antiquity* 50:803–18.

Gillespie, R., Gowlett, J. A. J., Hall, E. T. & Hodges, R. E. M. 1984. Radiocarbon measurement by accelerator mass spectrometry: an early selection of dates. *Archaeometry* 26:15–20.

Goodall, J. 1963. Feeding behaviour of wild chimpanzees: a preliminary report. *Symposia of the Zoological Society of London* 10:39–47.

Goodall, J. van Lawick 1970. Tool-using in primates and other vertebrates. In: Lehrman. P., Hinde, R. & Shaw, E. (eds) *Advances in the Study of Behaviour*. London: Academic Press, pp. 195–249.

Goodall, J. van Lawick 1971. *In the Shadow of Man*. London: Collins.

Goodman, M. 1976. Towards a genealogical description of the primates. In: Goodman, M. & Tashien, R. E. (eds) *Molecular Anthropology*. New York: Plenum Press, pp. 321–53.

Goodman, M., Baba, M. L. & Darga, L. L. 1983. The bearing of molecular data on the cladogenesis and times of divergence of hominoid lineages. In: Ciochon, R. & Corruccini, R. S. (eds) *New Interpretations of Ape and Human Ancestry*. New York: Plenum Press, pp. 67–86.

Gould, R. 1969. Subsistence behaviour among the western desert aborigines. *Oceania* 39:253–74.

Gould, R. 1980. *Living Archaeology*. Cambridge: Cambridge University Press.

Gould, S. J. 1966. Allometry and size in ontogeny and phylogeny. *Biological Reviews* 41:587–640.

Gould, S. J. 1977. *Ever Since Darwin: Reflections in Natural History*. London: Penguin.

Gould, S. J. 1980. Is a new and general theory of evolution emerging?

Paleobiology 6:119–30.

Gould, S. J. & Lewontin, R. 1979. The spandrels of San Marco and the panglossian paradigm: a critique of the adaptationist programme. *Proceedings of the Royal Society, London* B205:581–98.

Gould, S. J. & Vrba, E. S. 1983. Exaptation – a missing term in the science of form. *Paleobiology* 8:4–15.

Gowlett, J. A. J. 1984. Mental abilities of early man: a look at some hard evidence. In: Foley, R. (ed.) *Hominid Evolution and Community Ecology: Prehistoric Human Adaptation in Biological Perspective.* New York & London: Academic Press, pp. 167–92.

Gowlett, J. A. J., Harris, J. W. K., Walton, D. & Wood, B. A. 1981. Early archaeological sites, hominid remains, and traces of fire from Chesowanja, Kenya. *Nature* 294:125–9.

Grand, T. I. 1972. A mechanical interpretation of terminal feeding. *Journal of Mammalogy* 53:198–203.

Grant, P. R. 1972. Convergent and divergent character displacement. *Biological Journal of the Linnean Society* 4:39–68.

Gray, B. T. 1980. *Environmental reconstruction of the Hadar Formation (Afar, Ethiopia).* PhD thesis, Cape Western Reserve University.

Greenwood, P. N. 1974. The cichlid fishes of Lake Victoria, East Africa: the biology and evolution of a species flock. *Bulletin of the British Museum (Natural History) Zoological Supplement* No. 6.

Grine, F. 1981. Trophic differences between 'gracile' and 'robust' australopithecines: a scanning electron microscope analysis of occlusal events. *South African Journal of Science* 77:203–30.

Grove, A. T. 1967. *Africa South of the Sahara.* London: Oxford University Press.

Haeckel, E. 1876. *The History of Creation.* London: Murray.

Hall, K. R. L. 1962. Numerical data, maintenance activities and locomotion in the wild chacma baboon (*Papio ursinus*). *Proceedings of the Zoological Society of London* 139:181–220.

Hall, K. R. L. 1966. Behaviour and ecology of the wild patas monkey, *Erythrocebus patas*, in Uganda. *Journal of the Zoological Society, London* 148:15–87.

Hamilton, A. 1982. *Environmental History of East Africa.* New York & London: Academic Press.

Hamilton, W. D. 1964. The genetical theory of social behaviour. *Journal of Theoretical Biology* 7:1–52.

Hanson, C. B. 1980. Fluvial taphonomic processes: models and experiments. In: Behrensmeyer, A. K. & Hill, A. P. (eds) *Fossils in the Making.* Chicago: University of Chicago Press, pp. 156–81.

Harcourt, A., Harvey, P. H., Larson, S. G. & Short, R. V. 1981. Testis weight, body weight and breeding system in primates. *Nature* 293:55–7.

Harding, R. S. O. 1981. An order of omnivores: non-human primate diets in the wild. In: Harding, R. S. O. & Teleki, G. (eds) *Omnivorous Primates*. New York: Columbia University Press, pp. 191–214.

Harding, R. S. O. & Teleki, G. (eds) 1981. *Omnivorous Primates*. New York: Columbia University Press.

Harested, A. S. & Bunnell, F. L. 1979. Home range and body weight: a re-evaluation. *Ecology* 60:389–402.

Harper, J. 1977. *Population Biology of Plants*. New York & London: Academic Press.

Harris, D. R. 1980. Tropical savanna environments: definition, distribution, diversity and development. In: Harris, D. R. (ed.) *Human Ecology in Savanna Environments*. New York & London: Academic Press, pp. 3–30.

Harris, J. M. (ed.) 1983. *Koobi Fora Research Project Vol. 2. The Fossil Ungulates: Proboscidea, Perissodactyla, and Suidae*. Oxford: Clarendon Press.

Harris, J. W. K. 1983. Cultural beginnings: Plio-Pleistocene archaeological occurrences from the Afar, Ethiopia. *The African Archaeological Review* 1:3–31.

Harris, J. W. K. 1986. Archaeological evidence bearing on an understanding of adaptive behaviours of Late Pliocene hominids. *The Longest Record: The Human Career in Africa. A Conference in Honour of J. Desmond Clark* Berkeley, California, April 1986 (abstract).

Harvey, P. H. 1985. Intra-demic group selection and the sex ratio. In: R. M. Sibley & R. H. Smith (eds) *Behavioural Ecology: Ecological Consequences of Adaptive Behaviour*. Oxford: Blackwell, pp. 59–74.

Harvey, P. H. & Clutton-Brock, T. H. 1981. Primate home range size and metabolic needs. *Behavioural Ecology and Sociobiology* 8:151–55.

Harvey, P. H. & Clutton-Brock, T. H. 1985. Life history variation in primates. *Evolution* 39:559–81.

Hausfater, G. & Meade, B. J. 1982. Alternation of sleeping groves by yellow baboons (*Papio cynocephalus*) as a strategy for parasite avoidance. *Primates* 23:287–97.

Hay, R. L. 1976. *Geology of Olduvai Gorge*. Berkeley: University of California Press.

Hay, R. L. 1981. Lithofacies and environments of Bed I, Olduvai Gorge, Tanzania. In: Rapp, G & Vondra, C. F. (eds) *Hominid Sites: their Geologic Settings*. AAAS Selected Symposium No. 63. Boulder, Co.: Westview Press, pp. 25–56.

Hayden, B. 1981. Subsistence and ecological adaptations of modern hunter/gatherers. In: Harding, R. S. O. & Teleki, G. (eds) *Omnivorous Primates*. New York: Columbia University Press, pp. 344–421.

Hendey, Q. B. 1973. Fossil occurrences at Langebaanweg, Cape Province. *Nature* 244:13–14.

Hewes, G. W. 1961. Food transportation and the origins of bipedalism.

American Anthropologist 63:687–710.

Hewes, G. W. 1964. Hominid bipedalism: independent evidence for food-carrying theory. *Science* 146:416–18.

Hill, A. P. 1975. *Taphonomy of contemporary and Late Cenozoic East African vertebrates*. PhD Dissertation, University of London.

Hill, A. P. 1978. Hyaenas, bones, and fossil man. *Kenya Past and Present* 9:8–12.

Hill, A. P. 1979. Disarticulation and scattering of mammal skeletons. *Paleobiology* 5:261–74.

Hill, A. P. 1984. Hominids and hyaenas: taphonomy and hypothesis testing. In: Foley, R. (ed.) *Hominid Evolution and Community Ecology: Prehistoric Human Adaptation in Biological Perspective*. New York & London: Academic Press, pp. 111–28.

Hill, A. P. 1985. Early hominid from Baringo, Kenya. *Nature* 315:222–4.

Hill, A. P., Drake, R., Tauxe, L., Monaghan, M., Barry, J. C., Behrensmeyer, A. K., Curtis, G., Fine Jacobs, B., Johnson, N. & Pilbeam, D. 1985. Neogene palaeontology and geochronology of the Baringo basin, Kenya. *Journal of Human Evolution* 14:759–74.

Hill, K. 1982. Hunting and human evolution. *Journal of Human Evolution* 11:521–44.

Hladik, C. M. 1977. Chimpanzees of Gabon and chimpanzees of Gombe: some comparative data on diet. In: Clutton-Brock, T. H. (ed.) *Primate Ecology*. New York & London: Academic Press, pp. 481–501.

Hladik, C. M. 1981. Diet and the evolution of feeding strategies among forest primates. In: Harding, R. S. O. & Teleki, G. (eds) *Omnivorous Primates*. New York: Columbia University Press, pp. 215–54.

Hladik, C. M., Charles-Dominique, P. & Peters, J. J. 1980. Feeding strategies of five nocturnal prosimians in the dry forest of the west coast of Madagascar. In: P. Charles-Dominique (ed.) *Nocturnal Malagasy Primates*. New York: Academic Press, pp. 433–44.

Hodder, I. 1982. *The Present Past: an Introduction to Anthropology for Archaeologists*. London: Batsford.

Hoffman, A. 1979. Community palaeoecology as an epiphenomenal science. *Paleobiology* 5:357–79.

Hoffmeyr, J., Louw, G. & du Preeze, S. 1973. Incipient capture myopathy as revealed by blood chemistry of chased zebras. *Madoqua* Series I (7):45–50.

Horn, H. S. 1968. The adaptive significance of colonial nesting in the Brewer's blackbird (*Euphagus cyanocephalus*). *Ecology* 49:682–94.

Houston, A. F. & Davies, N. B. 1985. The evolution of co-operation and life history in the dunnock, *Prunella modularis*. In: R. M. Sibley & R. H. Smith (eds) *Behavioural Ecology: Ecological Consequences of Adaptive Behaviour*. Oxford: Blackwell, pp. 471–87.

Houston, D. C. 1979. Scavenging adaptations in the Serengeti. In: Sinclair, A. R. E. & Norton-Griffiths, M. (eds). *Serengeti: Dynamics of an*

Ecosystem. London: Academic Press, pp. 263–86.

Howell, F. C. 1978. The Hominidae. In: Maglio, V. & Cooke, H. B. S. (eds) *Evolution of African Mammals*. Cambridge, Mass.: Harvard University Press, pp. 154–248.

Hutchinson, G. E. 1957. Concluding remarks. *Cold Spring Harbour Symposium on Quantitative Biology* 22:415–27.

Huxley, J. 1924. Constant differential growth ratios and their significance. *Nature* 114:895–6.

Huxley, J. 1972. *Problems of Relative Growth* (2nd edition). New York: Dover.

Huxley, T. H. 1863. *Evidence as to Man's Place in Nature*. London: Williams & Norgate.

Imbrie, J. & Imbrie, K. P. 1979. *Ice Ages: Solving the Mystery*. London: Macmillan.

Ingram, Y. & Mount, Y. 1975. *Man and Animals in Hot Environments*. New York: Springer.

Isaac, G. 1965. The stratigraphy of the Peninj Beds and the provenance of the Natron *Australopithecus* mandible. *Quaternaria* 7:101–30.

Isaac, G. 1967. Towards an interpretation of occupation debris: some experiments and observations. *Kroeber Anthropological Society Papers* 37:31–57.

Isaac, G. 1971a. Whither archaeology? *Antiquity* 45:123–9.

Isaac, G. 1971b. The diet of early man: aspects of archaeological evidence from Lower and Middle Pleistocene sites in Africa. *World Archaeology* 2:278–98.

Isaac, G. 1972. Chronology and tempo of culture change during the Pleistocene: In: Bishop, W. W. & Miller, J. (eds) *Calibration of Hominoid Evolution*. Edinburgh: Scottish Academic Press, pp. 381–430.

Isaac, G. 1976. *Olorgesailie*. Chicago: University of Chicago Press.

Isaac, G. 1978a. Food sharing and human evolution: archaeological evidence from the Plio-Pleistocene of East Africa. *Journal of Anthropological Research* 34:311–25.

Isaac, G. 1978b. The food-sharing behavior of protohuman hominids. *Scientific American* 238 (4):90–108.

Isaac, G. 1981. Archaeological tests of alternative models of early hominid behaviour: excavation and experiments. *Philosophical Transactions of the Royal Society, London* B292:177–88.

Isaac, G. 1983. Bones in contention: competing explanations for the juxtaposition of artefacts and faunal remains. In: Clutton-Brock, J. & Grigson, C. (eds) *Animals and Archaeology: 1. Hunters and their Prey*. B. A. R. International Series No. 163. Oxford: B. A. R., pp. 3–19.

Isaac, G. 1984. The archaeology of human origins: studies of the Lower Pleistocene in East Africa 1971–1981. *Advances in World Archaeology* 3:1–79.

Isaac, G. & Crader, D. 1981. To what extent were early hominids carnivorous? An archaeological perspective. In: Harding, R. S. O. & Teleki, G. (eds) *Omnivorous Primates*. New York: Columbia University Press, pp. 37–103.

Janzen, D. H. 1980. When is it coevolution? *Evolution* 34:611–12.

Jarman, M. V. & Jarman, P. J. 1973. Daily activity of impala. *East African Wildlife Journal* 11:75–93.

Jarman, P. J. 1974. The social organization of antelope in relation to their ecology. *Behaviour* 48:215–67.

Jerison, H. J. 1961. Quantitative analysis of evolution of the brain in mammals. *Science* 133:1012–14.

Jerison, H. J. 1973. *Evolution of the Brain and Intelligence*. New York: Academic Press.

Jochim, M. A. 1981. *Strategies of Survival*. New York: Academic Press.

Johanson, D. C. & Edey, M. 1981. *Lucy: the Beginnings of Mankind*. New York: Simon & Schuster.

Johanson, D. C. & White, T. D. 1979. A systematic assessment of early African hominids. *Science* 203:321–30.

Johanson, D. C., Taieb, M. & Coppens, Y. 1982. Pliocene hominids from the Hadar Formation, Ethiopia (1973–1977): stratigraphic, chronologic, and palaeoenvironmental contexts. *American Journal of Physical Anthropology* 57:373–402.

Johnson, S. C. 1981. Bonobo: generalized hominid prototype or specialized insular dwarfs? *Current Anthropology* 22:363–75.

Jolly, C. 1970. The seed-eaters: a new model of hominid differentiation based on a baboon analogy. *Man* 5:5–26.

Jolly, C. 1972. The classification and natural history of *Theropithecus* (*Simopithecus*) (Andrews 1916) baboons of the African Plio-Pleistocene. *Bulletin of the British Museum (Natural History) Geology* 22:1–123.

Jungers, W. L. 1982. Lucy's limbs: skeletal allometry and locomotion in *Australopithecus afarensis*. *Nature* 297:676–78.

Jungers, W. L. 1985. Body size and scaling of limb proportions in primates. In: Jungers, W. L. (ed.) *Size and Scaling in Primate Biology*. New York: Plenum Press, pp. 345–81.

Jungers, W. L. & Stern, J. T. 1983. Body proportions, skeletal allometry and locomotion in the Hadar hominids: a reply to Wolpoff. *Journal of Human Evolution* 12:673–84.

Kalb, J. E., Oswald, E. B., Tebedge, S., Mebrate, A., Tola, E. & Peak, D. 1982. Geology and stratigraphy of Neogene deposits, Middle Awash Valley, Ethiopia. *Nature* 298:17–25.

Kaplan, D. 1978. *The Sociobiology Debate*. New York: Harper & Row.

Kavanagh, M. 1984. *A Complete Guide to Monkeys, Apes and Other Primates*. London: Jonathan Cape.

Kawai, M. 1965. Newly aquired pre-cultural behaviour of the natural troop of Japanese monkeys on Koshima Islet. *Primates* 6:1–30.

Kay, R. F. 1981. The nut-crackers – a new theory of the adaptations of the Ramapithecinae. *American Journal of Physical Anthropology* 55:141–51.

Kay, R. 1985. Dental evidence for the diet of *Australopithecus*. *Annual Review of Anthropology* 14:315–43.

Kay, R. F. & Hylander, W. L. 1978. The dental structure of mammalian folivores with special reference to primates and Phalangeroids (Marsupala). In: Montgomery, G. G. (ed.) *The Ecology of Arboreal Folivores*. Washington, D. C.: Smithsonian Institution Press.

Keeley, L. H. 1978. *Experimental Determination of Stone Tool Uses*. Chicago: University of Chicago Press.

Keeley, L. & Toth, N. 1981. Microwear polishes on early stone tools from Kenya. *Nature* 293:464–5.

Kennedy, G. E. 1984. The emergence of *Homo sapiens*: the post-cranial evidence. *Man* 19:94–110.

Kennett, J. P. 1977. Cenozoic evolution of antarctic glaciation, the circum-anatarctic ocean, and their implications on global palaeooceanography. *Journal of Geophysical Research* 82:3843–60.

Kingdon, J. 1981. *East African Mammals Volume III*. London: Academic Press.

King's College Sociobiology Group (eds) 1982. *Current Problems in Sociobiology*. Cambridge: Cambridge University Press.

Kleiber, M. 1961. *The Fire of Life: an Introduction to Animal Energetics*. New York: Wiley.

Klein, R. G. 1974. Environment and subsistence of prehistoric man in the Southern Cape Province, South Africa. *World Archaeology* 5:249–89.

Klein, R. G. 1983. The stone age prehistory of southern Africa. *Annual Review of Anthropology* 12:25–48.

Kortlandt, A. 1967. Experimentation with chimpanzees in the wild. In: Starck, D., Scheinder, R. & Kuhn, H. J. (eds) *Neue Ergebnisse der Primatologie*. Stuttgart: Fischer, pp. 208–24.

Kortlandt, A. 1972. *New perspectives on ape and human evolution*. Amsterdam: Stichting voor Psychobiologie.

Kortlandt, A. 1983. Facts and fallacies concerning Miocene ape habitats. In: Ciochon, R. & Corruccini, R. S. (eds) *New Interpretations of Ape and Human Ancestry*. New York: Plenum Press, pp. 465–514.

Kortlandt, A. 1984. Habitat richness, foraging range and diet in chimpanzees and some other primates. In: Chivers, D., Wood, B. A. & Bilsborough, A. (eds) *Food Acquisition and Processing in Primates*. New York: Plenum Press, pp. 119–60.

Krebs, J. & Davies, N. B. 1981. *Introduction to Behavioural Ecology*. Oxford: Blackwell.

Krebs, J. & Davies, N. B. (eds) 1984. *Behavioural Ecology*. (2nd edition). Oxford: Blackwell.

Kretzoi, M. 1975. New ramapithecines and *Pliopithecus* from the Lower Pliocene of Rudabanya in northeastern Hungary. *Nature* 257:578–81.

Kruuk, H. 1972. *The Spotted Hyaena*. Chicago: University of Chicago Press.

Kukla, G. J. 1975. Loess stratigraphy in Central Europe. In: Butzer, K. W. & Isaac, G. (eds) *After the Australopithecines*. The Hague: Mouton, pp. 99–188.

Kummer, H. 1968. *Social Organization of the Hamadryas Baboon*. Chicago: University of Chicago Press.

Kurtèn, B. 1953. On the variation and population dynamics of fossil and recent mammal populations. *Acta Zoologica Fennica* 76:1–122.

Ladell, W. S. S. 1964. Terrestrial animals in humid heat: man. In: Dill, D. B. (ed.) *Handbook of Physiology 4. Adaptation to the Environment*. Baltimore: Williams & Wilkins, pp. 625–59.

Latimer, B. 1984. The pedal skeleton of *Australopithecus afarensis*. *American Journal of Physical Anthropology* 63:182 (abstract).

Laurent, R. F. 1973. A parallel survey of equatorial amphibians and reptiles in Africa and South America. In: Meggars, B. J., Ayensu, E. S. & Duckworth, W. D. (eds) *Tropical Forest Ecosystems in Africa and South America: a Comparative Review*. Washington: Smithsonian Institution Press, pp. 259–66.

Layton, R. & Foley, R. in press. Human origins. In: Medawar, P. (ed.) *New Frontiers of Science*. London: Rainbow Press.

Le Gros Clark, W. E. 1949. *History of the Primates*. London: British Museum (Natural History).

Le Gros Clark, W. E. 1964. *The Fossil Evidence for Human Evolution* (2nd edition). Chicago: University of Chicago Press.

Leakey, L. S. B. 1967. An early Miocene member of the Hominidae. *Nature* 213:155.

Leakey, M. D. 1972. *Olduvai Gorge. Volume 3*. Cambridge: Cambridge University Press.

Leakey, M. D. 1978. Pliocene footprints at Laetoli, Northern Tanzania. *Antiquity* 52:133.

Leakey, M. D., Hay, R. L., Curtis, G. H., Drake, R. E., Jackes, M. K. & White, T. D. 1976. Fossil hominids from the Laetolil beds. *Nature* 262:460–6.

Lee, P. C. 1984. Ecological constraints on the social development of vervet monkeys. *Behaviour* 91:254–62.

Lee, R. B. 1968. What hunters do for a living, or, how to make out on scarce resources. In: Lee, R. B. & DeVore, I. (eds) *Man the Hunter*. Chicago: Aldine, pp. 30–48.

Lee, R. B. & DeVore, I. 1968. Problems in the study of hunters and gatherers. In: Lee, R. B. & DeVore, I. (eds) *Man the Hunter*. Chicago: Aldine, pp. 3–12.

Lewis, G. 1934. Preliminary notice of new man-like apes from India.

American Journal of Science 27:161.

Lewontin, R. 1978. Adaptation. *Scientific American* 239(3):157–69.

Livingstone, F. B. 1962. Reconstructing man's Pliocene pongid ancestor. *American Anthropologist* 64:301–95.

Lovejoy, C. O. 1979. A reconstruction of the pelvis of AL–288 (Hadar Formation). *American Journal of Physical Anthropology* 50:460 (abstract).

Lovejoy, C. O. 1980. Hominid origins: the role of bipedalism. *American Journal of Physical Anthropology* 52:250 (abstract).

Lovejoy, C. O. 1981. The origin of man. *Science* 211:341–50.

Lovejoy, C. O. & Heiple, K. G. 1970. A reconstruction of the femur of *A. africanus*. *American Journal of Physical Anthropology* 32:33–40.

Lumsden, C. J. & Wilson, E. O. 1980. Translation of epigenetic rules of individual behaviour into ethnographic patterns. *Proceedings of the National Academy of Sciences, U. S. A.* 77:4382–6.

MacArthur, R. H. & Pianka, E. R. 1966. On optimal use of a patchy environment. *American Naturalist* 100:603–9.

MacArthur, R. H. & Wilson, E. O. 1967. *The Theory of Island Biogeography*. Princeton: Princeton University Press.

McGrew, W., Baldwin, P. J. & Tutin, C. E. G. 1981. Chimpanzees in a hot, dry, open habitat: Mount Assirik, Senegal, West Africa. *Journal of Human Evolution* 10:227–44.

McHenry, H. M. 1974. How large were the australopithecines? *American Journal of Physical Anthropology* 40:329–40.

McHenry, H. M. 1975. Fossil hominid body weight and brain size. *Nature* 254:686–8.

McHenry, H. M. 1976. Early hominid body weight and encephalization. *American Journal of Physical Anthropology* 45:77–84.

McHenry, H. M. 1978. Fore- and hindlimb proportions of Plio-Pleistocene hominids. *American Journal of Physical Anthropology* 49:15–22.

McHenry, H. M. 1982. The pattern of human evolution: studies on bipedalism, mastication and encephalization. *Annual Review of Anthropology* 11:151–73.

McHenry, H. M. & Corruccini, R. S. 1981. *Pan paniscus* and human evolution. *American Journal of Physical Anthropology* 54:355–67.

McKinnon, J. R. 1974. The behaviour and ecology of wild orang-utan (*Pongo pygmaeus*). *Animal Behaviour* 22:3–74.

MacMahon, T. A. & Bonner, J. T. 1983. *On Size and Life*. San Francisco: Freeman.

McNab, B. K. 1963. Bioenergetics and the determination of home range size. *American Naturalist* 97:130–40.

McNab, B. K. 1974. On the energetics of endotherms. *Ohio Journal of Science* 74:370–80.

Maddock, L. 1979. The 'migration' and grazing succession. In: Sinclair, A. R. E. & Norton-Griffiths, M. (eds) *Serengeti: Dynamics of an Ecosystem*.

London: Academic Press, pp. 104–209.

Maglio, V. J. 1978. Patterns of faunal evolution. In: Maglio, V. J. & Cooke, H. B. S. (eds) *Evolution of African Mammals*. Cambridge, Mass.: Harvard University Press, pp. 603–20.

Marshall, L. G. & Corruccini, R. S. 1978. Variability, evolutionary rates and allometry in dwarfing lineages. *Paleobiology* 4:101–19.

Martin, R. A. 1980. Body mass and basal metabolism of extinct mammals. *Comparative Biochemistry & Physiology* 66a:307–14.

Martin, R. A. 1981. On extinct hominid population densities. *Journal of Human Evolution* 10:427–8.

Martin, R. D. 1981. Relative brain size and basal metabolic rates in terrestrial vertebrates. *Nature* 293:57–60.

Martin, R. D. 1983. *Human Brain Evolution in an Ecological Context* (52nd James Arthur Lecture on the Evolution of the Brain). New York: American Museum of Natural History.

Martin, R. D. 1984. Body size, brain size and feeding strategies. In: Chivers, D., Wood, B. & Bilsborough, A. (eds) *Food Acquisition and Processing in Primates*. New York: Plenum Press, pp. 73–104.

Martin, R. D. & May, R. 1981. Outward signs of breeding. *Nature* 293:7–9.

Matsu'ura, S. 1982. A chronological framework for the Sangiran hominids. *Bulletin of the Natural Science Museum of Tokyo* D8:1–53.

Maynard Smith, J. 1976a. Evolution and the theory of games. *American Scientist* 64:41–5.

Maynard Smith, J. 1976b. Game theory and the evolution of fighting. In: Maynard Smith, J. *John Maynard Smith on Evolution*. Edinburgh: Edinburgh University Press, pp. 8–28.

Maynard Smith, J. 1978. Optimization theory in evolution. *Annual Review of Ecology and Systematics* 9:31–56.

Maynard Smith, J. 1982. *Evolution Now: a Century after Darwin*. London: Macmillan.

Maynard Smith, J. 1983. *Evolution and the Theory of Games*. Cambridge: Cambridge University Press.

Mayr, E. 1963. *Animal Species and Evolution*. Cambridge, Mass.: Harvard University Press.

Mayr, E. 1982. Questions concerning speciation. *Nature* 296:609.

Mellor, D. 1974. New archaeology for old. *Cambridge Review* 95:71–2.

Mercer, J. H. 1978. West antarctic ice sheet and CO_2 greenhouse effect: a threat of disaster. *Nature* 259:321–5.

Milton, K. & May, M. L. 1975. Body weight, diet and home range area in primates. *Nature* 259:459–62.

Montagu, A. 1964. Comments on the human revolution by C. F. Hockett and R. Ascher. *Current Anthropology* 5:160–1.

Morbeck, M. E. 1983. Miocene hominoid from Rudabánya: implications from the postcranial skeleton. In: Ciochon, R. & Corruccini, R. S. (eds)

New Interpretations of Ape and Human Ancestry. New York: Plenum Press, pp. 369–404.

Moreau, R. E. 1969. Climatic changes and the distribution of forest vertebrates in West Africa. *Journal of Zoology* 158:39–61.

Mount, L. N. 1979. *Adaptations to a Thermal Environment*. London: Arnold.

Murphy, P. 1974. Primary productivity in tropical ecosystems. In: Leith, H. & Whittaker, R. H. (eds) *Primary Productivity of the Biosphere*. Berlin: Springer, pp. 217–34.

Nabakov, P. & McClean, M. 1980. Ways of native running. *Coevolution Quarterly* 4:21.

Napier, J. 1971. *Roots of Mankind*. London: George Allen & Unwin.

Napier, J. & Napier, P. 1967. *Handbook of Living Primates*. London: Academic Press.

Newell, N. D. 1949. Phyletic size increases – an important trend illustrated by fossil invertebrates. *Evolution* 3:103–24.

Newman, R. W. 1970. Why man is such a sweaty and thirsty naked animal: a speculative review. *Human Biology* 42:12–27.

Nishida, T. & Uehara, S. 1983. Natural diet of chimpanzees (*Pan troglodytes schweinfurthi*): long-term records from the Mahale Mountains, Tanzania. *African Studies Monographs* 3:109–30.

Oakley, K. P. 1966. *Frameworks for Dating Fossil Man* (2nd edition). London: Weidenfield & Nicholson.

Oakley, K. P., Campbell, B. & Mollison, T. H. 1977 *Catalogue of fossil hominids: Africa. (2nd edition)*. London: British Museum. (Natural History).

Oakley, K. P. & Montagu, M. F. A. 1949. A reconsideration of the Galley Hill skeleton. *Bulletin of the British Museum (Natural History) Geology* 1(2):25–48.

Olson, T. 1981. Basiocranial morphology of the extant hominoids and Pliocene hominids: the new material from the Hadar Formation, Ethiopia, and its significance in early hominid evolution and taxonomy. In: C. B. Stringer (ed.) *Aspects of Human Evolution*. Symposia for the Study of Human Biology No. 12. London: Taylor & Francis, pp. 99–128.

Oster, G. F. & Wilson, E. O. 1978. *Caste and Ecology in the Social Insects*. Princeton: Princeton University Press.

Owen, D. F. 1974. *What is Ecology?* London: Oxford University Press.

Passingham, R. 1982. *The Human Primate*. San Francisco: Freeman.

Patterson, B., Behrensmeyer, A. K. & Sill, W. D. 1970. Geology and fauna from a new Pliocene locality in Northwestern Kenya. *Nature* 226:918–21.

Pearson, R. 1978. *Climate and Evolution*. London: Academic Press.

Penck, A. & Brückner, E. 1909. *Die Alpen im Eiszeitalter*. Leipzig.

Peters, R. H. 1983. *The Ecological Implications of Body Size*. Cambridge: Cambridge University Press.

Peters, C. R. & O'Brien, E. M. 1981. The early hominid plant food niche: insights from an analysis of plant exploitation by *Homo*, *Pan* and *Papio* in eastern and southern Africa. *Current Anthropology* 22:127–40.

Peters, C. R. O'Brien, E. M. & Box, E. O. 1984. Plant types and seasonality of wild plant foods, Tanzania to southwestern Africa: resources for models of the natural environment. *Journal of Human Evolution* 13:397–414.

Pianka, E. 1978. *Evolutionary Ecology* (2nd edition). New York: Harper & Row.

Pickford, M. 1983. Sequence and environment of the Lower and Middle Miocene hominoids of western Kenya. In: Ciochon, R. L. & Corruccini, R. S. (eds) *New Interpretations of Ape and Human Ancestry*. New York: Plenum Press, pp. 421–40.

Pilbeam, D. 1968. The earliest hominids. *Nature* 219:1335.

Pilbeam, D. 1969. Tertiary Pongidae of East Africa: evolutionary relationships and taxonomy. *Peabody Museum of Natural History Bulletin* 31:1–185.

Pilbeam, D. 1972. *The Evolution of Man*. London: Macmillan.

Pilbeam, D. 1975. Middle Pleistocene hominids. In: Butzer, K. W. & Isaac, G. (eds) *After the Australopithecines*. The Hague: Mouton, pp. 809–56.

Pilbeam, D. 1979. Recent finds and interpretations of Miocene hominoids. *Annual Review of Anthropology* 8:333–52.

Pilbeam, D. 1984. The descent of hominoids and hominids. *Scientific American* 250(3):60–9.

Pilbeam, D. 1986. Distinguished lecture: hominoid evolution and hominoid origins. *American Anthropologist* 88:295–312.

Pilbeam, D. & Gould, S. J. 1974. Size and scaling in human evolution. *Science* 186:892–901.

Pilbeam, D. & Vaisnys, J. R. 1975. Hypothesis testing in palaeoanthropology. In: Tuttle, R. H. (ed.) *Palaeoanthropology: Morphology and Palaeoecology*. The Hague: Mouton, pp. 3–14.

Pilbeam, D., Mayer, G. E., Badgeley, C., Rose, M. D., Pickford, M., Behrensmeyer, A. K. & Shah, S. M. I. 1977. New hominoid primates from the Siwaliks of Pakistan and their bearing on hominoid evolution. *Nature* 270:689–95.

Pope, G. G. 1983. Evidence for the age of the Asian Hominidae. *Proceedings of the National Academy of Sciences, U. S. A.* 80:4988–92.

Post, D. 1981. Activity patterns of yellow baboons (*Papio cynocephalus*) in the Amboseli National Park. *Animal Behaviour* 29:357–74.

Post, D., Hausfater, G. & McCuskey, S. 1980. Feeding behaviour of yellow baboons (*Papio cynocephalus*): relationship to age, gender and dominance rank. *Folia Primatologica* 34:170–95.

Potts, R. 1982. *Lower Pleistocene Site Formation and Hominid Activity at Olduvai Gorge, Tanzania.* PhD Dissertation, Harvard University.

Potts, R. 1984a. Hominid hunters? Problems of identifying the earliest hunter/gatherers. In: Foley, R. (ed.) *Hominid Evolution and Community Ecology: Prehistoric Human Adaptation in Biological Perspective.* London: Academic Press, pp. 129–66.

Potts, R. 1984b. Home bases and early hominids. *American Scientist* 72:338–47.

Potts, R. & Shipman, P. 1981. Cutmarks made by stone tools on bones from Olduvai Gorge, Tanzania. *Nature* 291:577–80.

Pyke, G. H., Pulliam, H. R. & Charnov, E. L. 1977. Optimal foraging: a selective review of theory and tests. *Quarterly Review of Biology* 52:137–54.

Rak, Y. 1983. *The Australopithecine Face.* New York: Academic Press.

Raup, D. M. & Stanley, S. 1978. *Principles of Paleontology* (2nd edition), San Francisco: Freeman.

Ravey, M. 1978. Bipedalism: an early warning system for Miocene hominoids. *Science* 199:372.

Raza, S. M., Barry, J. C., Pilbeam, D., Rose, M. D., Shah, S. M. I. & Ward, S. 1983. New hominoid primates from the Middle Miocene Chinji Formation, Potwar Plateau, Pakistan. *Nature* 305:52–4.

Reader, J. 1981. *Missing Links.* London: Collins.

Reeve, E. C. B. & Huxley, J. S. 1945. Some problems in the study of allometric growth. In: Le Gros Clark, W. E. & Medawar, P. (eds) *Essays on Growth and Form.* Oxford: Clarendon.

Rensch, B. 1959. *Evolution Above the Species Level.* New York: Columbia University Press.

Repenning, C. A. & Fejfar, O. 1982. Evidence for earlier date of 'Ubeidiya, Israel, hominid site. *Nature* 299:344–7.

Rightmire, G. P. 1981. Patterns in the evolution of *Homo erectus. Paleobiology* 7:241–6.

Rightmire, G. P. 1984. *Homo sapiens* in sub-Saharan Africa. In: Smith, F. & Spencer, F. (eds) *The Origins of Modern Humans.* New York: Alan Liss, pp. 295–326.

Roberts, N. 1984. Pleistocene environments in time and space. In: Foley, R. (ed.) *Hominid Evolution and Community Ecology: Prehistoric Human Adaptation in Biological Perspective.* London: Academic Press, pp. 25–54.

Robinson, J. T. 1972. *Early Hominid Posture and Locomotion.* Chicago: University of Chicago Press.

Roche, H. 1980. *Premiers outils tailles d'Afrique.* Societé d'Ethnographie, France.

Roche, H. & Tiercelin, J. J. 1977. Decouverte d'une industrie lithique ancienne *in situ* dans la formation d'Hadar, Afar, central Ethiopie. *Comptes rendus de l'Académie des Sciences* 284–D:1871–74.

Rodman, P. S. & McHenry, H. M. 1980. Bioenergetics and the origin of hominid bipedalism. *American Journal of Physical Anthropology* 52:103–6.

Romer, A. S. 1959. *The Vertebrate Story*. Chicago: University of Chicago Press.

Rose, M. D. 1973. Quadrupedalism in primates. *Primates* 14:337–57.

Rose, M. D. 1983. Miocene hominoid postcranial morphology: monkey-like, ape-like, neither or both? In: Ciochon, R. & Corruccini, R. S. (eds) *New Interpretations of Ape and Human Ancestry*. New York: Plenum Press, pp. 405–20.

Rose, M. D. 1984. Food acquisition and the evolution of positional behaviour: the case of bipedalism. In: Chivers, D., Wood, B. & Bilsborough, A. (eds) *Food Acquisition and Processing in Primates*. New York: Plenum Press, pp. 509–24.

Rosenzweig, M. L. 1968. Net primary productivity of terrestrial communities: prediction from climatological data. *American Naturalist* 102:74–6.

Roth, W. 1901. Food: its search, capture and preparation. *North Queensland Ethnography Bulletin* No. 3.

Rothenbuhler, W. C. 1964. Behaviour genetics of nest cleaning in honey bees. *American Zoologist* 4:111–23.

Sailer, D. L., Gaulin, S. J. C., Booster, J. S. & Kurland, J. A. 1985. Measuring the relationship between dietary quality and body size in primates. *Primates* 26:14–27.

Sarich, V. M. 1971. A molecular approach to the question of human origins. In: Dolinhow, P. & Sarich, V. M. (eds) *Background for Man*. Boston: Little Brown, pp. 60–81.

Sarich, V. M. 1983. Appendix: retrospective on hominoid macromolecular systematics. In: Ciochon, R. & Corruccini, R. S. (eds) *New Interpretations of Ape and Human Ancestry*. New York: Plenum Press, pp. 137–50.

Sarich, V. M. & Wilson, A. C. 1967. Immunological time scale for hominoid evolution. *Science* 158:1200–3.

Sarich, V. M. & Wilson, A. C. 1973. Generation time and genomic evolution in primates. *Science* 179:1144–7.

Sartono, S. 1982. Characteristics and chronology of early men in Java. *Congrès International de Paléontologie Humaine*, Nice Prétirage, pp. 491–533.

Schaller, G. B. 1972. *The Serengeti Lion*. Chicago: University of Chicago Press.

Schaller, G. & Lowther, G. R. 1969. The relevance of carnivore behaviour to the study of early hominids. *Southwestern Journal of Anthropology* 25:307–41.

Schell, T. 1981. An American finds out that running with Pygmies is no small challenge. *Sports Illustrated* 11:6–7.

Schmidt-Neilson, K. 1975. *Animal Physiology: Adaptation and Environment*. Cambridge: Cambridge University Press.

Schoener, T. W. 1983. The controversy over interspecific competition. *American Scientist* 70:586–95.

Scott, K. 1986. Review of *Faunal Remains from Klasies River Mouth* by L. R. Binford. *Journal of Archaeological Science* 18:89–91.

Semenov, S. A. 1964. *Prehistoric Technology.* Bath: Adams & Dart.

Seyfarth, R. M., Cheney, D. L. & Marler, P. 1980. Monkey responses to three different alarm calls: evidence of predator classification and a semantic communication. *Science* 210:801–3.

Shackleton, N. & Opdyke, N. D. 1976. Oxygen-isotope and palaeomagnetic stratigraphy of equatorial Pacific core V28–238. Late Pliocene to Latest Pleistocene. In: Cline, R. M. & Hays, J. D. (eds) *Investigation of Late Quaternary Paleoceanography and Paleoclimatology.* Geological Society of America Memoir No. 145:449–64.

Shipman, P. 1982. Taphonomy of *Ramapithecus wickeri* at Fort Ternan, Kenya. *University of Missouri Museum Brief* No. 26.

Shipman, P. 1983. *Life History of a Fossil.* Cambridge, Mass.: Harvard University Press.

Shipman, P., Walker, A. C., Van Couvering, J., Hooker, P. & Miller, J. 1981. The Fort Ternan hominoid site, Kenya: geology, age, taphonomy and palaeoecology. *Journal of Human Evolution* 10:49–72.

Short, R. V. 1979. Sexual selection and its component parts: somatic and genital selection, as illustrated by man and the great apes. *Advances in the Study of Behaviour* 9:131.

Short, R. V. 1980. The great apes. *Journal of Reproduction and Fertility Supplement* 28:3–11.

Short, R. V. 1981. Sexual selection in man and the great apes. In: Graham, C. E. (ed.) *Reproductive Biology of the Great Apes.* London: Academic Press, pp. 319–41.

Sibley, C. & Ahlquist, J. 1984. The phylogeny of hominoid primates as indicated by DNA-DNA hybridization. *Journal of Molecular Evolution* 20:2–15.

Sigg, H. & Stolba, A. 1981. Home range and daily march in a hamadryas baboon troop. *Folia Primatologica* 36:40–75.

Silberbauer, G. 1981. *Central Kalahari Hunter–Gatherers.* Cambridge: Cambridge University Press.

Simons, E. 1961. The phyletic position of *Ramapithecus. Postilla* 57:1–9.

Simons, E. & Pilbeam, D. 1965. Preliminary revision of the Dryopithecinae (Pongidae, Anthropoidea). *Folia Primatologica* 3:81–152.

Skelton, R. R., McHenry, H. M. & Drawhorn, G. M. 1986. Phylogenetic analysis of early hominids. *Current Anthropology* 27:21–43.

Solomon, J. D. 1931. The geology of the implementiforous deposits in the Nakuru and Naivasha basins and the surrounding area in the Kenya Colony. In: Leakey, L. S. B. *The Stone Age Cultures of the Kenya Colony.* Cambridge: Cambridge University Press, pp. 245–66.

Speth, J. D. & Spielmann, K. A. 1983. Energy source, protein metabolism, and hunter–gatherer subsistence strategies. *Journal of Anthropological Archaeology* 2:1–31.

Stacey, F. D. 1969. *Physics of the Earth*. New York: Wiley.

Stahl, W. R. 1965. Organ weights in primates and other mammals. *Science* 150:1039–42.

Stanley, S. M. 1973. An explanation of Cope's rule. *Evolution* 27:1–26.

Stanley, S. M. 1975. A theory of evolution above the species level. *Proceedings of the National Academy of Sciences, U. S. A.* 72:646–50.

Stanley, S. M. 1979. *Macroevolution: Pattern & Process*. San Francisco: Freeman.

Stern, J. T. 1971. *Functional Myology of the Hip and Thigh of Cebid Monkeys and its Implications for the Evolution of Erect Posture*. Biblioteca Primatologia No. 14. Basel: Karger.

Stern, J. T. 1976. Before bipedality. *Yearbook of Physical Anthropology* 19:59–68.

Stern, J. T. & Susman, R. L. 1983. The locomotor anatomy of *Australopithecus afarensis*. *American Journal of Physical Anthropology* 60:279–317.

Steudel, K. 1980. New estimates of early hominid body size. *American Journal of Physical Anthropology* 52:63–70.

Street, F. A. & Grove, A. T. 1975. Environmental and climatic implications of Late Quaternary lake-level fluctuations in Africa. *Nature* 261:385–90.

Stringer, C. 1984. Human evolution and biological adaptation in the Pleistocene. In: Foley, R. (ed.) *Hominid Evolution and Community Ecology: Prehistoric Human Adaptation in Biological Perspective*. London: Academic Press, pp. 55–84.

Strugnell, R. G. & Pigot, C. D. 1978. Biomass, shoot production and grazing of two grasslands in the Ruwenzori National Park, Uganda. *Journal of Ecology* 66:73–96.

Struhsaker, T. T. 1967. Ecology of vervet monkeys (*Cercopithecus aethiops*) in Masai-Amboseli Game Reserve, Kenya. *Ecology* 48:891–904.

Suzuki, A. 1969. An ecological study of chimpanzees in savanna woodland. *Primates* 19:103–48.

Suzuki, A. 1975. The origin of hominid hunting: a primatological perspective. In: Tuttle, R. H. (ed.) *Socioecology and Psychology of Primates*. The Hague: Mouton, pp. 259–78.

Szalay, F. S. & Delson, E. 1979. *Evolutionary History of the Primates*. London: Academic Press.

Tanaka, J. 1976. Subsistence ecology of Central Kalahari San. In: Lee, R. B. & DeVore, I. (eds) *Kalahari Hunter–Gatherers*. Cambridge, Mass.: Harvard University Press, pp. 98–119.

Tanner, N. M. 1981. *On Becoming Human*. Cambridge: Cambridge University Press.

Taylor, C. R. & Rowntree, V. J. 1973. Running on two legs or four: which consumes more energy? *Science* 179:186–7.

Taylor, C. R., Schmidt-Nielson, K. & Raab, J. L. 1970. Scaling of energetic cost of running to body size in mammals. *American Journal of Physiology* 219:1104.

Teleki, G. 1975. Primate subsistence pattern: collector–predators and gatherer–hunters. *Journal of Human Evolution* 4:125–84.

Teleki, G. 1981. The omnivorous diet and eclectic feeding habits of chimpanzees in Gombe National Park, Tanzania. In: Harding, R. S. O. & Teleki, G. (eds) *Omnivorous Primates*. New York: Columbia University Press, pp. 303–43.

Thoillay, J. M. 1970. L'exploitation par les oiseaux de essaimages de fourmis et termites dans une zone du contact savane-forêt en Côte d'Ivoire. *Alauda* 38:255–73.

Thorne, A. & Macumber, P. 1972. Discoveries of Late Pleistocene man at Kow Swamp. *Nature* 238:316–19.

Thomas, D. H. 1978. *Figuring Anthropology*. New York: Holt, Rhinehart & Winston.

Thomson, D'Arcy, 1917. *On Growth and Form*. Cambridge: Cambridge University Press.

Thunnell, R. C. & Williams, D. F. 1983. The stepwise development of Pliocene–Pleistocene paleoclimate and paleooceanographic conditions in the Mediterranean oxygen isotope studies of DSDP Sites 125 and 132. In: Meulenkamp, J. E. (ed.) *Reconstruction of Marine Paleoenvironments*. Utrecht Micropalaeontological Bulletin No. 30, pp. 111–27.

Tinbergen, N. 1963. On aims and methods of ethology. *Zeitschrift für Tierpsychologie* 20:410–33.

Tite, M. S. 1972. *Methods of Physical Examination in Archaeology*. London: Academic Press.

Tobias, P. 1980. '*Australopithecus afarensis*' and '*A. africanus*': critique and alternative hypothesis. *Palaeontologica Africana* 23:1–17.

Torrence, R. 1983. Time budgeting and hunter–gatherer technology. In: Bailey, G. (ed.) *Hunter–Gatherer Economy in Prehistory: a European Perspective*. Cambridge: Cambridge University Press, pp. 11–22.

Trinkaus, E. 1981. Neanderthal limb proportions and cold adaptation. In: Stringer, C. (ed.) *Aspects of Human Evolution*. London: Taylor & Francis.

Trinkaus, E. 1982. *The Shanidar Neanderthals*. London: Academic Press.

Trinkaus, E. 1983. Neanderthal postcrania and the shift to modern humans. In: Trinkaus, E. (ed.) *The Mousterian Legacy*. B. A. R. International Series No. 164. Oxford: B. A. R., pp. 165–200.

Trinkaus, E. & Howells, W. W. 1979. The neanderthals. *Scientific American* 241(6):118–33.

Trivers, R. 1972. Parental investment and sexual selection. In: Campbell, B. G. (ed.) *Sexual Selection and the Descent of Man*. Chicago: Aldine, pp. 136–79.

Turner, A. 1984. Hominids and fellow-travellers: human migration into high latitudes as part of a large mammal community. In: Foley, R. (ed.) *Hominid Evolution and Community Ecology: Prehistoric Human Adaptation* *in Biological Perspective*. London: Academic Press. pp. 183–218.

Tuttle, R. H. 1975. Knuckle-walking and knuckle-walkers: a commentary on some recent perspective on hominoid evolution. In: Tuttle, R. H. (ed.) *Primate Functional Morphology and Evolution*. The Hague: Mouton, pp. 203–12.

Uzell, T. & Pilbeam, D. 1971. Phyletic divergence dates of hominoid primates: a comparison of fossil and molecular data. *Evolution* 25:615–35.

Van Couvering, J. A. H. 1980. Community evolution in East Africa during the Late Cenozoic. In: Behrensmeyer, A. K. & Hill, A. P. (eds) *Fossils in the Making*. Chicago: University of Chicago Press, pp. 272–97.

Van Couvering, J. A. H. & Van Couvering, J. A. 1976. Early Miocene mammal fossils from East Africa: aspects of geology, faunistics, and palaeoecology. In: Isaac, G. & McGown, E. (eds) *Human Origins: Louis Leakey and the East African Evidence*. Menlo Park, Ca.: W. A. Benjamin, pp. 155–207.

Van Schaik, C. P. & Van Hoof, J. 1983. On the ultimate causes of primate social systems. *Behaviour* 85:91–117.

Vincent, A. 1985. *Underground Plant Foods and Subsistence in Human Evolution*. PhD Dissertation, University of California, Berkeley.

Vita-Finzi, C. & Higgs, E. S. 1972. Prehistoric economy in the Mount Carmel area of Palestine. *Proceeding of the Prehistoric Society* 36:1–37.

Vrba, E. 1974. Chronological and ecological implications of the fossil Bovidae at Sterkfontein archaeological site. *Nature* 250:19–23.

Vrba, E. 1975. Some evidence on chronology and palaeoecology at Sterkfontein, Swartkrans and Kromdraai from the fossil Bovidae. *Nature* 254:301–4.

Vrba, E. 1976. The fossil Bovidae of Sterkfontein, Swartkrans, and Kromdraai. *Memoirs of the Transvaal Museum* 21:1–166.

Vrba, E. 1980. Evolution, species and fossils: how does life evolve? *South African Journal of Science* 76:61–84.

Vrba, E. 1985. Ecological and adaptive changes associated with early hominid evolution. In: Delson, E. (ed.) *Ancestors: the Hard Evidence*. New York: Alan Liss pp. 63–71.

Walker, A. C. 1967. Patterns of extinction among the subfossil Madagascan lemuroids. In: Wright, H. E. & Martin, P. S. (eds) *Pleistocene Extinctions: the Search for a Cause*. New Haven: Yale University Press, pp. 425–32.

Walker, A. C. 1976. Remains attributed to *Australopithecus* in the East Rudolf succession. In: Coppens, Y. et al. (eds) *Earliest Man and Environment in the Lake Rudolf Basin*. Chicago: University of Chicago Press, pp. 484–9.

Walker, A. C. 1981. Dietary hypotheses an human evolution. *Philosophical Transactions of the Royal Society, London* B292:47–64.

Walker, A. C. 1984. Extinction in hominid evolution. In: Nitecki, M. H. (ed.) *Extinctions*. Chicago: University of Chicago Press, pp. 119–52.

Walker, A. C. & Leakey, R. E. 1978. The East Turkana hominids. *Scientific American* 239(2):54–66.

Walker, A., Leakey, R. E., Harris, J. M. & Brown, F. H. 1986 2.5 Myr *Australopithecus boisei* from west of Lake Turkana, Kenya. *Nature* 322:517–22.

Walker, A. C. & Pickford, M. 1983. New postcranial fossils of *Proconsul africanus* and *Proconsul nyanzae*. In: Ciochon, R. & Corruccini, R. S. (eds) *New Interpretations of Ape and Human Ancestry*. New York: Plenum Press, pp. 325–54.

Ward, S. C. & Pilbeam, D. 1983. Maxillofacial morphology of Miocene hominoids from Africa and Indo-Pakistan. In: Ciochon, R. & Corruccini, R. S. (eds) *New Interpretations of Ape and Human Ancestry*. New York: Plenum Press, pp. 211–38.

Washburn, S. L. 1950. The analysis of primate evolution with particular reference to the origin of man. *Cold Spring Harbour Symposium on Quantitative Biology* 15:67–78.

Washburn, S. L. 1960. Tools and human evolution. *Scientific American* 203(3):3–15.

Washburn, S. L. 1967. Behaviour and the origin of man. *Proceedings of the Royal Anthropological Institute* 3:21–7.

Washburn, S. L. & Lancaster, C. S. 1968. The evolution of hunting. In: Lee, R. B. & DeVore, I. (eds) *Man the Hunter*. Chicago: Aldine. pp. 293–303.

Weiner, J. S. & Hellman, K. 1960. The sweat glands. *Biological Reviews* 25:141–86.

Weiss, M. L. & Mann, A. E. 1975. *Human Biology and Behaviour: an Anthropological Perspective*. Boston: Little, Brown & Co., p 89.

Western, D. 1973. *The Structure, Dynamics and Changes of the Amboseli Ecosystem*. PhD dissertation. University of Nairobi.

Western, D. 1975. Water availability and its influence on the structure and dynamics of a large mammal ecosystem. *East African Wildlife Journal* 13:365–80.

Western, D. 1979. Size, life history and ecology in mammals. *African Journal of Ecology* 17:185–205.

Wheeler, P. 1984. The evolution of bipedality and loss of functional body hair in hominids. *Journal of Human Evolution* 13:91–8.

Wheeler, P. 1985. The loss of functional body hair in man: the influence of thermal environment, body form and bipedality. *Journal of Human Evolution* 14:23–8.

White, M. 1978. *Modes of Speciation*. San Francisco: Freeman.

White, T. D. & Harris, J. 1977. Suid evolution and correlation of African hominid localities. *Science* 198:13–21.

White, T. D., Johanson, D. C. & Kimbel, W. H. 1983. *Australopithecus africanus*: its phyletic position reconsidered. In: Ciochon, R. & Corruccini, R. S. (eds) *New Interpretations of Ape and Human Ancestry*. New York: Plenum Press, pp. 721–80.

Wiens, J. A. 1977. On competition and variable environments. *American Scientist* 65:590–7.

Williams, G. C. 1966. *Adaptation and Natural Selection*. Princeton: Princeton University Press.

Williams, J. G. 1971. *Guide to the Parks of East Africa*. London: Collins.

Williamson, P. G. 1981. Palaeoecological documentation of speciation in Cenozoic molluscs from Turkana basin. *Nature* 293:437–43.

Wilson, D. S. 1980. *The Natural Selection of Populations and Communities*. Menlo Park, Ca.: Benjamin Cummings.

Wilson, E. O. 1975. *Sociobiology: the New Synthesis*. Cambridge, Mass.: Harvard University Press.

Wolpoff, M. H. 1973. Posterior tooth size, body size and diet in South African gracile australopithecines. *American Journal of Physical Anthropology* 39:375–94.

Wolpoff, M. H. 1983. Lucy's little legs. *Journal of Human Evolution* 12:443–53.

Wolpoff, M. H. 1984. Evolution in *Homo erectus*: the question of stasis. *Paleobiology* 10:389–406.

Wood, B. 1984. The origins of *Homo erectus*. *Courier Forschungsinstitut Senkenberg* 69:99–111.

Wrangham, R. W. 1977. Feeding behaviour of chimpanzees of Gombe National Park, Tanzania, In: Clutton-Brock, T. (ed.) *Primate Ecology*. London: Academic Press, pp. 504–37.

Wrangham, R. W. 1980. An ecological model of female bonded primate groups. *Behaviour* 75:262–300.

Wynne-Edwards, V. C. 1962. *Animal Dispersion in Relation to Social Behaviour*. Edinburgh: Oliver & Boyd.

Yellen, J. E. 1977. *Archaeological Approaches to the Present: Models for Reconstructing the Past*. London: Academic Press.

Zihlman, A. L., Cronin, J. E., Cramer, D. L. & Sarich, V. M. 1978. Pygmy chimpanzee as a possible prototype for the common ancestor of humans, chimpanzees and gorillas. *Nature* 275:744–6.

Zihlman, A. L. & Lowenstein, J. M. 1983. *Ramapithecus* and *Pan paniscus*: significance for human origins. In: Ciochon, R. & Corruccini, R. S. (eds) *New Interpretations of Ape and Human Ancestry*. New York: Plenum Press, pp. 677–94.

Author index

A page number in italics refers to a figure or table

Subject index

A page number in italics refers to a figure or table